Department of the Environment

Coastal Planning and Management:
A Review

Rendel Geotechnics
61 Southwark Street
London
SE1 1SA

London: HMSO

Acknowledgements

This report was prepared as part of a research project entitled **Review of Planning Policy for the Coast and Earth Science Information in Support of Coastal Planning and Management**. The project was funded by the Department of the Environment under its planning research programme (Contract No. PECD 7/1/403).

This report was written by Mr E.M. Lee of Rendel Geotechnics, with guidance provided by Dr A.R. Clark (Rendel Geotechnics), Mr A.S. Freeman (Rendel Planning) and Dr J.C. Doornkamp (Nottingham University).

Background research and specialist advice has been provided by:

Dr R Moore	Rendel Geotechnics
Dr S Burnett	Rendel Geotechnics
Mr S Crawhurst	Rendel Planning
Mr K Hargest	Rendel Planning
Dr S Davidson	Rendel Science and Environment
Prof D Brunsden	King's College, University of London
Dr J Pethick	Institute of Estuarine and Coastal Studies, University of Hull
Mr D Court	Consultant

Preface

Preface

The management of the coast has become a very contentious issue over the last decade. The reasons for this are many and varied; from the threat of rising sea levels, continued pressure for coastal development, ever-increasing demands for tourism and water-based recreation, to fears about a long-term decline in the quality of the natural environment.

Many different groups have their own views about the effectiveness of the ways in which the coastline is managed. Many have advocated radical change to overhaul the current management framework; others see gradual evolution as the way forward.

This Report has attempted to steer a course through the many and varied positions adopted by the numerous bodies with an interest in coastal management. This has not proved an easy task. Often the adopted positions are in direct conflict with other interests, often the evidence for misuse or damage is disputed. All too frequently coastal managers are unaware of the legislative and administrative provisions outside their immediate area of interest, although these provisions could influence their approach to management.

There is clearly a need for a Report that describes the nature of the framework for coastal management in the UK which is written for the non-specialist. This Report attempts to fill that need. Its purpose is to provide an informed, readable and relatively non-technical appreciation of coastal management in the UK based on a general review of the main legislative and administrative provisions.

The Report should not be viewed as a comprehensive directory of all relevant provisions, issues and perceptions. Each of the main administrative systems have been described in a level of detail that hopes to inform the interested reader. For those who seek further detail, there is no substitute for accessing and analysing the enormous volume of Acts of Parliament, statutory instruments, byelaws, regulations, planning guidance, policy statements, etc. that have been referred to throughout the Report.

The views expressed in this Report are those of the consultants (Rendel Geotechnics) and not necessarily of the Department of the Environment or of the individuals consulted.

MARK LEE
August 1993

Executive Summary

Introduction

In recent years there has been considerable concern about the effectiveness of the existing legal and administrative frameworks that have evolved to control or regulate activity in the coastal zone. These concerns have been articulated by many groups such as the Marine Conservation Society, the RSPB and the Wildlife Link. This high profile has been enhanced by the House of Commons Environment Committee report on Coastal Zone Protection and Planning (1992) and the subsequent Government response.

Coastal managers are faced with the challenge of reconciling a number of conflicting and often incompatible demands, including:

- facilitating economic development;

- meeting the demands of the tourism and recreation industry;

- protecting areas of scenic, geological or ecological importance;

- protecting vulnerable communities against the effects of erosion and flooding.

Finding the right balance can lead to conflicts. On one hand many existing communities and business interests feel that conservation policies restrict local economic growth, whilst others feel that areas of national importance are being progressively spoilt by inappropriate development. The potential threat of rising sea levels is likely to heighten these concerns.

The Department of the Environment (DoE) has recently issued policy guidance on coastal planning to assist planners, developers and others in the forward planning of land use and control of development (DoE, 1992; PPG 20). This report has been prepared as part of the DoE research contract

PECD 7/1/403 which addresses 2 major themes that are of direct relevance to planning in the coastal zone:

- the wider context of coastal management within which the planning system operates (Task 1); and

- the technical information on the physical environment needed to support decision making in the coastal zone (Task 2).

This Report addresses the first of these Tasks. The preliminary results of Task 1 were used by the DoE to provide a foundation for the PPG, although the report examines many wider management issues which lie beyond the control of the statutory planning system. For a wider audience, the Report aims to present a synthesis of the enormous volume of legislation, policy advice and research relevant to management of the coastal zone in the UK.

Defining the Coastal Zone

There can be no single definition for many stretches of coast. One of the key problems is the need to reconcile the contrasting perspectives of those involved with the **management of coastal resources** (eg sea fisheries, waste disposal, marine aggregates) and **management of coastal hazards** (eg erosion and flooding). The approach adopted by this study (Figure 1) has recognised the importance of both the human and physical geographical systems (the **interactive** and **dynamic** zones, respectively) and the narrow **hazard zone** where they interact.

Particular coastal environments present a unique combination of **resources** and **constraints** to and **opportunities for** development or use, which need to be taken into account in the management of a coastline. The nature and significance of these

Figure 1 Defining the coastal zone

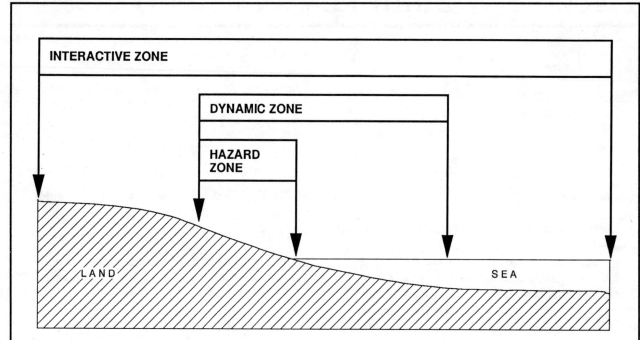

The concept of risk as the interaction of the human environment with the physical environment is illustrated below. Only when the two systems are in conflict do hazards such as landsliding become a threat to the community. Of particular importance is the fact that as urban development increases, intensifies or spreads into vulnerable areas so the potential impact of hazards increases.

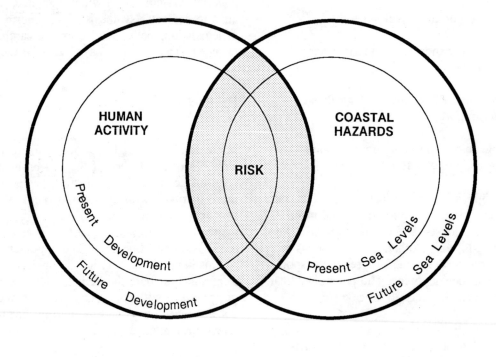

factors will depend on a combination of:

- **the physical character**; landforms, materials and processes;

- **the natural heritage**; landscapes, habitats and living resources;

- **the coastal use**; past and present development, historic interest and technological hazards.

The development and use of the coastal zone is influenced by these three characteristics which are interlinked to produce the unique nature of a stretch of coast. It is clear, therefore, that planning and management considerations will not be uniform around the coast, but reflect a combination of **local** (eg site conditions), **regional** (eg demand for employment opportunities; sediment transport), **national** (eg demand for aggregates for the construction industry) and **international** (eg pollution of the seas around the UK) factors.

The Dynamic Nature of the Coastal Zone

The coastline may be viewed as a series of interlinked physical systems, comprising both offshore and onshore elements. Sediment (clay, silt, sand, gravel etc.,) is moved around the coast by waves and currents in a series of linked systems **(sediment transport cells)**. Simple cells comprise an arrangement of sediment source areas (eg eroding cliffs, the sea bed), areas where sediment is moved by coastal processes and sediment sinks (eg beaches, estuaries or offshore sinks). Along a particular stretch of coast there may be a series of such cells, often operating at different scales. Change in one part of a cell can lead to adjustment to other parts. This has important implications for any development in the coastal zone which interferes with the movement of sediment around the coast (eg harbour breakwaters, groynes, etc.,).

These longshore sediment transport cells are not the only important physical systems acting within the coastal zone. **Estuaries** provide an important link between these coastal cells and rivers; **mudflats and salt marshes** have developed where fine grained sediment (clay and silt) is laid down in sheltered areas with high tidal ranges; **coastal sand dunes** have developed as a result of wind–blown sand transport; major **coastal landslide systems** are found on many soft rock coasts; **high, near–vertical cliffs** occur along hard rock coasts,

providing an almost passive barrier against the effects of wave attack.

Many parts of the coast are subject to natural hazards ranging from flooding to erosion and deposition. These processes are, of course, natural phenomena that have become significant hazards because they have increasingly imposed themselves upon vulnerable communities. On the other hand, these coastal processes are essential for maintaining the value of many coastal landscapes and habitats. Without continued erosion, the famous white chalk cliffs of the Seven Sisters would become drab and less spectacular.

Coastal Resources

The varied nature of the coastline also provides significant benefits of shelter and deep water for ports and harbours, breeding grounds for fish and shellfish and opportunities for recreation and tourism. The sea bed has become an important source of sand and gravel for the construction industry and, increasingly, for use in beach recharge schemes.

The coast also provides important locational benefits for heavy industry and energy generating facilities. Coastal waters are used as coolants in nuclear and thermal power stations and the coast itself provides convenient locations for the reception, processing and distribution of imported fuels and raw materials. For many years the coast has also been viewed as a potential source of energy through wave power and tidal power.

Coastal landforms have an important role in protecting the coastline from erosion and flooding. Salt marshes, for example, are capable of absorbing a large proportion of the wave energy arriving at the coast and, thus, provide a valuable defence from sea floods. Beaches, spits and bars perform a similar role in dissipating wave energy and can protect the open coast from erosion. The sediment supplied by the erosion of cliffs can be important to sustain these landforms and, hence, natural coastal defences.

The coastline also provides unique opportunities to view the varied geological structure of the UK and to see natural processes shaping the landscape. The scale and continuity of geological exposures along the coast is rarely matched inland. In addition, many sections of the coast are of international importance because they are agreed reference points for the world's geological history.

Coastal Planning

Coastal **planning** and **management** are not synonymous. Planning relates to the operation of the **statutory planning system** which, in England and Wales, has its basis in the Town and Country Planning Act 1990 (as amended). This legislation clearly defines a narrow role for planning in the coastal zone as it is concerned solely with the development and use of **land**, with the limit of local planning authority jurisdiction normally around low water mark. In addition, planning legislation should not normally be used to secure objectives achievable under other legislation. However, the planning system, through development plans and control of development, is an important instrument in determining the way the coast is developed and conserved.

The Effectiveness of Current Land Use Policies

The planning system is entirely capable of taking into account the human, natural heritage and physical elements of the coastal environment. However, there is a difference between what **can be achieved** within the present framework and what **is achieved** by many local planning authorities.

Since 1947, the planning system has been effective in arresting the spread of piecemeal development along the **scenic undeveloped coast**. For example, in England and Wales, land use policies within development plans have played an important role in the success of designated National Parks and AONBs and those stretches of coastline defined as heritage coasts, following advice given in:

- DoE Circular 12/72 (WO 36/72) Planning of the Undeveloped Coast (now cancelled by PPG 20);

In Scotland, protection of National Scenic Areas has been achieved by means of development control restrictions outlined in:

- SDD Circular 51/77 Development Control in National Scenic Areas (as amended by Circular 9/87);

Local planning authorities have to balance conservation interests with the need to make adequate provision for development and economic growth. Nature conservation designations such as National Nature Reserves, Local Nature Reserves and SSSIs provide protection for areas of the **undeveloped** coastline as well as some developed stretches. Many estuaries lie within the **developed** coast, but have been recognised to be of international conservation importance, reflected by their designation as Ramsar and SPA sites.

The planning system is an important instrument in achieving nature conservation objectives above LWM, through the inclusion of land use policies within development plans that take into account the following guidance (see also Table 6.2 for advice in Scotland):

- DoE Circular 32/81 (WO 50/81) Wildlife and Countryside Act 1981 (to be cancelled by the forthcoming PPG Nature Conservation);

- DoE Circular 27/87 (WO 52/87) Nature Conservation (to be cancelled by the forthcoming PPG Nature Conservation);

- DoE Circular 1/92 (WO 1/92) Planning Controls over SSSIs (to be cancelled by the forthcoming PPG Nature Conservation);

- PPG 7 The Countryside and Rural Economy.

Concern has been expressed, however, over the inconsistent or inadequate treatment of many nature conservation objectives within development plans.

The planning system has also had a significant role in protecting sites of archaeological interest (above LWM). The importance of protecting sites of national value, in England, has recently been stressed in:

- PPG 16 Archaeology and Planning.

Advice on policies for historic buildings and conservation areas is contained in:

- DoE Circular 8/87 (WO 61/87) Historic Buildings and Conservation Areas – Policy and Procedures.

The planning system has been less effective in addressing issues related to the **physical character** of the coast. Indeed, the prevailing view, in the past, has been that hazards such as erosion, landsliding and flooding are a matter for the developer and not a planning issue. This has led to coastal development in vulnerable locations and demands for coast protection or sea defences funded by the public purse once the threats become apparent. These works often have implications for other interests as they may seriously affect the amenity and ecological value of the coast and give rise to conflict between local interests and conservation bodies. In recent years, however, the Government has emphasised the need for these problems to be taken into account in development plans in England and Wales, through:

- PPG 14 Development on Unstable Land;

- PPG 20 Coastal Planning;

- DoE Circular 30/92 (MAFF FD 1/92; WO 68/92) Development and Flood Risk;

Within the context of this advice, the planning system has an important role in minimising risks, especially in light of the possible effects of sea-level rise, through refusing permission to develop in vulnerable locations or making permission conditional on special building measures. To date, however, no advice specifically addressed at the management of natural hazards has been issued in Scotland.

Coastal Management: Powers and Responsibilities

Planning forms only one of a number of control and regulatory systems in the coastal zone, which are concerned with the "**management**" of a wide range of activities from port and harbour operations to oil and gas exploration. However, the wide range of policies, decisions and management practices adopted by each of the bodies with a responsibility in the coastal zone can have a direct effect on planning objectives.

The role of regulating change and improving environmental conditions in the coastal zone is split between many authorities and bodies including central government, local authorities, the conservancy councils, harbour authorities, sea fisheries committees, the NRA, River Purification Authorities, Internal Drainage Boards, landowners and voluntary organisations. In the past the coastal zone has tended to be seen as the boundary between the land and the sea, rather than an integrated unit. This is reflected by different legislative and administrative provisions for

controlling activity on **land**, the **sea bed** and at **sea**.

In addition, three separate mechanisms have evolved to manage the impact of man on the physical environment and to minimise the risks associated with coastal development:

- protecting the quality of coastal habitats and landscapes (**conservation**);

- maintaining the quality of coastal waters (**pollution control**);

- safeguarding coastal development from erosion and flooding (**coastal defence**).

Powers generally relate to a requirement to perform specific duties, such as maintaining water quality (eg the NRA, under the Water Resources Act 1991 or the River Purification Authorities under the Control of Pollution Act 1974), protecting sites of conservation value (eg English Nature and its counterparts in Scotland and Wales, under the Wildlife and Countryside Act 1981), management of efficient port and harbour facilities (harbour authorities, under the Harbours Act 1964) and protection against the effects of erosion (coast protection authorities, under the Coast Protection Act 1949).

Most of the current coastal zone responsibilities reflect past economic climates (eg harbour authorities, with the importance of many traditional ports having declined in recent years), historic ownership patterns (eg CEC), the result of urgent needs for action to prevent loss of life and investment (eg the powers for flood defence), have been acquired in response to specific EC directives (eg monitoring bathing water quality by the NRA or RPAs) or simply developed because of a pressing need for regulation of a rapidly expanding industry (eg CEC's role in the control of marine fish farming in Scotland).

The complexity of arrangements in the UK is further heightened by the different legislative provisions, policy context and responsible authorities that form the framework for coastal management in each of the four constituent countries; England, Scotland, Wales and Northern Ireland. Just as there can be unique issues along particular coastlines, there can be contrasting responses in the four separate countries. For the sake of brevity this Report has been biased towards the management framework in England and Wales, although significant differences have been highlighted where appropriate. It is clear, however, that there can be no single statement on the effectiveness of coastal management in the UK; each country has adopted its own responses to the issues that are currently relevant along their coastlines.

Coastal Management: The Framework

The framework for coastal management can be viewed as a complex system; change in one area (eg increased demand, intensification of use or change in management practice) will often lead to change and tension elsewhere. The effect of the heritage coast definition is an example, diverting development towards less valued landscapes and estuaries where it may cause conflict with other conservation interests.

The key elements of the various regulatory systems in England and Wales are summarised in Table 1, which highlights that there is no consistent approach. Management takes place at a variety of scales from local to national, often not in the context of strategic plans or clearly defined national strategies and with varying degrees of public participation or access to the decision making process.

In general, the framework comprises three key components:

- **legislation and regulations** which define responsibilities and provide powers;

- **policy advice** which sets the management context;

- **linkages** between authorities, managers and users through which decision makers can take into account the views of other interests.

With separate legislation and policy for many of the different types of coastal activity, the linkages provide the means for:

- anticipating problems before they arise;

- coordinating management decisions to ensure that uses do not interfere with other interests;

- ensuring that coastal management reflects local needs as well as national policy;

- resolving conflicts when they arise.

Measuring the Effectiveness of the Framework for Coastal Management

Chapters 3 to 8 of this Report include a brief outline of the current legislative and administrative frameworks for controlling activity in the coastal zone: Coastal Defence (Chapter 3); Pollution Control (Chapter 4); Conservation (Chapter 5); Control of Development on Land (Chapter 6); Regulation of Development on the Sea Bed (Chapter 7); Regulation of Activities on and in the Sea (Chapter 8).

These Chapters have also addressed the **effectiveness** of the provisions in terms of the extent to which the administrative systems:

- consider coastal dynamics;

- take the environmental effects of a project into account;

- take into account the interests of other groups; and

- enable coordinated decision making across the coastal zone.

The main issues of concern within each of the areas of interest are described in the relevant Chapters and are summarised in Table 2. Individual issues can, of course, be addressed in a variety of ways, including new legislation or regulations and policy guidance. Indeed, this is a common characteristic of coastal management in the UK where the frequent amendments make it difficult to determine exactly what the current position is. However, it is important to view these concerns in a broader context which examines how decision making in one administrative system can lead to conflict with other interests. These interlinkages have been analysed in terms of two dominant issues in coastal management:

- the effects of protecting vulnerable communities from coastal hazards (**hazard management**);

- the effects of reconciling competing coastal activities or land uses (**resource management**).

Table 1 Summary of the main features of the various regulatory systems relevant to coastal management in England and Wales

REGULATORY SYSTEM	LEGISLATION	AUTHORITY	SCALE OF DECISION-MAKING	PREPARATION OF STRATEGIC PLANS	CONSULTATION	ENVIRONMENTAL DUTIES	PUBLIC PARTICIPATION
Coast Protection	Coast Protection Act 1949 (Also see Table 3.2)	Maritime district councils as promoters or regulators of schemes.	Local, but increasingly within context of National (MAFF/WO) and Regional (Coastal Defence Group) considerations, (Table 3.1).	Trend towards regional scale plans, through Coast Defence Groups, (Table 3.6).	Wide ranging consultation required under 1949 Act, (Table 3.8)..	None.	Proposals advertised, anybody may object. If objections are not withdrawn a local inquiry or hearing can be held.
Sea Defence	Water Resources Act 1991 Land Drainage Act 1991 (Also see Table 3.2)	NRA as promoters or regulators of schemes	Regional, but increasingly in context of Regional and National Coastal Defence Strategies, (Table 3.1).	Trend towards regional scale shoreline management plans.	Limited requirements to consult. Guidelines published by MAFF/DOE/WO which recommend consultation with a wide range of conservancy agencies and groups.	- to further conservation of natural heritage. - to have regard for sites of archaeological interest. - to take into account effect of proposals on conservation interests.	None.
Waste Disposal at Sea	Food and Environment Protection Act 1985 Part II	MAFF	National.	No.	No specific consultation requirements, (Table 4.1).	- to protect the marine environment and its living resources.	None.
Discharge of Prescribed Processes	Environmental Protection Act 1990	HMIP	National.	No.	Limited consultation, including NRA and MAFF, (Table 4.1).	None.	Local inquiry or hearing may be held in relation to discharge application.
Discharge to Water	Water Resources Act 1991	NRA	Regional.	No.	Must consult EN/CCW before carrying out or authorising works that may affect an SSSI, (Table 4.1).	- to further conservation of natural heritage. - to have regard for sites of archaeological interest. - to take into account effect of proposals on conservation interests.	NRA required to give notice of discharge consents in press. Objections can be made and may lead to a local inquiry.
Development on Land	Town and Country Planning Act 1990 Planning and Compensation Act 1991	Local planning authority	Local, but within context of national and regional policy guidance, (Tables 6.1 and 6.2).	Preparation of development plans. All planning decisions made in accordance with policies in development plans, unless material considerations indicate otherwise.	Wide ranging consultation required when preparing development plans and determining planning applications, (Tables 6.6 and 6.7).	No formal duties.	Public consulted in development plan preparation Objections may lead to an Examination in Public or local inquiry.

Table 1 (cont...)

REGULATORY SYSTEM	LEGISLATION	AUTHORITY	SCALE OF DECISION-MAKING	PREPARATION OF STRATEGIC PLANS	CONSULTATION	ENVIRONMENTAL DUTIES	PUBLIC PARTICIPATION
Landscape Conservation - National Parks - AONBs	National Parks and Access to the Countryside Act 1949.	Secretary of State, proposed by Countryside Commission and CCW.	National	Management plans prepared by countryside body and local authority.	Local authority, (Table 5.4).	Defined by conservation legislation.	Public informed by notice in national and local press. Local inquiry or hearing may be held to resolve objections.
Landscape Conservation - heritage coast	None	Defined by Countryside Commission and CCW, together with local authorities.	Local and National.	Management plans prepared by countryside body and local authority, (Table 5.5).	Landowners and other bodies concerned, (Table 5.4).	Defined by conservation legislation.	Public invited to comment.
Wildlife Conservation - National Nature Reserves	National Parks and Access to the Countryside Act 1949.	Secretary of State, proposed by conservancy council.	National.	Management plans.	No formal requirements. Agreement with owner, leasee or occupier, (Table 5.4).	Defined by conservation legislation.	Notice published in press. Local inquiry or hearing may be held to resolve objections.
Wildlife Conservation - SSSIs	Wildlife and Countryside Act 1981.	Secretary of State, proposed by conservancy council.	National.	Nature Conservation and Geological Conservation Reviews.	Owners and occupiers, (Table 5.4).	Defined by conservation legislation.	None.
Wildlife Conservation - Marine Nature Reserves	Wildlife and Countryside Act 1981.	Secretary of State, proposed by conservancy council.	National.	Management plans.	Secretary of State shall consult with any appropriate group. Extensive informal consultation by conservancy council.	Defined by conservation legislation.	Notice given to all interested parties. Local inquiry or hearing may be held to resolve objections to designation or byelaws.
Archaeology - scheduled monuments and archaeological areas	Ancient Monuments and Archaeological Areas Act 1979.	Secretary of State, local authority.	National and Local.	None.	Consultation with local authorities, (Table 5.4).	Defined by conservation legislation.	Notice in national and local press. Local inquiry or hearing may be held.
Archaeology - wrecks	Protection of Wrecks Act 1973.	Secretary of State, DNH.	National.	None.	Any appropriate bodies, (Table 5.4).	None.	None.

Table 1 (cont...)

REGULATORY SYSTEM	LEGISLATION	AUTHORITY	SCALE OF DECISION-MAKING	PREPARATION OF STRATEGIC PLANS	CONSULTATION	ENVIRONMENTAL DUTIES	PUBLIC PARTICIPATION
Development in Harbours: Harbour orders (Also see Table 6.3).	Harbours Act 1964.	DTp.	National.	No.	No specific consultation requirements.	Harbour authorities must have regard to: - conservation of the natural heritage. - preserving freedom of access to archaeological or historic sites. - the effect of proposals on	Local inquiry or hearing may be held to resolve objections to applications for harbour orders.
Land drainage consents.	Water Resources Act 1991.	NRA control through byelaws.	Regional.	No; although may operate within context of shoreline management plans.	No specific requirements.	NRA has statutory environmental duties (see Sea Defence, above).	Byelaws advertised with notices served to affected parties. Local inquiries may be held to resolve objections.
Marine Aggregate Extraction	None.	Government: DoE coordinates Government View Procedure.	National.	No.	Wide ranging consultation carried out. (See Table 7.1)	None.	Applications advertised in press.
Marine Fish Farming	None.	CEC.	National.	No; but Scottish Office (199 guidance does identify locational and operational constraints.	CEC invite comments from a wide range of bodies. (See Table 7.1)	Crown Estate Commissioners must maintain and enhance the value of the estate, with due regard to requirements of good management.	Applications advertised in press.
Oil and Gas	None.	DTi.	National.	No.	Wide ranging consultation carried out. (See Table 7.1)	None.	None.
Shipping	Various Merchant Shipping Act.	DTp.	National.	No.	No specific requirements.	None.	None.

Table 1 (cont...)

REGULATORY SYSTEM	LEGISLATION	AUTHORITY	SCALE OF DECISION-MAKING	PREPARATION OF STRATEGIC PLANS	CONSULTATION	ENVIRONMENTAL DUTIES	PUBLIC PARTICIPATION
Sea Fishing	Various Fisheries Acts. (See Table 8.1).	MAFF Sea Fisheries Committees may make byelaws.	National and Regional.	No.	No specific requirements.	None.	Local inquiries or hearing can be held to resolve objections to sea fisheries byelaws. Byelaws must not affect rights under Private Acts or Royal Charter.
Near Shore Recreation	Public Health Act 1936, 1961 Local Government (Miscellaneous Provisions) Act 1976.	Local Authority may make byelaws.	Local.	No.	No specific requirements.	None.	Byelaws must be consistent with byelaws made by harbour authorities. Secretary of State may hold a local inquiry to resolve objections to byelaws.

Hazard Management: Protection of Vulnerable Communities

Coastal defence works have been very successful in protecting communities, industrial developments or heritage sites from the threat of erosion and flooding. However, construction of the defences has had a range of effects on the coastal zone; from "coastal squeeze", the encouragement of further development behind the defences to the disruption of sediment transport around the coast. Many of these concerns are now the focus of attention of the recently established coastal defence groups, often through **shoreline management plans**, or have been addressed in recent planning policy advice.

From a planning perspective, however, there remain two key areas of concern:

- the need for earth science information to support coastal planning;

- the need for greater coordination between coastal planning and coastal defence.

Resource Management: Reconciling Competing Demands

The key issues involved in coastal resource management are outlined in Chapter 9, reflecting pressures in both the landward and seaward elements of the coastal zone. The impacts of these coastal activities range from interference with the rights of other users or diverting incompatible uses to other locations, to the decline or damage in conservation interests through land claim or disturbance.

Perhaps the most pressing issue for resource management is the problem of coordinating activity and decision making across the coastal zone. Particular difficulties experienced in the area immediately above and below LWM, especially for the protection of intertidal habitats.

The planning system is an important source of protection for many of these sites through the inclusion of policies in development plans. Problems have arisen, however, because the boundaries of conservation sites such as SSSIs are drawn along MLWM, coinciding with the normal limit of local authority jurisdiction. Adjacent areas, below this level, are often of equal scientific importance but are not afforded protection through the planning system. This has significant implications for bird communities, especially in estuaries.

In this context, the seaward limit of the planning system is arbitrary and does not reflect the nature of some coastal issues which may involve development immediately below LWM (eg the construction of a marina or barrage). In such circumstances there is no provision under existing legislation for local planning authorities to extend their jurisdiction seawards, in contrast to the powers of coast protection authorities under the Coast Protection Act 1949. Local authorities can, of course, seek to extend their jurisdiction through special legislation, as was the case with the Zetland County Act 1974 which gave Shetland Council powers to control development within territorial waters.

It is likely that the new order making procedures introduced by the Transport and Works Act 1992 will address some of the issues in controlling developments above and below LWM.

Considerable difficulties have also been experienced in providing protection to wildlife and archaeological sites in the marine environment, where conservation may be in direct conflict with traditional rights of navigation and fishing.

Management Plans

In recent years some local authorities have become more aware of the complex issues that can arise in the coastal zone. This has led a number of individual authorities to address these issues in non–statutory **coastal management plans** or **estuary management plans**.

It is clear that management plans are becoming an important element in the coordination of decision making over hazard and resource management issues. Although the three separate types of plan that are emerging (shoreline, estuary and coastal) address different aspects of management in different parts of the coastal zone there is potential for considerable overlap both in terms of the issues covered and the participating authorities and bodies.

These management plans can be complemented by appropriate land use policies within development plans. However, their present ad–hoc nature and

overlapping areas of interest may hinder their role in improving the effectiveness of coastal planning. Indeed, there is currently no mechanism for coordinating different plans covering the same stretch of coast, nor linking with plans produced in neighbouring authorities.

The Report presents a framework for the integration of coastal planning and management plans, based on:

– appreciation of the nature of the **coastal environment**;

– the **information needs** for planning and management;

– the development of appropriate **strategies** at national, regional and local scale;

– the appropriate **responses** to planning and management issues.

Amongst the key points highlighted by this framework are:

– both planning and management strategies should be appropriate to the relevant coastal **system** (eg sediment transport cell, coastal landslide system, estuary, etc.);

– planning and management strategies need to be prepared in the context of an appreciation of the **constraints** resulting from the dynamic nature of the relevant coastal system;

– the need for decision making to be supported by surveys of coastal **resources** and monitoring to determine how they are responding to current levels of exploitation and usage;

– the important role of **Environmental Assessment** in ensuring that activities do not have an adverse effect on the coastal system;

– the central role of strategic plans highlights an increased emphasis on **preventive** measures rather than reacting to individual problems at specific sites.

The planning system can address land use issues of relevance to the overall coastal management objectives, with **regional planning guidance** providing an opportunity for addressing issues that need to be considered on a wider scale than a single county or district. Management plans could provide the necessary strategic framework for

B

Table 2 Key issues of concern in the coastal zone

Coastal Defence (Chapter 3)

Lack of appreciation of powers available to coast protection authorities for controlling removal of material from the sea bed (para 3.14).

Legacy of defence works which have disrupted sediment transport or promoted accelerated erosion (paras 3.32–3.35).

Establishment of coastal defence groups which reflect pattern of sediment movement rather than administrative boundaries (para 3.44).

Lack of reliable and useful data on coastal processes on which policy decisions can be made (para 3.51).

Lack of coordination between coastal defence strategy and land use planning (para 3.54).

No requirement for EA with coast protection schemes (para 3.57)

Limited consideration of leisure sailing interests in sea defence schemes (para 3.65).

Problems of reconciling coast protection and conservation interests (paras 3.71–3.75).

Absence of coordinated decision making for schemes that involve works immediately above and below LWM (para 3.78).

Separation of coast protection and sea defence responsibility in England and Wales (para 3.80).

Pollution Control (Chapter 4)

Concerns over garbage disposal regulations at sea outside special areas (para 4.10).

Limited resources allocated to deal with accidental spillages at sea (para 4.37).

Concerns that bathing water improvements apply to only a limited part of the coastline (para 4.44).

Lack of agreement over the effects of contaminants on marine life, reflecting inadequate scientific information (para 4.49).

Concern from port authorities over the cost of providing garbage reception facilities (para 4.50).

Potential confusion between authorities and bodies with a responsibility for pollution control and conservation, as highlighted by the Kimya incident in Caernarfon Bay (para 4.56).

Concerns over the achievement of bathing water quality standards (para 4.62).

Conservation (Chapter 5)

The need for additional protection for areas of landscape conservation value in Scotland (para 5.9).

The omission of important nature conservation sites from the SSSI network (para 5.8).

The lack of protection for wetland sites which meet Ramsar criteria, but lie outside the SSSI network (para 5.33).

The limited number of important wrecks protected by the 1973 Act (para 5.47).

The lack of resources for identifying new archaeological sites in coastal waters (para 5.49).

Lack of reliable information about recent habitat loss (para 5.62).

The potential effects of sea level rise on intertidal habits and the need to consider options for restoring habitats (paras 5.63–5.65).

The need to recognise the value of submerged archaeological sites as indicators of long term coastal changes (para 5.66).

The effect of the heritage coast definition on concentrating "unsuitable" development in estuaries (para 5.67).

The lack of formal consultation arrangements for SSSI designation and concerns that national conservation interests can take precedence over the local economy (para 5.72).

The potential effects of common law rights and traditional activities, permitted development and development authorised by private Acts on SSSIs (para 5.73).

The lack of progress in designating Marine Nature Reserves (para 5.79).

Concerns over the preservation of archaeological sites below LWM (paras 5.84–5.85).

The problems involved in achieving conservation objectives for habitats covering the intertidal range because of the limit of local authority jurisdiction (para 5.88).

The Planning System (Chapter 6)

The reluctance of some local planning authorities to take landslide and flood risk into account when preparing development plans and determining planning applications (paras 6.40–6.56).

The absence of specific planning policy advice concerning coastal risks in Scotland (para 6.57).

Concerns that a number of activities that do not require express planning permission may increase the risk to adjacent properties from natural hazards (para 6.58 and 6.61).

Table 2 (cont) ....

The Planning System (cont ...)

The lack of coordination between land use planning and coastal defence strategy (paras 6.67–6.70).

The absence of a mechanism to provide compensation to property owners affected by stricter development control in areas prone to landsliding, erosion or flooding (para 6.73).

Lack of consideration of NRA water quality objectives in development plan policies (para 6.74).

Inconsistent or inadequate treatment of conservation issues in development plans (paras 6.78–6.80).

Calls to improve the effectiveness of the heritage coast definition (para 6.81).

Lack of consideration of leisure sailing interests in development plans (paras 6.84–6.85).

Concerns over lack of local planning authority powers to control activities below LWM, especially within estuaries (paras 6.98–6.102).

Ports and Harbours (Chapter 6)

Concerns over the exercise of certain permitted development rights within operational land (paras 6.88–6.89).

Concerns over the effects of maintenance dredging on marine conservation interests (para 6.90).

Concerns over harbour authority's role in facilitating new marina developments (paras 6.91–6.93).

Marine Aggregate Extraction (Chapter 7)

The lengthy periods required for the Government View Procedure and the absence of a right to appeal over rejected applications (para 7.15).

Concerns about the potential impact of dredging on coast erosion and marine conservation interests, and the lack of reliable information on the mobility of sea bed materials (paras 7.30–7.31).

Concerns over the limited local involvement in decision making procedures and the absence of local planning authority jurisdiction below LWM (paras 7.40 and 7.59).

Marine Fish Farming (Chapter 7)

The perceived conflict of interest arising out of CEC's role as the "competent authority" for environmental assessment and their financial responsibilities in managing the Crown Estate (paras 7.36–7.38).

The limited consideration of marine conservation interests in the Very Sensitive Area definition (para 7.43).

Concerns over the onshore impacts of the rapid expansion of the marine fish farming industry and the absence of local planning authority jurisdiction below LWM (para 7.45).

Sea Use (Chapter 8)

Problems of enforcement of byelaws to control recreational craft and water sports (para 8.22).

Concerns about the effects of sea uses on marine conservation interests, resulting from disturbance, discharge of pollutants and trawling (para 8.25).

addressing local hazard and resource management issues. However, in contrast with the planning system, there is no national or regional guidance on the aims and objectives of coastal management. There is also no statutory equivalent to the development control process for ensuring that coastal activities are in accordance with management plan policies.

The Geographical Context for Coastal Planning and Management

In the past, there has been a tendency for individual local authorities to concentrate on local issues such as protection of the undeveloped coast, provision of tourist and recreation facilities and preservation of valuable habitats. However, coastal processes often operate over a much broader scale than individual local authority boundaries. As a result land use policies in one area may have an effect on the coastal zone in neighbouring areas.

Decision making by coastal authorities needs to reflect an awareness of the appropriate scale of physical or ecological systems. Whilst the importance of **sediment transport cells** for coastal defence along many parts of the UK coast cannot be disputed, it is by no means clear that such cells will be relevant for other aspects of coastal management, most notably land use planning and regulation of sea uses. Indeed, many coastal problems need to be considered in the context of the behaviour of the appropriate **coastal landform**. In Ventnor, Isle of Wight, the local planning authority is concerned with ensuring that development or redevelopment does not affect the stability of adjacent parts of a landslide system.

Broad sediment transport cells are not necessarily the most appropriate framework for ensuring that a strategic view is taken over all coastal zone issues. However, the principle that decision making should be based on an awareness of both the **site** and the **situation** is of major importance to coastal managers. This awareness should extend to an understanding of how the effects of activities at a particular location can be transmitted over a wider area and vice versa ie. the **area of influence**. In the case of migratory bird feeding grounds or the spread of marine pollutants this may require an appreciation of the international context. In the case of housing development away from the dynamic zone, the area of influence will be much smaller.

Understanding Coastal Behaviour

Most coastal landforms are not static. Understanding how landforms have developed in the past can give a valuable insight into the potential for future change and provide a scientific basis for planning and management policies. For example, the assessment of ground behaviour at Ventnor, Isle of Wight, has enabled landslide management strategies to be developed that take into account the historical patterns of ground movement and structural damage.

Coastal managers should be aware of the potential for coastal change and the interactions between coastal processes, landforms and the habitats which they support. These changes can be **periodic** (cyclic) with the landforms or habitats responding to events by altering their shape or nature and then recovering and returning to the previous state. Examples include changes in beach profiles in response to storms or the periodic reductions in plant and animal communities in response to changes in environmental conditions. In other instances, change is **progressive** as in the retreat of an eroding cliff. Distinguishing between long term progressive change and cyclic change with periodicities of many decades is a particular problem for coastal managers faced by only a limited period of records. In addition, many of the environmental effects of coastal zone development or activity may take many decades to become apparent.

In the past coastal change has tended to be regarded as detrimental to human interests, with the emphasis placed on resisting rather than accommodating or avoiding the effects of coastal processes. This is readily apparent in past attitudes to coastal defence, but has also influenced approaches to coastal conservation. Understanding coastal changes can be a fundamental component of effective shoreline management and soft engineering; from allowing unprotected cliffs to erode and supply sediment to beaches to the regeneration of salt marshes through managed retreat. On the Anglian coast, for example, the NRA has recognised the importance of the need to understand the operation of coastal processes and their effect on coastal landforms. Long term monitoring of coastal behaviour is also necessary for establishing the impact of exploitation of coastal resources and assessing maximum sustainable yields from coastal waters.

Improving the Framework for Coastal Management

It is not the aim of this Report to recommend particular changes to the framework for coastal management in the UK. However, the developing interest in management plans for both hazard and resource management is a clear indication that the framework for coastal management is changing in response to pressing issues on particular coasts. However, this development is likely to be constrained by the ad hoc nature of these plans and their uncertain relationship with the statutory regulatory frameworks such as the planning system.

Solutions involving major institutional or legislative change should not be viewed as a panacea for coastal management. Effective coastal management will depend on close coordination and cooperation between different interest groups to ensure that acceptable solutions are found to the conflicting resources demands. Indeed, it is clear that the links between bodies representing different interests provide the opportunity to ensure that the enormous variety of points of view are heard. In many areas and activities, however, there is a need to strengthen existing mechanisms for coordination.

It is important that the future framework for coastal management is suitable for both hazard and resource management, whilst ensuring that these two key elements are not considered in isolation. The regulatory frameworks should take into account the interests of other coastal zone users and provide effective mechanisms for resolving conflicts. Effective coastal management should also involve a broad strategic perspective at national and regional level and an appreciation of the nature of coastal change, including an awareness of the implications of sea level rise. Decision making needs to be based on adequate scientific understanding of coastal constraints and resources and able to take into account the potential effects of activities or uses on other coastal zone interests. This will require an improved understanding of coastal systems and the interrelationships between coastal landforms and the habitats which they support.

Contents

Chapter 1
Introduction: The Physical Nature of the Coastal Zone

Chapter 2
Background to the Legal and Administrative Framework

Chapter 3
Coastal Defence

Chapter 4
Pollution Control

Chapter 5
Conservation

Chapter 9
Issues in Coastal Planning and Management

Appendix A

List of Figures

List of Tables

List of Abbreviations

AONB	Area of Outstanding Natural Beauty
AoSP	Area of Special Protection (Birds)
ASSI	Area of Special Scientific Interest (Northern Ireland)
BATNEEC	Best Available Techniques Not Entailing Excessive Cost
CCC	Country Conservancy Council (English Nature, Scottish Natural Heritage, Countryside Council for Wales)
CCS	Countryside Commission for Scotland
CCW	Countryside Council for Wales
CEC	Crown Estate Commissioners
CERAC	Coastal Engineering Research Advisory Committee
DEn	Department of Energy
DCPN	Development Control Policy Note
DoE	Department of the Environment
DoE (NI)	Department of the Environment (Northern Ireland)
DNH	Department of National Heritage
DTi	Department of Trade and Industry
DTp	Department of Transport
EA	Environmental Assessment
EC	European Community
EN	English Nature
ES	Environmental Statement
FOOCG	Fisheries and Offshore Oil Consultative Group
GCR	Geological Conservation Review
GDO	Town and Country Planning General Development Order 1988
GVP	Government View Procedure
HMIP	Her Majesty's Inspectorate of Pollution
HMIPI	Her Majesty's Industrial Pollution Inspectorate
HRL	Hydraulics Research Ltd, Wallingford
HWM	High water mark
ICES	International Council for Exploration of the Sea
IDB	Internal Drainage Board
IPC	Integrated pollution control
JNCC	Joint Nature Conservation Committee
LWM	Low water mark
MAFF	Ministry of Agriculture, Fisheries and Food
MARPOL	International Convention for the Prevention of Pollution from Ships 1973
MCA	Marine Consultation Area
MLWS	Mean low water, spring tides
MNR	Marine Nature Reserve
MOD	Ministry of Defence
MPA	Marine Protected Area
MPCU	Marine Pollution Control Unit
MPG	Minerals Planning Guidance note
NCC	Nature Conservancy Council
NCR	Nature Conservation Review

NGO	Non–government organisation
nm	Nautical Mile (1852 yards)
NRA	National Rivers Authority
PDO	Potentially Damaging Operation
PPG	Planning Policy Guidance note
RIGS	Regionally important geological site
RPA	River purification authority
RPG	Regional Planning Guidance note
RSPB	Royal Society for Protection of Birds
RYA	Royal Yachting Association
SCOPAC	Standing Conference on Problems Associated with the Coastline
SDD	Scottish Development Department
SFC	Sea fisheries committee
SOAFD	Scottish Office Agriculture and Fisheries Department
SPA	Special Protection Area
SSSI	Site of Special Scientific Interest
STWS	Storm tide warning service
UDP	Unitary Development Plan
UK	United Kingdom
WO	Welsh Office
WWF	World Wide Fund for Nature

1 Introduction: The Physical Nature of the Coastal Zone

Introduction

1.1 Although substantial stretches of the UK coastline remain largely undeveloped, many areas are subject to considerable development pressures affecting the amenity and conservation value. This is particularly so along the south and east coasts of England and in the major industrial estuaries such as the Mersey, Tyne and Clyde. In recent years, there has been ever increasing pressure for development along the coast, especially for tourist and recreation facilities, large scale industrial development and housing. In some areas the siting of tidal barrages, port expansion, oil and gas pipelines, marine fish farms, coastal quarries and land reclamation schemes have heightened concerns over the conservation of the coastal environment.

1.2 The Department of the Environment (DoE) has recently issued policy guidance on coastal planning to assist planners, developers and others in the forward planning of land use and control of development (DoE, 1992; PPG 20). This report has been prepared as part of the DoE research contract PECD 7/1/403 which addresses two major themes that are of direct relevance to planning in the coastal zone:

- the wider context of coastal management within which the planning system operates (Task 1); and

- the technical information on the physical environment needed to support decision making in the coastal zone (Task 2).

1.3 This report addresses the first of these Tasks (Tables 1.1 and 1.2). The preliminary results of Task 1 were used by the DoE to provide a foundation for the PPG, although it must be recognised that this report examines many wider management issues which lie beyond the control of the statutory planning system. For a wider audience, the report aims to present a synthesis of the enormous volume of legislation, policy advice and research relevant to management of the **coastal zone** in the UK (see Figure 1.1, Table 1.3 and Appendix A which contains a detailed definition of the coastal zone).

1.4 In preparing the report it quickly became apparent that the framework for coastal management is rapidly changing. Details presented in the various sections should be seen as an indication of the picture during the period 1992–1993. However, this picture is likely to become quickly out-of-date as new legislation, regulations or advice is prepared by the relevant Government departments or authorities. However, it is hoped that the broader perspective and general conclusions may have a longer relevance.

Physical constraints to development on the coast

1.5 Many parts of the coast are subject to natural hazards ranging from flooding to erosion and deposition. However, the prevalent view in the past has been that these are problems for the developer and not planning issues. This has led to coastal development in vulnerable locations and demands for coast protection or sea defences funded by the public purse once the threats become apparent. These works often have implications for other interests as they may seriously affect the amenity and ecological value of the coast and give rise to conflict between local interests and conservation bodies. It is likely that the possible effects of sea level rise might heighten the potential for such conflict.

C

1.6 That coastal planning has taken insufficient account of the dynamic nature of the coast is largely due to a lack of awareness of the physical environment and the limited use of technical information in support of decision making. This is certainly not unique to the coastal zone. It has been recognised that one of the main problems facing land use planning is that few planners have an earth science background and few earth scientists have a planning background, and hence there is often a communication gap between the two groups (eg Brook and Marker, 1987).

Table 1.1 The aims and objectives of the study

This report presents the results of the Department of the Environment (DoE) research contract PECD 7/1/403 entitled **Planning policy for the coast and earth science information in support of coastal planning and management.** The aims of this research are to:

- review the existing situation with regard to the agencies and mechanisms relevant to planning and management in the coastal zone as a basis for Planning Policy Guidance;

- provide a report for planning and management practitioners on the use of earth science information in decision making in the coastal zone to assist implementation of guidance;

- disseminate results to appropriate audiences to help ensure that these are applied.

This report addresses the first of these aims and presents a **review of coastal planning and management policy and responsibility.**

The objectives of this task are to:

- review the powers, policies and other involvement of all bodies with an interest in planning and managing the coastal zone;

- identify the nature and effectiveness of powers, policies and actions for the planning, management and conservation of the coastal zone in the UK;

- consider policies and practice in coastal planning in Europe and overseas, including European Community policies and proposals which may affect or influence planning, management and conservation in the coastal zone;

- provide a report which identifies the key issues for coastal zone planning as an input to Planning Policy Guidance (now issued as PPG 20; DoE, 1992).

1.7 In this context the DoE have promoted a number of important initiatives. First, a series of broad national reviews of physical hazards (landsliding; erosion, deposition and flooding; natural underground cavities; undermined ground; foundation conditions; seismic risk) have been carried out to provide general indications of those areas where these factors might be material planning considerations.

1.8 The DoE has also been actively encouraging the development of **applied earth science mapping** so that geological, geomorphological, hydrological, soil and rock data can be made available to planners, engineers, developers and others whose decisions are affected by ground conditions. In recent years the DoE, together with the Welsh Office and Scottish Development Department, has commissioned in excess of 40 such studies. The broad aim of all these has been to produce earth science information in a format that is readily accessible by non-specialists in the earth sciences. Examples range from the "green field" site at Glenrothes, Fife (Nickless, 1982), an urban-fringe zone and rural zone around Bath (Forster et al., 1985) and a coastal area of tourist potential and conservation value in Torbay (Doornkamp, 1988).

1.9 Such maps provide a snapshot of possible limitations in an area which could be directly set against other factors which are already considered by the planner, such as existing and proposed land-uses, conservation and amenity areas, agricultural land potential, communications and natural habitats (Figure 1.2). It should perhaps be stressed that the aim is not that earth science information should necessarily override all other factors but that it should be capable of being considered alongside those other factors and given a weighting appropriate to the particular circumstances. Indeed, applied earth science mapping can heighten the awareness of the physical conditions prevailing within an area and should, if used correctly, enable further detailed investigations to focus on key factors which may otherwise have been overlooked, such as the presence of potential unstable ground conditions or flood risks. In other instances awareness of the geological conditions may prevent the approval of planning permission in cases which could lead to considerable effects on surrounding properties or other interests.

1.10 The consequences of not taking into account the nature of the physical environment are most acute on the coast because, unlike most inland areas, the coastal landscape cannot be considered to be stable. The coastline may experience rapid and major changes, sometimes over a matter of decades. For example, in the 14th century Wisbech was a thriving coastal port, it now lies 30km inland (Astbury, 1958). At Studland, Dorset, four large ridges of sand have developed since 1607, the last of which has formed since 1930. During a single storm during the autumn of 1694, 16 fertile farms in the Culbin area, covering 20–30km^2, were overwhelmed by up to 30m of wind blown sand (the Culbin Sands Disaster; Bain, 1922; Lamb, 1991). In 1829 the entire village of Kettleness, north of Whitby, slid into the sea, overnight, and the inhabitants had to be rescued by ships lying offshore (Jones and Lee, in press). Removal of a natural headland, in the 1860s, as part of a harbour development at Ventnor, Isle of Wight, led to accelerated beach erosion and landslide activity, over the next decade (Lee et al, 1991).

Table 1.2 The programme of work

In order to achieve these objectives the following programme of work was undertaken largely between September–November 1991:

- reviewing and taking stock of in-house information held by Rendel Geotechnics and the DoE;

- undertaking a desk study of legislation, government advice, development plans, proposals for coastal planning and management by interest groups and relevant literature on coastal planning and management, both UK and foreign;

- preparing a working definition of the coastal zone appropriate to this task, for use in the study;

- surveying and interviewing key agencies with responsibilities for planning and regulating activities in the coastal zone, to a maximum of 25 contacts;

- surveying other interested key parties;

- interviewing, in depth, a sample of 5 local authorities, including discussions with key individuals.

Account was taken, where appropriate, of the different legal and administrative bases for planning and government which exist in Scotland and Northern Ireland.

The dynamic nature of the coastal zone

Coastal landforms and processes

1.11 In general, coastal environments and processes can be characterised by the type of coast, the nature of the sediment involved and the position along the shore profile (the line through HWM to LWM and beyond; Pethick & Burd, 1993):

(a) **open coasts;** high energy environments dominated by solid materials:

   – low shore **rocky platforms;**

   – upper shore **rocky cliffs.**

(b) **bays;** intermediate energy environments characterised by non–cohesive materials (ie sands and gravels):

   – low shore **shingle and sand beaches;**

   – upper shore **shingle ridges and sand dunes.**

(c) **estuaries;** low energy environments with cohesive materials (muds):

   – low shore **mudflats;**

   – upper shore **salt marshes.**

1.12 In turn, the shore profile position is characterised by a set of dominant processes:

(a) **low shore;** sediment transport and deposition.

(b) **upper shore;** biological processes, erosion and flooding.

1.13 The evolution of coastal landforms is part of a complex response to the prevailing conditions. Features such as beaches, shore platforms and cliffs act as buffers against erosion, absorbing the wave energy arriving at the coast until a balance is reached. Most places have not reached this point and so continue to change. Orford Ness, for example, has grown 6km in length since around 1500. Others are relict forms created under different environmental conditions, such as Chesil Beach which rolled onshore during the period of major sea level rise between 15,000 and 5,000 years ago. If such features are destroyed there is no natural mechanism to recreate them under the present environmental conditions.

Figure 1.1 Defining the coastal zone

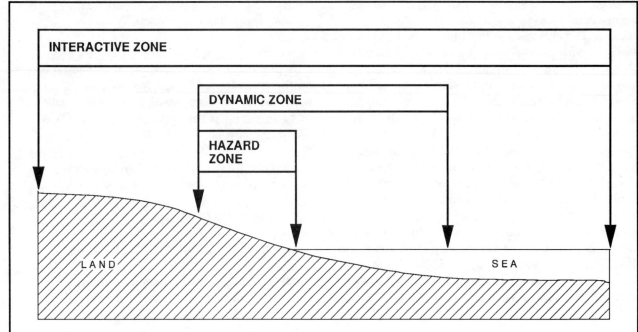

The concept of risk as the interaction of the human environment with the physical environment is illustrated below. Only when the two systems are in conflict do hazards such as landsliding become a threat to the community. Of particular importance is the fact that as urban development increases, intensifies or spreads into vulnerable areas so the potential impact of hazards increases.

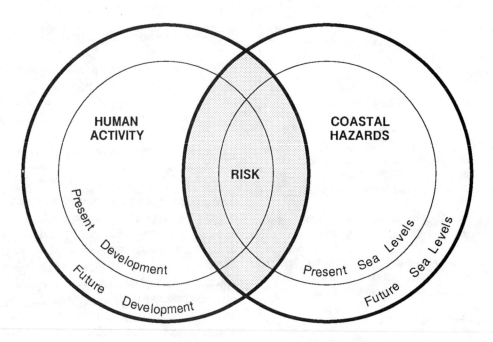

1.14 The coastline itself is in a delicate balance between the wave energy, tidal regime, resistance of the rocks and the supply of sediments. Where there is a small tidal range of less than 2m, as on the east coast of Norfolk the wave action is concentrated over a narrow range. This makes the waves more effective in shaping the shoreline and features such as sandy beaches and spits dominate. In areas with larger tidal ranges, as in Lincolnshire, tide–related landscapes dominate with features such as salt marshes and mudflats (Figures 1.3 and 1.4).

1.15 Changes or adjustments in form only occur when the resistance of the landscape is exceeded by the force of an event. Not all events cause change; **formative events** are those which most effectively shape the coastline. In some instances they may be very rare large events (high magnitude, low frequency) as is often the case for major coastal landslides. Smaller, more frequent events may dictate the characteristic form of eroding clifflines or salt marshes.

1.16 **Storm surges** are an important example of a rare event that can cause considerable damage to coastal environments. In general surges on the UK coast are single waves that have developed in response to rapidly moving low pressure cells (depressions) which tend to increase the tidal height. The transformation of these waves in the shallow coastal waters can cause a surge wave with a height of 2m or more. The occurrence of these storm surges and their prediction is of considerable importance to coastal managers.

Coastal Systems

1.17 The coastline may be viewed as a series of interlinked physical systems, comprising both offshore and onshore elements. Sediment (clay, silt, sand, gravel etc.,) is moved around the coast by waves and currents in a series of linked systems (**sediment transport cells**). Simple cells comprise an arrangement of sediment source areas (eg eroding cliffs, the sea bed), areas where sediment is moved by coastal processes and sediment sinks (eg beaches, estuaries or offshore sinks; Figure 1.5). Along a particular stretch of coast there may be a series of such cells, often operating at different scales (Figure 1.6). It is recognised that change in one part of a cell can lead to adjustment to other parts (Bray et al, 1991). This has important implications for any development in the coastal zone which interferes with the movement of sediment around the coast (eg harbour breakwaters, groynes, etc.,).

1.18 These longshore sediment transport cells are not the only important physical systems acting within the coastal zone. **Estuaries** provide an important link between these coastal cells and rivers, with their form and character determined by the tidal range, the river flows and the degree of mixing between the fresh and saline waters; extensive **mudflats and salt marshes** have developed where fine grained sediment (clay and silt) is laid down in sheltered areas with high tidal ranges; **coastal sand dunes** have developed as a result of wind–blown (aeolian) sand transport; **major coastal landslide systems** are found on many soft rock coasts, having been produced by repeated marine erosion since the rise in sea level at the end of the last glaciation (around 100m over the last 14,000 years), although contemporary

Table 1.3 A three–tier approach to defining the coast

This definition recognises the importance of both the human and physical systems and the narrow zone in which the two systems interact to create coastal risks (Figure 1.1):

(i) a broad coastal activity zone, or **interactive zone** where human activities are influenced by or can influence the quality of the whole coastal zone. This zone may extend as far inland or seaward as necessary to control activities which may have an impact on the coast.

(ii) a coastal process zone, **the dynamic zone** (within the interactive zone), which is directly affected by offshore and nearshore natural processes (eg storm surges, erosion, deposition, flooding, landslides). The limits of this zone may be more rigorously defined using geomorphological and ecological criteria.

(iii) a narrow **hazard zone** defined as the landward area potentially susceptible to damage from coastal processes. Such damage may include potential loss of life as well as property damage.

The boundaries of this zone may be the same as the landward limits of the dynamic zone, but the areas defined need to be classified according to the magnitude and frequency of damaging events. If development has already taken place in such areas special management considerations may be needed.

These zones also have definable limits along the coastline, corresponding with physical systems, such as estuaries or sediment cells, for the dynamic zone and administrative areas for the interactive zone. A combination of these physical and human system boundaries are relevant in the hazard zone.

Figure 1.2 Key ground characteristics for planning and development, Torbay (after Doornkamp, 1988)

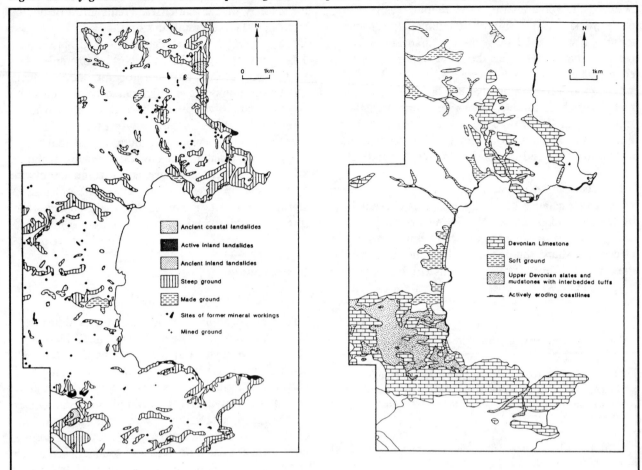

GROUND CHARACTERISTICS	DESCRIPTION
Cavernous limestone	Extent of Middle Devonian limestone affected by solution weathering to a variable degree. Possible presence of extensive soil–filled solution pipes, caverns and swallow holes in bedrock. Infill may contain large voids. Extent of solution weathering cannot be determined without investigation.
Upper Devonian slates and mudstones with interbedded tuffs	Outcrop of interbedded and interdigitated mudrocks and tuffs. Problems due to extreme local variation in foundation strata and depths of weathering causing associated difficulties in excavation and foundation design.
Soft ground	Alluvial, colluvial, estuarine and marine deposits. Low bearing capacities due to shear strengths, high compressibility soft silts and clays, with sand and gravel layers and bands of peat. Possibility of high groundwater tables and flooding.
Actively eroding coastlines	Areas of active coastal landsliding ranging from rockfalls to translational failures.
Ancient coastal landslides	Sites of long–term instability. Problems may result from periodic movements.
Active inland landslides	Areas of presently unstable ground.
Ancient inland landslides	Ancient landslides, presently stable but could be reactivated.
Steep slopes	Slopes steeper than 1:5.
Sites of former mineral workings	Problems associated with steep rock faces or infill material of variable bearing capacity.
Undermined ground	Sites of former iron and tin workings.
Landfill sites	Waste disposal sites.

6

Figure 1.3 Tidal systems around Great Britain and the associated tidal ranges at the coast (after Pethick, 1984)

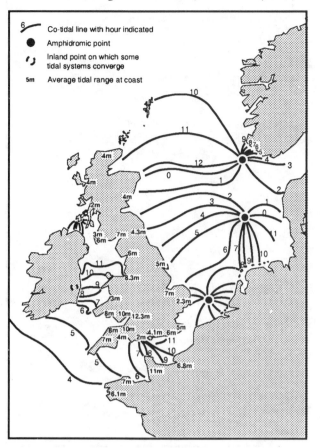

movements are often in response to other factors such as weathering and changes in groundwater conditions; **high, near-vertical cliffs** occur along hard rock coasts, providing an almost passive barrier against the effects of wave attack.

1.19 The great diversity of coastal landscapes around the UK coast is reflected in the variety of coastal planning and management issues that occur.

Coastal hazards

1.20 The coast is a very dynamic environment. Severe onshore gales can cause huge waves to batter the coastline. In 1979, for example, low-lying parts of the Isle of Portland were badly affected by 15m high waves which demolished property, smashed cars and severed communication links with the mainland (Perry, 1981). The UK coast is littered with wrecks which sank or ran aground in high seas. For example, the biggest disaster in the history of ocean racing occurred during the Fastnet yacht race in August 1979 when a severe gale sunk 23 boats and drowned 17 competitors.

1.21 Large areas of the coast and low lying land adjacent to tidal estuaries are vulnerable to flooding from the sea as a result of storm surges. In December 1663 Samuel Pepys wrote in his diary:

> "there was last night the greatest tide that ever was remembered in England to have been in this river, all Whitehall having been drowned."

1.22 Belfast city centre was flooded 125 times between 1916 and 1972, often as a result of high spring tides (Prior & Betts, 1974). Over 300 people were killed by the east coast floods on 31 January 1953 when over 800km^2 were flooded as a result of a storm surge (Grieve, 1959). However, perhaps the most severe flooding in the UK occurred in 1606 in Severnside when about 2000 people were drowned as the sea defences were overtopped (Perry, 1981).

1.23 Stretches of coast are prone to rapid retreat because of coastal erosion. Along the Holderness coast, for example, Valentin (1971) calculated erosion rates of between 1 and 6m a year since 1852. It is known that over 200km^2 of land has been lost over the last thousand years, including at least 26 villages listed in the Domesday survey of 1086. Similar, albeit less dramatic, rates of retreat have been recorded for Lincolnshire between Mablethorpe and Skegness and the Norfolk coast from Happisburgh to Weybourne. Further south, on the Suffolk coastline between Lowestoft and Thorpness severe erosion has been a major long-term problem, particularly at Dunwich where all that remains is a fragment of the cemetery.

1.24 Stretches of cliffed coastline are affected by landslides ranging from small rockfalls to massive areas of landsliding such as on the west Dorset coast between West Bay and Lyme Regis. A recent review of the recorded extent of landsliding in Great Britain revealed 1302 separate coastal examples, although there are likely to be many more as yet unrecorded (Geomorphological Services Ltd 1987; Jones & Lee, in press). Many slides have caused problems for communities on the coast, ranging from damage to property and services in Ventnor, Isle of Wight (Lee & Moore, 1991; Lee et al, 1991) to loss of life, as happened when a party of schoolchildren were caught in a sudden rock slide in Lulworth Cove, in 1977 (Jones & Lee, in press).

1.25 Deposition of sediment within estuaries can lead to significant channel maintenance problems for port and harbour authorities. The port of Colraine, Northern Ireland, for example, was noted

Figure 1.4 The relationship between tidal ranges and landforms around the coast of Great Britain (after Pethick, 1984)

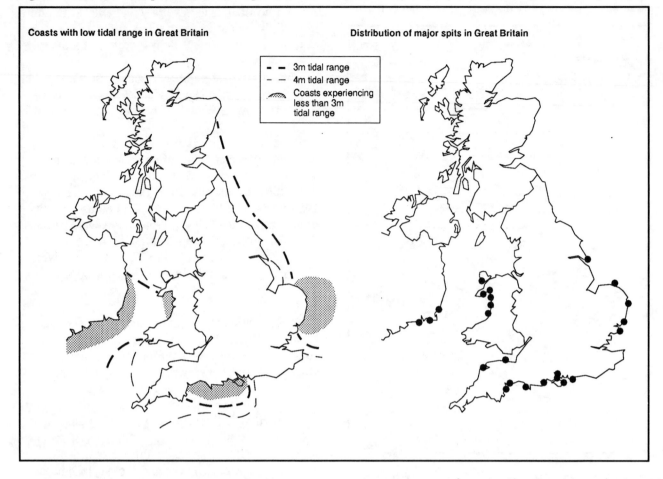

Coasts with low tidal range in Great Britain

Distribution of major spits in Great Britain

— — 3m tidal range
– – 4m tidal range
Coasts experiencing
less than 3m
tidal range

for the problematic shoals at the mouth of the River Bann. These shoals were reported to have migrated over 200–250m before training works between 1883–1889 arrested the movement. Over the next 40 years a small sand shoal accumulated and impaired navigation. Since 1975 120,000m^3 of sand has been dredged from the channel, although it is reported that this action may have led to erosion of adjacent beaches (Carter, 1988).

1.26 These coastal processes are, of course, natural phenomena that have become significant hazards because they have increasingly imposed themselves upon vulnerable communities. In this sense, urban growth and land use changes have transformed these processes into community hazards.

Coastal Resources

1.27 It would be wrong to imply that coastal processes are wholly detrimental to the economy through causing losses from erosion, deposition and flooding. It should be recognised that these processes are essential for maintaining the value of

many coastal landscapes and habitats. Without continued erosion, the famous white chalk cliffs of the Seven Sisters would become drab and less spectacular.

1.28 The varied nature of the coastline also provides significant benefits of shelter and deep water for ports and harbours, breeding grounds for fish and shellfish and opportunities for recreation and tourism. The sea bed has become an important source of sand and gravel for the construction industry and, increasingly, for use in beach recharge schemes. In 1989 marine sources provided nearly 21M tonnes of sand and gravel or 8% of the total production of England and Wales.

1.29 It is recognised, however, that in many coastal locations there is little sedimentation, with much of the sand and gravel resource being a legacy of the Pleistocene glaciations. The present input by rivers is largely trapped in their estuaries and nearshore; elsewhere the sea bed comprises sediments that are sorted and redistributed by currents and storms (Cook and Taylor, 1992). The marine sand and gravel resource is, therefore, finite. It has been estimated that, with increased

Figure 1.5 Coastal sediment transport model for West Dorset (after Bray, 1990)

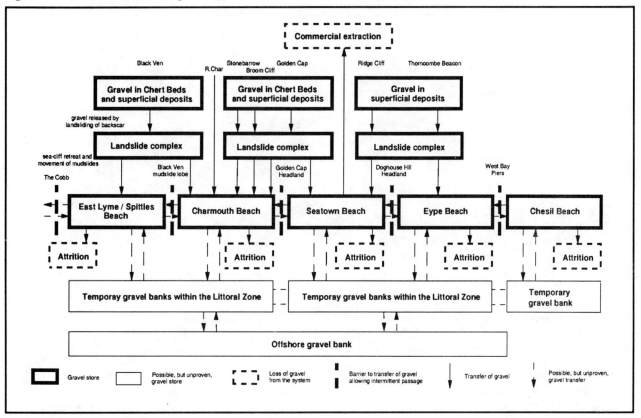

extraction rates, the identified accessible resources might be available for only the next 25 years or so.

1.30 Following the Verney Report of 1976 (DoE, 1976), the demand for aggregates in southern England has led to the development of the concept of coastal superquarries (with a production of the order of 10M tonnes a year) to supply crushed rock aggregate. In 1988 Foster Yeoman opened their Glensanda quarry in Loch Linnhe, west Scotland, and proposals exist for other sites on the Scottish coast (Figure 1.7). Coastal quarries are, of course, not a recent development; the Isle of Portland, for example, has long been a major source of building stone. However, superquarries are distinctive because of the scale of operations and the great distances over which material would be transported (Whitbread and Marsay, 1992).

1.31 The coast also provides important locational benefits for heavy industry and energy generating facilities. Coastal waters are used as coolants in nuclear and thermal power stations and the coast itself provides convenient locations for the reception, processing and distribution of imported fuels and raw materials. For many years the coast has also been viewed as a potential source of energy through wave power and tidal power.

1.32 Coastal landforms also have an important role in protecting the coastline from erosion and

flooding. Salt marshes, for example, are capable of absorbing a large proportion of the wave energy arriving at the coast and, thus, provide a valuable defence from sea floods. Beaches, spits and bars perform a similar role in dissipating wave energy and can protect the open coast from erosion. Conversely, the sediment supplied by the erosion of cliffs can be important to sustain these landforms and, hence, natural coastal defences.

1.33 The coastline also provides unique opportunities to view the varied geological structure of the UK and to see natural processes shaping the landscape. The scale and continuity of geological exposures along the coast is rarely matched inland. In addition, many sections of the coast are of international importance because they are agreed reference points for the world's geological history.

The diversity of coastal habitats

1.34 The coastal zone supports a great diversity of plant and animal communities; the reed beds, lagoons and islands of Minsmere, Suffolk are home to over 100 species of breeding and migratory birds; the Farne Islands are a major nesting site for sea birds and the principle breeding grounds of the

9

Figure 1.6 Principal sediment pathways along the south coast, between Lyme Regis and West Sussex (after Bray et al, 1991)

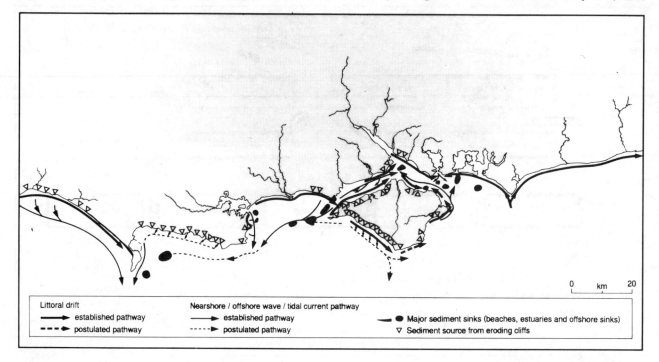

Littoral drift
→ established pathway
- - -► postulated pathway

Nearshore / offshore wave / tidal current pathway
→ established pathway
- - -► postulated pathway

●— Major sediment sinks (beaches, estuaries and offshore sinks)
▽ Sediment source from eroding cliffs

0   km   20

grey seal; the Wash is the most important estuarine habitat in the UK, supporting over 250,000 waterfowl each winter.

1.35 Estuaries and rock coasts sustain highly productive ecosystems, with the potential for supplying nutrients to adjacent areas (Davidson et al, 1991). The ecology of the Irish Sea, for example, is supported by a series of estuaries around its landward margins. This chain of estuaries is of importance in maintaining fish and bird populations and provides a series of feeding stops for migratory birds (Carter, 1992).

1.36 It is important to appreciate that the ecology of the coastline has developed within the framework provided by the physical environment. Thus the major coastal habitats (sand dunes, salt marshes, inter tidal sands and mudflats, shingle structures, saline lagoons, soft cliffs, coastal heath, grasslands, hard rock cliffs) are dependent on and vulnerable to erosion, deposition and flooding processes.

1.37 These habitats are vulnerable to any changes that may occur within coastal systems, either as a result of extreme natural events or human interference. In a study of habitat loss, CERC (1992) identified that salt marshes and inter tidal mudflats have suffered significant losses in recent decades. For example, Burd (1992) reported between 10–40% loss of salt marsh areas in south east England since 1973, mainly due to erosion. Losses of other habitats has been on a smaller

scale, often related to human interference (CERC, 1992). The rapid movement of pollutants around the coast, from accidental spillages or unlicensed discharges, is also a recurrent threat to many habitats.

Sea level rise

1.38 There has been much debate in recent years of the global warming/rising sea level issue. The Intergovernmental Panel on Climate Change has identified the extent to which rising sea levels are in evidence around the world, and the extent to which further rises may be expected (Houghton et al 1990). The Second World Climate Conference (Jager and Ferguson, 1991) reached similar conclusions, which in the case of the British Isles suggest that there could be a rise of between 50 and 70 cm over the next 100 years. However, it is clear that this rise would not be the same in all parts of Britain since long–term vertical land movements are still taking place in some areas, and the more northerly parts (eg the coastal margins of the Highlands of Scotland) may continue to see a relative drop in sea level (Figures 1.8 & 1.9).

1.39 As yet, British tidal gauge records show no clear evidence of an acceleration in the rate of sea level rise (Woodworth, 1990; Woodworth et al, 1991). However, even if there is no acceleration, mean sea level is predicted to rise by as much as 10cm over the next 20 years on parts of the south

10

Figure 1.7 Coastal superquarries: main locations of interest

- Principal geological resources of technical interest

North Scotland

Shetland

Western Isles & West Coast

Figure 1.8 Estimated current rates of crustal movement (mm/yr) in Great Britain (after Shennon, 1989).

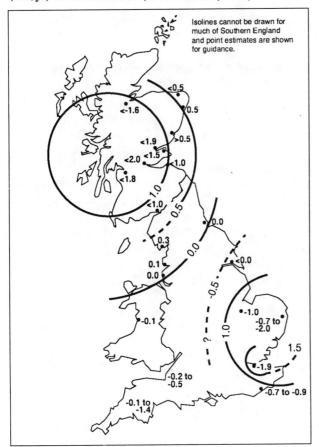

Isolines cannot be drawn for much of Southern England and point estimates are shown for guidance.

coast (Bray et al, 1992). Allowances given by MAFF (November 1991; see also DoE Circular 30/92) for the design or adaption of coastal defences with an effective life beyond 2030 range from 6mm per year (south east and southern England) to 4mm per year (north west and north east England) and 5mm per year (the remainder of England and Wales).

1.40   Where a sea–level rise is experienced, there may well be a tendency for increased erosion of soft cliffs to take place and, consequently, the build up of some beaches. Unprotected coastal lowlands may be flooded more frequently, although salt marshes could grow in height as sea level rises and, therefore, continue to provide natural protection. In places, salt water could intrude into underground freshwater (coastal aquifers).

1.41   There may even be some changes in sea currents, brought about by wave refraction, leading to changes in sediment supply and distribution with the effect that there could be a shift in the location of areas of erosion and deposition. Some salt marshes and mudflats may, therefore, be at risk if they are unable to maintain adequate accretion during the period of sea level rise and, consequently, valuable ecological sites might be threatened. Where habitats abut coast defence structures the intertidal zone could be progressively squeezed into an ever narrower zone, with a consequent effect on coastal habitats and wintering bird populations (Doody, 1991).

1.42   The specific effects of sea level rise will depend on the character of the coastline at a particular location. Coastal responses to sea level rise are likely to be complex and, to a large extent, unpredictable. Much will depend on local conditions including wave regime, changes to beach profiles and the availability of sediment.

1.43   In addition to the obvious threats to unprotected lowlands, some sand dunes, marshlands and mudflats (Figure 1.10), sea level rise will heighten those coastal management problems which are already experienced. In this context it is important to emphasise that present–day storms are capable of generating water heights several metres above average levels. The issue of global warming and the potential for sea level change raises not so much the issue of the specific policies that are required to meet it as the need to have in place an appropriate coastal management context to effectively cope with such problems as and when they have been more precisely defined.

11

Figure 1.9 Recent sea level changes (mm/year) around Great Britain (after Carter, 1989)

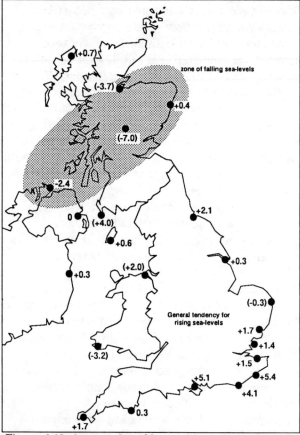

Figure 1.10 Areas vulnerable to rising sea levels around Great Britain (after Whittle, 1989; ITE, 1989 and Doody, 1991)

Measuring the effectiveness of coastal planning and management

1.44 One of the key objectives of this Task has been to measure the effectiveness of planning and management within the coastal zone (Table 1.1). However, effectiveness can only be measured against set criteria. For the present purposes the criteria must reflect the central themes of the research, namely to demonstrate the links between the planning system and the management of other activities, and to highlight the need to take into account the dynamic nature of the coastal environment.

1.45 Following a brief description of the background to the legal and administrative framework (Chapter 2), Chapters 3–8 outline the main features of the 3 "systems" to protect the coastal environment (coastal defence, pollution control and conservation) and the 3 broad administrative systems which control development in the coastal zone: on land, on the sea bed and at sea. After briefly describing the legislative or regulatory frameworks, the effectiveness of each "system" is examined in terms of 4 criteria which reflect the unique problems facing coastal managers:

– to what extent does the system consider coastal dynamics?

– to what extent does the system take the environmental effects of a project into account?

– to what extent does the system take into account the interests of other groups?

– to what extent does the system enable coordinated decision making across the coastal zone?

1.46 Chapter 9 includes an appraisal of the key issues for the coastal zone, some of which have been addressed in Planning Policy Guidance note 20: Coastal Planning (DoE, 1992).

References: Chapter 1

Astbury, A.K., 1958, The black fens. Cambridge: Golden Head Press.

Bain, G., 1922, The Culbin Sands or the story of a buried estate. Nairn (Nairnshire Telegraph).

Bray, M.J., 1990, Coastal sediment transport model for West Dorset. In R.J. Allison (ed) Landslides of the Dorset coast. BGRG Field Guide.

Bray, M.J., 1991 The SCOPAC sediment transport study. Proceedings of the SCOPAC conference on Coastal Instability and Development Planning, Southsea.

Bray, M.J., Carter, D.J., & Hooke, J.M., 1991, Coastal Sediment Transport Study. Reports to SCOPAC, Department of Geography, Portsmouth Poly.

Bray, M.J., Carter, D.J., & Hooke, J.M., 1992, Sea-level rise and Global Warming: Scenarios, Physical Impacts and Policies. Report to SCOPAC, Department of Geography, Portsmouth Poly.

Brook, D., & Marker, B., 1987, Thematic geological mapping as an essential tool in land use planning. In Culshaw, M.G., Bell, F.G., Cripps, J.C. & O'Hara, M., (eds) Planning and Engineering Geology. Geol. Soc. Eng. Grp. Spec. Public. No. 4, 211-214.

Burd, F., 1992, Erosion and vegetation change on the saltmarshes of Essex and north Kent between 1973 and 1988. Research 7 Survey in Nature Conservation No.42, NCC Peterborough.

Cambridge Environmental Research Consultants Ltd, 1992, Targets for coastal habitat recreation. English Nature Research Report No.35.

Carter, R.W.G., 1988 Coastal Environments: An introduction to Physical, Ecological and Cultural Systems of Coastlines. Academic Press.

Carter, R.W.G., 1989, Rising sea level. Geology Today, 5, 63-67.

Carter, R.W.G., 1992 Coastal conservation. In M.G. Barrett (ed) Coastal zone planning and management, Thomas Telford, 21-36.

Cook, P.J. & Taylor, L.E., 1992, Sustaining the coastal zone and its resources. British Geological Survey Technical Report WB/92/30.

Davidson, N.C., d'A Laffoley, D., Doody, J.P., Way, L.S., Gordon, J., Drake, C.M., Pienkowski, M.W., Mitchell, R. & Duff, K.L., 1991, Nature conservation and estuaries in Great Britain. Nature Conservancy Council.

Department of the Environment, 1976, Aggregates: The Way Ahead. (The Verney Report). HMSO.

Department of the Environment, 1992, Coastal Planning. PPG 20, HMSO.

Doody, J.P., 1991 Global warming and sea-level change on British estuaries. In N C Davidson et al (eds) Nature conservation and estuaries in Great Britain 381-387. Nature Conservancy Council.

Doornkamp, J.C. (ed), 1988, Applied earth science background: Torbay. GSL Publications.

Forster, A., Hobbs, P.R.N., Monkhouse, R.A. & Wyatt, R.J., 1985, Environmental Geology Study; Parts of west Wiltshire and southeast Avon. British Geological Survey Environmental Geological Study.

Geomorphological Services Ltd., 1987, Review of research into landsliding in Great Britain. Series D Vol.3 Legislative and Administrative Provisions and a review of overseas practice. Report to DoE.

Grieve, H., 1959, The Great Tide. Chelmsford: Essex County Council.

Houghton, J.T., Jenkins, G.J. & Ephraums (eds) 1990, Climate change: The IPCC Scientific Assessment. Cambridge Univ. Press.

Institute of Terrestrial Ecology, 1989, Climate change, rising sea level and the British coast. Institute of Terrestrial Ecology research publication No.1, HMSO.

Jager, J. & Ferguson, H.L. (eds), 1991, Climate change: science impacts and policy. Cambridge Univ. Press.

Jones, D.K.C., & Lee, E.M., in press, Landsliding in Great Britain: a review for the Department of the Environment. HMSO.

Lamb, H.H., 1991, Historic storms of the North Sea, British Isles and Northwest Europe. Cambridge University Press.

Lee, E.M., & Moore, R., 1991, Coastal Landslip Potential Assessment, Isle of Wight Undercliff, Ventnor. DoE.

Lee, E.M., Doornkamp, J.C., Brunsden, D., & Noton, N.H., 1991, Ground Movement in Ventnor, Isle of Wight. DoE.

Nickless, E.F.P., 1982, Environmental geology of the Glenrothes district, Fife Region. Institute of Geological Sciences Report No. 82/15.

Perry, A.H., 1981, Environmental hazards in the British Isles. George Allen & Unwin.

Pethick, J., 1984, An introduction to coastal geomorphology. Arnold.

Pethick, J., & Burd, F., 1993, Coastal defence and the environment: a guide to good practice. MAFF.

Prior, D.B., & Betts, N.I., 1974, Flooding in Belfast. Irish Geography, 7, 1-18.

Shennon, I., 1989, Holocene crustal movements and sea level changes in Great Britain. J. Quaternary Science, 4, 77-89.

Valentin, H., 1971. Land loss at Holderness. In J A Spears (ed.) Applied coastal geomorphology. London. Macmillan, 116-137.

Whitbread, M. & Marsay, A., 1992, Coastal superquarries to supply south-east England aggregate requirements. Ove Arup Economics and Planning. HMSO.

Whittle, I.R., 1989, Lands at risk from sea level rise in the UK. In J.C. Doornkamp (ed) Greenhouse effect and rising UK sea levels, 85–93. M1 Press.

Woodworth, P.L., 1990, A search for accelerations in records of European mean sea level. Int.J.Climatol, 10, 129–143.

Woodworth, P.L., Shaw, S.M. & Blackman, D.L., 1991, Secular trends in mean tidal range around the British Isles and along the adjacent European coastline. Geophys. J. Internat. 104, 593–609.

2 Background to the Legal and Administrative Framework

Introduction: Activities that require a coastal location.

2.1 Although opportunities for development on the coast may be restricted by coastal hazards (eg erosion and flooding) and important natural resources (eg habitats and landscapes), there is a range of activities that require a coastal location. Examples are described throughout this report in the context of the regulatory procedures which control them; ports and harbours, marinas and moorings, major developments such as oil and gas terminals, mineral extraction such as superquarries and marine aggregates, marine fish farming, sea fisheries, energy generation and sewage treatment and disposal works.

2.2 Of particular importance are **tourism and recreation**, which can make a valuable contribution to the local economy in many coastal areas (Table 2.1). The growth in tourism has been accompanied by significant changes in demand away from traditional seaside holidays towards more specialist interest and activity holidays. Thus, whilst the demand for tourist facilities has been expanding, there has been a decline in many seaside resorts.

2.3 Although the nature of facilities and development needed to support tourism are not fundamentally different from other types of development, the industry can have a significant impact on other coastal activities and interests; it may lead to disturbance of coastal habitats or increased pressure for recreational facilities on the undeveloped coast.

2.4 The growth of the tourism and recreation industries are, however, only one of the issues facing coastal management. These issues often involve reconciling conflicting and incompatible demands, including:

- facilitating economic development;

- meeting the demands of the tourist industry;

- protecting areas of historic, scenic, geological or ecological importance;

- protecting vulnerable communities against the effects of erosion and flooding.

2.5 Finding the right balance can lead to conflicts between the different interests. Indeed, many existing communities and business interests sometimes feel that conservation policies restrict local employment opportunities and economic growth, whilst others may regard areas of national importance as being progressively spoilt by inappropriate development. The potential threat of rising sea levels is likely to heighten these concerns and provide a focus for many aspects of coastal planning and management.

Coastal Planning and Management

2.6 Coastal **planning** and **management** are not synonymous. Planning relates to the operation of the **statutory planning system** which has its basis in the Town and Country Planning Act 1990 (as amended). This legislation clearly defines a narrow role for planning in the coastal zone as it is concerned solely with the development and use of **land**. The planning system can be an instrument to achieve some coastal management objectives through shaping and guiding development and land use through policies and proposals in development plans and through development control decisions. However, management of the coastal zone also

Table 2.1: Government policy for tourism (adapted from DoE, 1992; PPG 21 Tourism)

Government policy on tourism is coordinated by the respective Departments of Natural Heritage for England, Wales and Scotland. The 3 statutory national tourist boards have responsibility for promoting and developing tourism, advising Government and local authorities on matters affecting tourism. Many of the functions of the national boards are devolved to the independent regional tourist boards which include representatives from local authorities and businesses.

The Government is committed to encouraging tourism whilst at the same time conserving those qualities in the environment that are a major attraction for tourism. Its policy is directed at securing a proper balance between:

- maximising the economic and employment benefits that tourism can bring;

- promoting geographical and seasonal spread of tourism;

- encouraging the development of non-traditional destinations as well as the more popular visitor locations;

- respecting the needs of the tourist industry and its customers;

- safeguarding of the environment; and

- protecting the interests of the communities that cater for its needs, but feel its effects.

Policies for tourism must be fully consistent with the Government's environmental strategy as set out in the White Paper "This Common Inheritance" (HMSO, 1990). The central objective is to achieve **sustainable development**. Advice on how this can be achieved is presented in the reports of the **Tourism and Environment Task Force** (see English Tourist Board, 1991).

---

involves matters not concerned with land use, arising from other local authority functions and powers or activities controlled by other authorities or bodies.

2.7 Planning forms only one of a number of control and regulation systems in the coastal zone, which are concerned with the **"management"** of a wide range of activities from port and harbour operations to oil and gas exploration. However, the wide range of policies, decisions and management practices adopted by each of the bodies with a responsibility in the coastal zone can have a direct effect on planning objectives.

2.8 In recent years there has been an increasing trend for development projects that involve the use of all three elements of the coastal zone: the land, the sea and the sea bed. Examples include the redevelopment of docks and boatyards as combined marina, residential and commercial projects in the Solent (Prescott, 1990) and the urban regeneration of derelict docklands such as on Teesside. These projects and other issues, such as the effect of land claim on estuary birdlife, the disturbance of habitats by increased water-based recreation and the possible effects of marine aggregate dredging on coastal erosion rates, have led many local authorities to show an increasing awareness of the effects of sea-based activities outside their jurisdiction, resulting in conflicts of interest between organisations with interests or responsibilities in the coastal zone.

2.9 There has also been growing awareness of the potential adverse effects of many coastal activities and marine pollution on the seas around the UK. Ministerial conferences involving all the countries bordering the North Sea have been held in 1984, 1987 and 1990, to consider proactive action, including the establishment of a **North Sea Task Force**. The task force comprises scientists and policy makers from the 8 maritime countries, the Commission of the European Communities and the International Council for the Exploration of the Sea (ICES) and has produced a 5 year Plan of Action (North Sea Task Force, 1989; 1990a; 1990b).

2.10 Similar concerns about marine pollution and sea use led to the formation of the **Irish Sea Study Group** in 1985 to report on the environmental health of the sea (Irish Sea Study Group, 1990). This identified 4 topics of concern: nature conservation; waste inputs and pollution; exploitation of living marine resources; and planning, development and management. The study established 3 principle objectives for managing the Irish Sea:

- the sustainable use of all of its resources, including its living, waste absorbing, recreational and wildlife assets;

- the passing on to future generations of environmental assets at least as good and diverse as those available at present;

- the responsible use of its non-renewable resources, such as gas and minerals.

2.11 The study concluded:

"the management of its resources cannot be carried out in isolation if a serious attempt is to be made to achieve the objectives of sustainable use and the passing on of the natural heritage to future generations. At present the responsibilities and powers for managing the seas resources are too widely dispersed among different authorities, and some rationalisation of responsibilities is needed. This is particularly important in the coastal zone where there is a strong need for developments on each side of the land/sea boundary to be coordinated, at least within each region." (Irish Sea Study Group, 1990).

2.12 Concerns about the ability to achieve "sustainable use" has led to close scrutiny of the management objectives of many coastal zone activities by interested groups. For example, the Marine Conservation Society recently undertook a questionnaire survey of interested bodies to support their calls for a major reappraisal of how the coastal zone is managed (Gubbay, 1990). This study identified a number of issues of concern amongst the respondents, including:

– a lack of a national policy or strategy for use of the coastal zone;

– a lack of a planning regime for the sea;

– the number of government agencies involved in marine matters and the level of integration between land and sea–based users in the planning and management of coastal activities.

2.13 These concerns were reiterated and expanded with 22 case studies in a paper produced by Wildlife Link (1991). Many of the examples cited in this paper reflect difficulties that have arisen from the administration of an interlinked and dynamic environment by a wide variety of bodies with activity–based responsibilities. The paper recommended, as many have done before, that an integrated approach to coastal zone management should be developed:

"Coastal zone management can provide practical solutions to tackling these problems through a system which links planning for both land and sea, developing integrated policies rather than dealing with sectoral interests in isolation, and having initiatives and support at local, regional and national levels." (Wildlife Link, 1991).

2.14 The high profile interest in coastal management issues was also reflected by the variety of sponsors, speakers and delegates at the **European Workshop on Coastal Zone Management** held in Poole, Dorset during 1991. This workshop was supported by the DoE and identified a number of critical areas of concern where action was urgently needed (Countryside Commission, 1991). Amongst the key recommendations of the workshop were:

– the European Community should play a key role in developing strategies for the coastal zone, by giving high priority to integrating the special needs of coastal zones in relevant community policies, and by establishing the appropriate international framework and funding mechanisms;

– each European coastal nation should prepare a comprehensive strategy for its coastal zone. This should involve local, regional, national and international action.

Bodies involved in management of the coastal zone.

2.15 The role of regulating change and improving environmental conditions in the coastal zone is split between many authorities and bodies including central government, local authorities, harbour authorities, sea fisheries committees, the NRA, River Purification Authorities, Internal Drainage Boards, landowners and voluntary organisations. It is possible, however, to recognise 3 broad systems which act to administer and control human activity in the different elements of the coastal zone: land, sea bed and the sea (Figure 2.1).

2.16 In addition, 3 separate mechanisms have evolved to manage the impact of man on the physical environment and to minimise the risks associated with coastal development:

– protecting the quality of coastal habitats and landscapes (conservation);

– maintaining the quality of coastal waters (pollution control);

– safeguarding coastal development from erosion and flooding (coastal defence).

2.17 Whilst the statutory planning system has closely defined limits, the coastal environment is

D

Figure 2.1: Management of the coastal zone

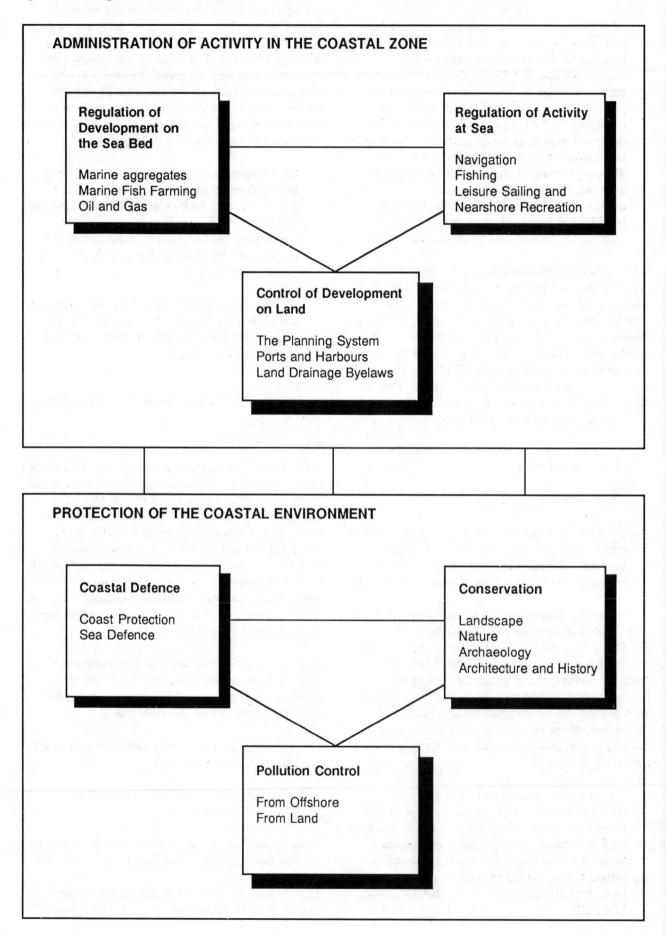

ADMINISTRATION OF ACTIVITY IN THE COASTAL ZONE

Regulation of Development on the Sea Bed

Marine aggregates
Marine Fish Farming
Oil and Gas

Regulation of Activity at Sea

Navigation
Fishing
Leisure Sailing and
Nearshore Recreation

Control of Development on Land

The Planning System
Ports and Harbours
Land Drainage Byelaws

PROTECTION OF THE COASTAL ENVIRONMENT

Coastal Defence

Coast Protection
Sea Defence

Conservation

Landscape
Nature
Archaeology
Architecture and History

Pollution Control

From Offshore
From Land

Alkali and Radiochemical Inspectorate
Cadw (Wales)
Countryside Commission
Countryside Council for Wales
Crown Estate Commissioners
Department of Agriculture (Northern Ireland)
Department of Economic Development (Northern Ireland)
Department of the Environment
Department of the Environment (Northern Ireland)
Department of National Heritage
Department of Trade and Industry
Department of Transport
English Heritage
English Nature
Foreign and Commonwealth Office
Harbour Authorities
Health and Safety Executive
Historic Scotland
HM Customs and Excise
HM Industrial Pollution Inspectorate
HM Inspectorate of Pollution
Home Office
Joint Nature Conservation Committee
Local Authorities
Ministry of Agriculture, Fisheries and Food
Ministry of Defence
National Governing Bodies of Sports
National Rivers Authority
Natural Environment Research Council
Royal Commission on the Historical Monuments of England (and equivalents in Scotland and Wales)
Regional Tourist Boards
River Purification Authorities (Scotland)
Scottish Natural Heritage
Scottish Office Agriculture and Fisheries Department
Scottish Office Environment Department
Sea Fisheries Committees
Sports Council
Trinity House
Welsh Office

affected by the broader range of policies, decisions and actions made by the numerous bodies with responsibilities in the coastal zone (Table 2.2). In this context it is important to recognise that the planning system cannot be considered to operate in isolation and, hence, its relationships with other "systems" needs to be understood in order to identify the way in which coastal zone planning and management objectives can be achieved.

The Legal and Administrative Framework.

2.18 Distinct legal systems operate for England and Wales, for Scotland and for Northern Ireland. Separate provisions or statutes are generally prepared for Scotland and Northern Ireland and these are highlighted in the text where relevant. However, it is not always possible to make specific detailed comments about the effectiveness of the coastal management approach in Scotland and Northern Ireland although it is clear they address similar problems, even if this is done in different ways.

2.19 Although individuals enjoy public rights to navigation and fishing in tidal waters and customary rights of bathing, there are many constraints on land and sea use through legislation. Most legislation concerning uses of the coastal zone has been prepared by the Government of the day, or introduced by backbench MPs or peers (private Members Bills). Such **public and general Acts** may apply to the whole UK, although normally there are separate provisions or different statutes for Scotland and Northern Ireland. Thus the **Town and Country Planning Act 1990** applies to England and Wales, but there is a separate Act for Scotland (the **Town and Country Planning (Scotland) Act 1972**).

2.20 **Private Acts** may be sought by local authorities, statutory undertakers (including harbour authorities) or developers to provide authorisation for certain projects or purposes. Bills for private Acts are not introduced by an MP, but are sought by the person or body promoting them, who must deposit a petition for the Bill in Parliament, together with a copy of the Bill itself. In recent years the proposed construction of barrages in Cardiff Bay and across the mouth of the River Tees have been the subject of private Bills.

2.21 A third form of legislation is the hybrid Act which is a combination of both a public and private Act. It is public in that it raises questions of public policy; its private element derives from the fact that it treats a particular private interest in a different way from the interests of other persons or bodies in the same category or class. Recent examples include the **Channel Tunnel Act 1987** and the **Severn Bridges Act 1992**.

2.22 Private Acts have been very important in facilitating the development of railways, canals, ports and harbours and the creation of public utilities such as electricity, gas and water. Such

Acts enabled railway companies to acquire compulsorily any land not already in their ownership which was needed for the construction and operation of the system. In addition, the companies could obtain immunity from claims in nuisance (and related torts). Indeed, the very nature of such an operation can give rise to liability in nuisance by, for example, noise and fumes. If the system is run under statutory powers, however, the operator will, as a general rule, be liable only where an action is carried out in a way which the courts consider to be negligent (Durkin et al, 1992).

2.23 In the case of ports and harbours, private Acts have been used to provide immunity from liability for interfering with public rights of navigation. Under common law these rights extend over all navigable tidal waters and any interference with them is actionable as a public nuisance. For this reason, any structure placed below HWM, such as a jetty or pier, will constitute an obstruction and so must be authorised by statute.

2.24 The **Transport and Works Act 1992** has changed the basis on which statutory authority for major infrastructure developments will be obtained. The Act introduces a new order-making system in England and Wales under which proposals for railway, tramway and other guided transport projects, inland waterways and other schemes which interfere with navigation will be approved outside Parliament (other than schemes of national importance, where Parliament will be asked to approve the broad policy and principles). Under the order developers will be able to secure all of the powers they could have secured by means of a Private Bill, including deemed planning permission, compulsory acquisition of land and the repeal or amendment of provisions in earlier private enactments.

2.25 In addition to making primary legislation, Parliament may delegate to central government powers to make subordinate legislation in the form of **Statutory Instruments**. These have the same authority as statutes but within narrower limits. Statutory Instruments are prepared by the relevant government department to regulate a wide range of matters in the coastal zone, including oil and gas operations or merchant shipping activity (eg the Petroleum Production (Seaward Areas) Regulations 1988; the Merchant Shipping (Prevention of Pollution from Garbage) Regulations 1988).

2.26 **Byelaws** may provide rules for the control of certain activities in specified areas. Powers to make byelaws for specific purposes have been granted to local authorities, the NRA, harbour authorities, sea fisheries committees, the 3 Country Conservancy Councils (English Nature, Scottish Natural Heritage and the Countryside Council for Wales), the Countryside Commission and the National Trust. The National Trust, for example, may make byelaws to control damage to Trust land and exclude the public from specified areas (**National Trust Act 1971** S.24). All byelaws, however, need to be confirmed by a higher authority, generally the appropriate Secretary of State.

2.27 The UK is a member of the **European Community** the policies of which are enforced in member states through:

- **regulations**; these are automatically enforceable in the member states without the need for implementing legislation (eg Environmentally Sensitive Areas established under Article 19 of EC Council Regulation 797/85; see Chapter 5);

- **directives**; these are binding as to their objectives, but require member states to implement them through suitable national legislation (eg **EC Directive on Bathing Waters** (76/160/EEC) is implemented through the **Water Resources Act 1991**, see Chapter 4).

2.28 The Commission is currently preparing a directive on strategic environmental assessment, requiring compulsory plans for sustainable development for the whole of the Community's coasts. This initiative may, ultimately, provide a broad framework in which more detailed requirements of coastal zone management will operate.

2.29 In addition, the Commission proposes to establish a **legal instrument** for planning and protection of the Community's coastal zones in order to:

- reinforce coastal land use and sea use planning procedures in member states;

- avoid threats to the environment as a result of economic development;

2.30 This instrument, if enacted, would require member states to:

- formulate coastal zone management plans;

- balance the demands of economic development and conservation of natural resources;

- identify environmentally sensitive coastlines (by means of an inventory);

- establish coastal protection schemes for all environmentally sensitive coastal zones and areas interacting with them;

- submit physical planning projects within the coastal zone to an environmental impact assessment.

Environmental Assessment

2.31 Although environmental issues have always been a factor in determining planning applications and other forms of authorisation (eg granting of oil and gas exploration licences), the UK is bound by **EC Directive 85/337/EEC** on "the assessment of the effects of certain public and private projects on the environment". This directive requires an **environmental assessment** (EA) to be carried out before development consent is granted for certain types of major project, listed in 2 Annexes to the directive. For Annex I projects EA is mandatory. For Annex II projects EA is required if there are likely to be significant environmental effects. Where EA is required, the developer must prepare and submit an **environmental statement** setting out their own assessment of the likely environmental effects of the proposed development.

2.32 The statutory planning system is one of the main instruments for taking account of an EA in the decision making process, under the **Town and Country Planning (Assessment of Environmental Effects) Regulations 1988**. The regulations apply to certain projects that require planning permission under the **Town and Country Planning Act 1990**. The relevant projects are listed in 2 Schedules corresponding to the Annexes from the EC directive.

2.33 DoE Circular 15/88 (WO 23/88) provides guidance to local planning authorities for assessing

Table 2.3 Statutory consultation in the Environmental Assessment procedures, for England and Wales. Note: similar procedures apply in both Scotland and Northern Island

ACTIVITY	CONSULTEES
1. Development subject to planning control. Town and Country Planning (Assessment of Environmental Effects) Regulations 1988	Any principal council for the area, Countryside Commission, English Nature or CCW, HMIP (for waste operations). Any body required by Article 18 of the GDO 1988 (see Table 6.6).
2. Land drainage improvement – permitted development (see Chapter 6) Land Drainage Improvement Works (Assessment of Environmental Effects) Regulations 1988	The drainage body considers whether EA is needed. A copy will be sent to English Nature/CCW, the Countryside Commission and any other interested authority or organisation. The statement may be inspected by the public.
3. Ports and Harbours – applications for revision or empowerment orders (see Chapter 6) Harbour Works (Assessment of Environmental Effects) Regulations 1988 – activities not covered by 1 and 3 above The Harbour Works (Assessment of Environmental Effects) (No.2) Regulations 1989	The relevant Minister decides on the need for EA. The statement must be published and EN/CCW, the Countryside Commission, HMIP and the relevant local authority are invited to comment. The Minister may require the proposals to be considered at a public enquiry.
4. Marine Aggregate Extraction DoE, 1989	DoE/WO in consultation with Government Departments consider the need for EA, which forms part of a broad consultation procedure (the Government View Procedure)
5. Marine Fish Farming Environmental Assessment (Salmon Farming in Marine Waters) Regulations 1988	DoE/WO decide on the need for EA, guided by indicative criteria. The statement forms part of a broad consultation procedure (see Table 7.1)
6. Oil and Gas	EA is required by DTi in all cases where a licence block is within 25 miles of the coast or in a sensitive area. The study must be carried out in consultation with other Government Departments, local authorities, EN/CCW and all interested parties.

Figure 2.2 Environmental Assessment Procedures

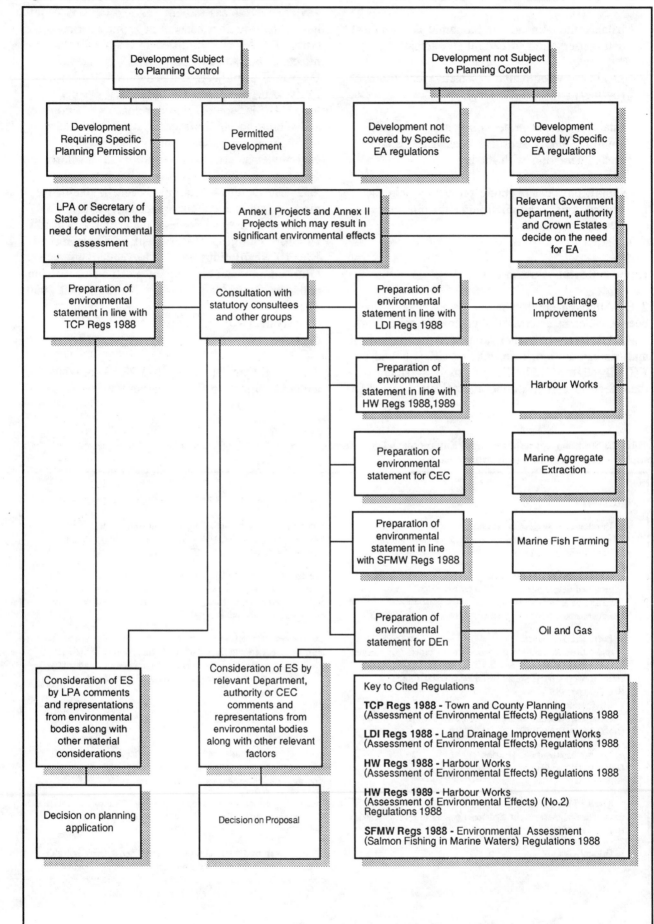

the significance for Annex II projects that require planning permission:

- whether the project is of more than local importance;

- whether the project is intended for a particularly sensitive or vulnerable location;

- whether the project is thought likely to give rise to particularly complex or adverse effects, for example, in terms of the discharge of pollutants.

2.34 However, these are only general guidelines. In addition, DoE Circular 15/88 sets out indicative criteria and thresholds for some Annex II projects. It is the responsibility of the **competent authority** to make a judgement on the need for an EA on the basis of the indicative criteria and other relevant factors such as the nature, scale and location of a project.

2.35 Similar procedures apply in Scotland (see **SDD Circular 13/1988 Environmental Assessment Implementation of the EC Directive**) and **Northern Ireland (see Planning (Assessment of Environmental Effects Regulations) Northern Ireland 1989**).

2.36 Many projects which may have a significant environmental effect lie outside the planning system, particularly activities on the sea bed. For such activities specific regulations (eg the Environmental Assessment (Salmon Farming in Marine Waters) Regulations 1988) or non–statutory procedures (eg criteria for EA as part of the Government View Procedure for marine aggregate extraction) have been prepared (Table 2.3; Figure 2.2).

2.37 In addition to giving an indication of the likely environmental effects of a project, EA also provides an opportunity for a number of interested parties to comment upon the proposals (Table 2.3). At the same time a formal EA can help inform the public of the sensitive issues relevant to a particular project.

References: Chapter 2

Countryside Commission, 1991 Europe's coastal crisis : a co–operative response. European Workshop on Coastal Zone Management, 1991 Poole Dorset.

Department of the Environment, 1989, Procedure note for offshore dredging of sand, gravel and other minerals.
Department of the Environment, 1992, Tourism. PPG 21, HMSO.
Durkin, J., Lane, P. & Peto, M., 1992, The Transport and Works Act 1992: planning for infrastructure developments. Blackstone Press.
English Tourist Board, 1991, Tourism and the Environment – Maintaining the Balance. English Tourist Board.
Gubbay, S., 1990 A Future for the Coast : Proposals for a UK Coastal Zone Management Plan. Marine Conservation Society and The World Wide Fund for Nature.
Her Majesty's Stationary Office, 1990, This Common Inheritance. Britain's Environmental Strategy. Government White Paper.
Irish Sea Study Group, 1990, The Irish Sea, an environmental review.
North Sea Task Force, 1989, Five year plan. North Sea Environment Report No.1.
North Sea Task Force, 1990a, Important issues in enhancing scientific understanding of the North Sea environment. North Sea Environment Report No.2.
North Sea Task Force, 1990b, Monitoring master plan. North Sea Environment Report No.3.
Prescott, R.N., 1990 Current concerns of coastal planning. In J. Houston & C.R. Jones (eds) Planning and Management of the Coastal Heritage, Symposium Proceedings, Southport, 1989, 16–20.
Wildlife Link, 1991, A selection of case studies illustrating the need for coastal zone management in the UK.

3 Coastal Defence

Introduction

3.1 Over the last century considerable importance has been placed on the need to defend coastal communities, industrial and commercial development, transport routes and agricultural land from the threat of erosion or flooding. It is current policy to ensure that the UK has the coastal defence systems it needs to safeguard the future of the land (MAFF, 1989) and some 11.5% of Britain's coast is protected in some way by banks, walls, groynes or esplanades. A recent statement by the Minister emphasised the Government's commitment to reducing risks to people, to important infrastructure and to the environment from flooding and coastal erosion (John Gummer, 24.2.1993).

3.2 The administration of coastal defence strategies involves two related management systems: **coast protection** and **sea defence**. Stated simply, **coast protection** is the protection of land from erosion and encroachment by the sea, whereas **sea defence** is the defence against flooding and inundation. Whilst this may appear a somewhat arbitrary distinction, it has arisen because of the historical responsibilities of coast protection authorities and river boards (now the NRA in England and Wales). Whereas coast protection reflects a need to mitigate the effects of erosion, sea defences were constructed as an integral part of land drainage schemes to prevent flooding in river valleys.

3.3 Powers to carry out works to defend the coastline of England and Wales are contained in **The Coast Protection Act 1949**, the **Water Resources Act 1991** and **The Land Drainage Act 1991**, of which the former relates to coast protection and the two 1991 Acts to sea defence, respectively (Figure 3.1). In Scotland, coast protection and flood defence of non-agricultural land are the responsibility of the island and regional councils under the 1949 Act and the **Flood Prevention (Scotland) Act 1961**. Schemes are promoted by these authorities and have to be approved by the Secretary of State for Scotland.

3.4 These powers are **permissive**; the authorities are not required to undertake works and are expected only to promote schemes which are of benefit to the community. Indeed, although central and local government has often taken the lead in the promotion, funding and construction of coast defence works, **the primary responsibility for protecting property or land lies with the owner**.

3.5 In England and Wales responsibility for coastal defence is split between a number of authorities:

- coast protection; maritime district and metropolitan borough councils;

- sea defence; NRA, Internal Drainage Boards and maritime district councils.

3.6 Following the transfer of policy responsibility for coast protection, in England, from DoE in 1985, a single Government department (MAFF) is now responsible for making available grants towards capital expenditure under both the 1949 and 1991 Acts. Under the Acts it is generally the responsibility of the appropriate authority to determine the need for works and promote schemes. MAFF has no powers to direct that one particular scheme should be undertaken in preference to another (MAFF, 1989). In Wales, the responsibility for both functions has always been with the Welsh Office.

3.7 Since 1986, there has been a significant increase in Central Government funding for coast defence, reflecting the need for additional capital works to reduce flood risk and to repair defences damaged in the winter storms of 1989/1990.

Figure 3.1 Coastal Defence: A summary of the legal and administrative framework

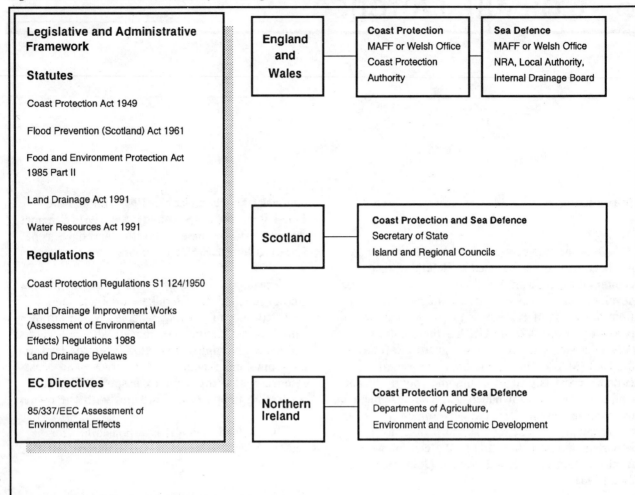

Legislative and Administrative Framework

Statutes

Coast Protection Act 1949

Flood Prevention (Scotland) Act 1961

Food and Environment Protection Act 1985 Part II

Land Drainage Act 1991

Water Resources Act 1991

Regulations

Coast Protection Regulations S1 124/1950

Land Drainage Improvement Works (Assessment of Environmental Effects) Regulations 1988
Land Drainage Byelaws

EC Directives

85/337/EEC Assessment of Environmental Effects

England and Wales

Coast Protection
MAFF or Welsh Office
Coast Protection Authority

Sea Defence
MAFF or Welsh Office
NRA, Local Authority, Internal Drainage Board

Scotland

Coast Protection and Sea Defence
Secretary of State
Island and Regional Councils

Northern Ireland

Coast Protection and Sea Defence
Departments of Agriculture, Environment and Economic Development

Authorisation Procedures : All coastal defence works above LWM require planning permission although sea defence improvements are permitted development under GDO (see Chapter 6). All works below LWM require a licence under the Food and Environment Protection Act 1985 Pt II (as amended by the Environmental Protection Act, 1990), and require the consent of the Department of Transport under the Coast Protection Act 1949 S.34. to ensure they do not present a hazard to navigation. A lease for use of the sea bed is usually required from the Crown Estate Commissioners.

The NRA (under the Water Resources Act 1991), local authorities and IDBs (under the Land Drainage Act 1991) and Scottish local authorities (under the Flood Prevention (Scotland) Act 1961) have the power to make byelaws for flood defence purposes.

3.8 MAFF and the Welsh Office have been developing a comprehensive policy framework for coastal defences, the aims and objectives of which are (see Table 3.1):

- to encourage the provision of adequate and cost effective flood warning systems;

- to encourage the provision of adequate, technically, environmentally and economically sound and sustainable flood and coastal defence measures;

- to discourage inappropriate development in areas at risk from flooding or coastal erosion.

3.9 The primary aim of the MAFF/Welsh Office strategy is to safeguard lives and minimise stress and disruption to the community. As a result priority is given to flood warning systems and capital works designed to protect people and property.

3.10 In addition to construction of sea walls and embankments, grant aid is available for beach renewal, the funding of strategic coastal defence studies and beach management operations within an agreed strategic plan.

3.11 In Northern Ireland, the Departments of Agriculture, Environment and Economic

Table 3.1 Objectives of the draft MAFF/Welsh Office strategy for coastal defence in England and Wales (issued in February 1993).

A. To encourage the provision of adequate and cost effective flood warning systems by:

- funding a Storm Tide Warning Service and keeping the effectiveness of that Service and of emergency procedures under review;
- funding a national network of tide gauges to give continuous records of sea levels at key positions for use by the Storm Tide Warning Service and in national and international research and development (R&D);
- providing grant aid for technically, environmentally and economically sound flood warning systems;
- funding a relevant R&D programme; and
- providing relevant guidance to operating authorities.

B. To encourage the provision of adequate, technically, environmentally and economically sound and sustainable flood and coastal defence measures by:

- encouraging the development of catchment plans and coastal cell or shoreline management plans and issuing guidance on the environmental issues and targets which should be addressed in them;
- encouraging the development of groups reflecting common interests within identified coastal cells to address those interests and share information and experience through the MAFF/WO Coastal Defence Forum;
- providing guidance to operating authorities on technical standards, on the integration of environmental factors into defence operations, and on project appraisal techniques;
- issuing indicative target standards of protection;
- issuing guidance on priorities for grant funding;
- requiring operating authorities applying for government grant to address a range of options for defence works with a view to adopting the best practical and environmentally sound option and maximising value for money;
- providing grant aid for technically, environmentally and economically sound defence measures which take account of the interrelationship between processes and measures elsewhere in the coastal cell or catchment area;
- encouraging appropriate maintenance of defences;
- encouraging the preparation of water level management plans for SSSIs and the working with policies on Environmentally Sensitive Areas to ensure that environmentally sound management is taken into account where appropriate;
- funding a relevant R&D programme.

C. To discourage inappropriate development in areas at risk from flooding or coastal erosion by liaising with the DoE on guidance to local authorities.

Development share the responsibility for coast protection. There is no legislation governing these functions.

Coast Protection: England, Wales and Scotland

3.12 The 1949 Act empowers coast protection authorities (maritime district councils in England and Wales; regional and island councils in Scotland (S.1)) to carry out such coast protection works, whether within or outside their area, as may be needed for the protection of any land in their area (S.4). In addition, a number of bodies have statutory powers to carry out works through various common law rights or Local Acts (Table 3.2).

3.13 Coast protection authorities should be viewed as having two functions: **promoting** their own

schemes under the 1949 Act and **regulating** protection works by landowners or bodies with statutory powers. Indeed, they have wide–ranging powers to regulate or control activities which might affect the general coast protection of their areas. The prior approval of the relevant coast protection authority is required before any such works can be carried out (S.16), except for works carried out by persons or bodies covered by S.17 (mainly those with statutory powers under other Acts; see Table 3.2). However, before proceeding with any works these bodies must notify the coast protection authority which may lodge an objection with the appropriate Minister.

3.14 Coast protection authorities may also make orders under S.18 of the 1949 Act (subject to confirmation by the Minister) to prohibit removal of material from any portion of the seashore within their area or lying to seaward. South Wight Borough Council (Figure 3.2), Thanet District

Table 3.2 Summary of coastal defence powers and the requirement to consult with the local authority (LA) or the NRA, in England and Wales

Body and Source of Power/Rights	Requirement to Consult Local Authority or NRA
1. Sea Defence	
Riparian owner – Common Law	No
NRA – Water Resources Act 1991	No
– Land Drainage Act 1991	No
– Local Acts	Subject to Act
Local Authority	
– Land Drainage Act 1991 S.17	NRA
– Local Government Act 1972 S.137	No
– Local Acts	Subject to Act
Internal Drainage Board	
– Land Drainage Act 1991 S.7	No
– Local Acts	Subject to Act
Highway Authorities	
– as owners	No
– Highway Acts	No
British Rail	
– as owners	No
– Local Acts	Subject to Act
Other Bodies	
– Local Acts	Subject to Act
2. Coast Protection	
Riparian owner – Common Law	LA/NRA 1949 Act S.16
Local Authority	
– Coast Protection Act 1949	NRA 1949 Act S.5
– Local Acts	LA/NRA 1949 Act S.17
Highway Authority	
– as owner	LA/NRA 1949 Act S.17
– Highway Acts	LA/NRA 1949 Act S.17
British Rail	
– as owner	LA/NRA 1949 Act S.17
– Local Acts	LA/NRA 1949 Act S.17
Harbour Authority	
– Local Acts	LA/NRA 1949 Act S.17
– Harbours Act 1964	LA/NRA 1949 Act S.17
Other Bodies	NRA 1949 Act S.16

Council, the Borough of Port Talbot and Rhuddlan Borough Council are amongst the few coast protection authorities to have sought such powers. Many local authorities, however, use other powers to control mineral extraction along the coast. Grampian Regional Council Economic Development and Planning Department, for example, has established a presumption against extraction from coastal sand dunes and all rivers (Grampian Regional Council, 1990).

3.15 When an application is made to a coast protection authority for consent to carry out works, the authority should give notice to neighbouring coast protection authorities and any relevant drainage authority (S.16) and consider any representations that arise.

3.16 When coast protection authorities decide to **promote** works other than those of maintenance or emergency, the Act requires them to advertise and consult widely. These requirements apply to schemes promoted under S.5 (voluntary schemes) and S.8 (using compulsory powers). In England and Wales this consultation procedure includes: the NRA, Internal Drainage Boards, neighbouring maritime district councils, the County Council, sea fisheries committees, harbour, conservancy and

Figure 3.2 Isle of Wight coastal protection areas

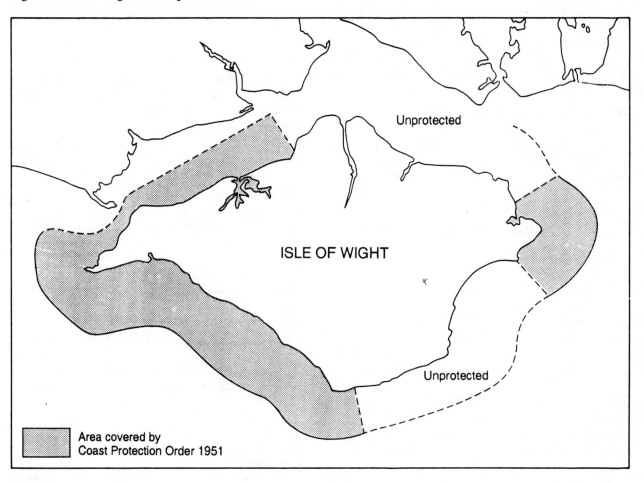

Unprotected

ISLE OF WIGHT

Unprotected

Area covered by
Coast Protection Order 1951

navigation authorities, Government Departments, the Crown Estate Commissioners and the nature conservancy agencies (S.5; **Regulations SI 124/1950**). In Scotland, the bodies to be consulted are given in the **Coast Protection (Notices) (Scotland) Regulations, 1988**.

3.17 Objections to schemes can be made on the grounds that the works will be detrimental to the protection of any land or interfere with the exercise of statutory duties of others (S.5). If these objections are not withdrawn they are resolved by a local inquiry or hearing (S.5).

3.18 Although the provisions of the 1949 Act apply in general to all tidal waters, many estuaries are partly excluded (Fourth Schedule to the Act). This has caused concern in Hampshire where much of the Lymington, Beaulieu and Hamble rivers, Southampton Water and Portsmouth, Langstone and Chichester Harbours lie outside the area covered by the Act. As a result, erosion problems in these areas have been left to individual landowners to tackle (Hampshire County Council, 1991). However, the Minister responsible is

empowered to vary the areas covered by the Act, if the need arose.

Sea Defence: England and Wales

3.19 The NRA has a statutory obligation to exercise a general supervision over all matters relating to flood defence throughout England and Wales, in accordance with the **Water Resources Act 1991**. The authority can **promote** its own schemes and **regulate** defence works by other bodies (see below). Under the 1991 Act the NRA has the power to maintain existing defences and to improve and construct new defences against sea water and tidal water (S.165). These responsibilities are undertaken through ten **Regional Flood Defence Committees**, each containing a majority of local councillors and chaired by Ministerial appointees. This local representation reflects the fact that apart from grant aid on capital schemes and some charges for services, the NRA's flood defence expenditure is funded by levies on constituent County Councils.

3.20 Under the 1991 Water Resources Act (S.105) the NRA is required to carry out surveys in relation to its flood defence functions, indicating where flooding problems are likely. The results of these surveys should be copied to the appropriate local planning authorities in order to inform them as they carry out their development plan and development control functions (see Chapter 6).

3.21 In addition to the NRA, a number of other bodies have powers or rights to construct sea defences (Table 3.2). These include landowners, internal drainage boards (responsible for administering areas with special drainage needs such as the Fens), highway authorities, British Rail and local authorities. In all cases these powers are **permissive**, as is the case for coast protection.

3.22 In order to carry out its supervisory role over all flood defence matters, consent from the NRA is required for any proposed works affecting sea defences or watercourses. Each NRA region has produced its own set of byelaws for flood defence purposes (made under the 1991 Act S.210 and Schedule 25), specifically for securing the efficient working of any defence works or drainage system. Although the details vary between regions, byelaws are generally made for preventing activities that may endanger the stability of or cause damage to sea defences. Table 3.3 lists some of the relevant byelaws from NRA Southern Region.

3.23 All byelaws require the confirmation of the appropriate Minister and should not interfere with the operation of byelaws made by navigation, harbour or conservancy authorities. The byelaws are advertised with notice served to any affected parties. Local inquiries may be held to resolve objections.

3.24 Under S.14 of the **Land Drainage Act 1991** Internal Drainage Boards have powers to implement measures in their areas, principally to reduce the flooding of agricultural land but may also protect urban areas. Maritime district councils (coast protection authorities) are provided with powers to protect land against flooding under the same section. Thus, two, and sometimes three, authorities have powers to carry out sea defence works along a stretch of coastline. The division of responsibility between the NRA and local authorities has traditionally been resolved at a local level, with the NRA generally accepting responsibility for defences which protect large areas of urban or agricultural land where failure could lead to disastrous flooding. The local authorities are generally responsible for sea defences at coastal resorts, especially where the defences have an amenity function.

3.25 Under the Water Resources Act, 1991 (S.166) the NRA has the power to provide and operate flood warnings. Warnings of storm surges are provided by the **Storm Tide Warning Service** (STWS) of the Meteorological Office, set up after the 1953 floods and funded mainly by MAFF. The distribution of surges is heavily biased towards the winter months with little surge activity experienced in the summer months. The STWS, therefore operates on a seasonal basis with 24 hour a day manning from 1st September to the end of April, with a general eye kept on the situation over the summer.

3.26 Warnings for East coast surges are issued for any of the 5 Divisions (Figure 3.3) where a flood risk is calculated to exist for a particular tide. Within each division a "reference port" has been nominated and the tidal level determined at which sea defences in the division may be overtopped. An initial "alert" is issued 12 hours before the time of high water at the reference port. This is followed

Figure 3.3 East coast Storm Tide Warning Service: Coastal divisions and reference ports

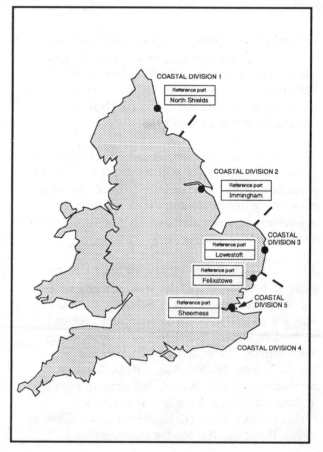

Table 3.3 Summary of sea defence byelaws: NRA Southern Region

Repairs to Buildings on Sea Defences;

Control of Animals;

Acts endangering Stability of or causing Damage to Sea Defences:

- removal or disturbance of material on the sea bed in the vicinity of any groyne or other works in the sea that form part of the sea defences;

- removal or disturbance of material from any part of the Authority Area below MHWM to 200m inland from the sea defences;

- excavation or work that may cause damage to the defences, on any land or cliff adjoining the sea defences;

- disturbance of vegetation growing on sea defences.

Erections, Excavations etc affecting Sea Defences:

- construction or excavation between MLWM and 15m of the landward side of any sea defence;

Driving of Animals and Vehicles on Sea Defences;

Deposit on Sea Defences:

- placement of any goods or materials within 15m of the landward side of any sea defences;

Prevention of Interference with Sea Defences;

Maintenance and Alterations of Floodgates etc

Control of Vessels;

Control of Vermin on Sea Defences;

Damage to Sea Defences by grazing of Animals

---

by a second message 4–7 hours before high water; a cancellation, alert confirmed or danger (if the danger level is likely to be exceeded by over 0.2m).

3.27 These primary warnings are issued to the Police and NRA and result in local flood rooms being activated. Local colour warnings (yellow, amber, red) are initiated by the NRA and public warnings by the Police acting on the advice of the NRA.

Sea Defence: Scotland

3.28 In Scotland, schemes to protect non-agricultural land are promoted by the island and regional councils under the provisions of the **Flood Prevention (Scotland) Act 1961** (S.1&2). Under

this legislation councils are authorised to prevent or mitigate the flooding of land in their area (S.1). These powers can be exercised on land outside the boundary of the authority (S.3).

3.29 The 1961 Act does not differentiate between river and coastal flooding. However, it is generally only applied to river systems in urban areas. Under the 1961 Act S.6 regional councils have the power to make byelaws to prevent the obstruction of any watercourse in their area that may result in flooding of non-agricultural land and to regulate depositing materials near watercourses. However, no such byelaws are believed to be in existence. In many instances sea defence works are undertaken through other legislation. For example, the **Roads (Scotland) Act 1984** makes provision for the protection of roads from natural hazards, which makes it particularly convenient for application in coastal situations. Works can be undertaken on an emergency basis and the Scottish Office funding provided retrospectively.

3.30 In Scotland, **The Agriculture (Scotland) Act, 1970** enables river purification authorities to provide and operate flood warning systems. These, however, tend to be directed towards providing warnings of river floods.

3.31 Flood defence of agricultural land is the responsibility of the owner.

The effectiveness of the coastal defence system

The extent to which coastal dynamics are considered

3.32 The coastal zone has an inheritance of what were (in modern terms) poorly designed coastal defence structures, many built over 100 years ago. Seaside promenades built to protect fashionable Victorian resorts, such as at Scarborough, have caused many problems because their design has promoted beach erosion in front of the sea wall (Keay, 1941). Many artificial harbours such as the Cobb at Lyme Regis, which was permanently attached to the land in 1756, have had a significant impact in disrupting natural sediment transport around the coast, leading to problems of accelerated erosion and beach depletion (Brunsden, 1991). Many coastal defences were built after the 1953 East Coast floods and the foundations of these are increasingly under threat from wave scour as they approach the end of their design life (Clayton, 1990). These problems, together with the uncertainties of the impact of sea-level rise and the devastating effects of the 1990 floods along the North Wales coast, have focused a great deal of attention on the future needs for coastal defence, especially in England and Wales (eg Clayton, 1989; Parker, 1989; McNichol, 1990; National Audit Office, 1992).

3.33 Indeed, in a study of coast protection in East Anglia, Clayton (1980) drew attention to broader problems that are the legacy of the approach to coastal defence over the last century:

"Comparison of areas lost and gained by coastal erosion in the early years of this century with (erosion and deposition in) recent years, shows that the building of coastal defences along parts of the (East Anglian) coast was effective in reducing net land loss. At that time selection of relatively easy sites

coupled with the continuing drift of sand from feeder bluffs showed the advantage in terms of net area to be gained by accepting the erosion of high cliffs and consolidating the progradation of neighbouring low-lying areas. Public pressure, willingly accepted by engineers, has brought extension of the defences to 60% of the coast, but no improvement in the erosional balance. Indeed, the successful stabilisation of some of the lower cliffs has removed local sand sources, so that the longer transport paths from the major feeder bluffs are now dominant. Current attempts to extend the defences to these active cliff systems seem unlikely to be successful in the long term although they may give a temporary reduction in basal removal by waves and thus in cliff retreat. Our work suggest that... the removal of these inputs of sand to the system would initiate a decline in beach volumes that could build up to catastrophic proportions", (Clayton, 1980).

3.34 These observations highlight a major failure to consider the cumulative impact of individual schemes on coastal landforms, such as cliffs and beaches, further along the coast and a lack of awareness of the role of natural processes in providing and maintaining coastal defences. By disrupting the links between sediment sources and protective beaches, coastal defence work in one place has often led to accelerated erosion in another.

3.35 In this context, there has been widespread criticism from conservation groups, local authorities, engineers and academics interviewed during the course of this study, of the impact that schemes built on one section of the coast have had on an adjacent section. For example, a recent paper by Wildlife Link (1991) on reported conflicts in the coastal zone cites the coast protection problems of Christchurch Bay:

"groynes erected by Bournemouth Borough Council have been resisting movement of sediment into Christchurch Bay. This has had an incremental effect around the bay and led Christchurch Borough Council to build a series of groynes to trap sediment.... In the absence of a coherent strategy for coast protection the problem has gradually moved on from council to council. The solution for each one has been considered in isolation from the possible impacts on the area under the jurisdiction of the adjacent council", (Wildlife Link, 1991).

3.36 It is interesting to note that mechanisms for resolving such conflicts are included within the 1949 Act. The fact that they appear not to have been effective in this situation probably rests more with a lack of awareness of coastal sediment transport when the schemes were conceived.

3.37 Over the last decade there have been significant changes in the approach to coastal defence issues. Most notable have been the advocacy of **soft engineering** approaches, **regional coordination** between authorities and the development of the concept of **shoreline management**.

(i) Soft engineering

3.38 Traditional coastal defences involve a combination of:

- breakwaters and sea walls designed to oppose wave energy;

- groynes designed to increase sediment storage on the shore;

- flood embankments and barrages designed to reduce the threat of elevated water levels.

3.39 These traditional measures are known as **hard engineering** solutions in which natural forces are opposed by structures. The success of this approach is clearly demonstrated by the extensive development which has taken place along the coast where, previously, natural hazards would have caused considerable damage. However, the presence of these fixed structures can generate problems for coastal managers. Most notably, these problems include the disruption of sediment transport and the reduction in intertidal area and, hence, coastal habitats (ie. "coastal squeeze";Table 3.4).

3.40 There has, however, been a recent shift towards approaches which aim to work with natural systems by manipulating coastal processes to the benefit of environmental interests as well as protecting coastal communities (Pethick & Burd, 1993). Examples of this "**soft engineering**" approach include beach feeding and managed retreat (Table 3.5). Beach feeding is the most widely used soft engineering technique and involves counteracting natural loss of beach sediment by artificial recharge (Brampton, 1992; West, 1992). The source of material is usually offshore. The success of the technique has, however, placed additional demands on sea bed

Table 3.4 Coastal squeeze (prepared from Davidson et al, 1991)

Many coastal activities have led to a reduction in the width of the intertidal zone and, hence, the balance of habitats within this zone. This "squeeze" has operated on both the existing high-water and low-water marks:

High-water; land reclamation schemes have displaced the high-water mark seaward, often covering the whole range of intertidal shore levels. These land claims have had substantial and long-term effects on the remaining habitats of an estuary, through the modification of tidal currents, sediment transport and location of tidal channels.

Tidal and storm surge barriers tend to depress the high-water mark, so that upper salt marshes become dry and develop terrestrial vegetation. These sea defences can increase periods of tidal inundation at the upper tidal levels or alter depositional patterns and steepen the shore.

Low-water; dredging deepens and widens the subtidal channel for shipping, directly removing parts of the subtidal and lower intertidal areas. Barriers and barrages restrict tidal amplitude, raising low-water mark. In extreme cases, such as leisure barrages, this can lead to the removal of the tidal influence, so that low-water is effectively raised to high-water level.

The overall implication of coastal squeeze has been a progressive long-term decline in the estuarine and intertidal habitats. The maintenance of the diversity and variety of the UK's estuaries is considered vital for their continued health and to provide the conditions needed to support both conservation and shellfish interests.

sand and gravel resources (see Chapter 7).

3.41 Soft engineering options are seen by many as the best way of achieving multiple sustainable use of coastal environments and form a central component of English Nature's **Campaign for a Living Coast** (see Chapter 5).

(ii) Regional coordination

3.42 There have been important advances in the way coast defences are coordinated at a regional level over the last decade. Since the **Carmarthen Bay Group** first met in February 1985 informal coastal groups have been established throughout England and Wales for the purpose of encouraging coordination and exchange of information (Figure 3.4 and Table 3.6). These groups have no statutory powers (although similar bodies could be formed as **coast protection boards** under the 1949 Act S.2), but provide fora for strategic planning of coastal defences within the context of sediment transport

E

Table 3.5 Examples of soft engineering approaches to coastal defence (after Pethick & Burd, 1993)

Stable Bays; coastal bays can reduce shoreline erosion and tidal flooding by acting as discrete cells which trap sediment and lead to the development of stable beaches. They also tend to reduce the wave energy per unit length of coast. Example: Dinas Dinlle, Gwynedd.

Beach Recharge: non cohesive materials; replacing lost sediment by artificial recharge. Source material is usually from offshore dredging, but can be from dredging of navigation channels. Example: Mablethorpe to Skegness, Lincolnshire.

Managed Retreat; a controlled move back from the present shore defence location, allowing shoreline landforms to develop and provide a degree of natural defence. Example: Northey Island, Essex.

Dune Management; improving natural flood defences by dune building. Example: Sefton, Merseyside.

Cliff Management; toe protection, slope reprofiling and drainage to reduce the likelihood of instability. Example, Whitby, North Yorkshire.

cells or coastal process units (see below).

3.43 Perhaps the most influential of these groups has been **The Standing Conference on Problems Associated with the Coastline (SCOPAC)** which is a forum for coast protection authorities, county councils, 3 Harbours Authorities, the NRA, English Nature, Southern Sea Fisheries and the Solent Protection Society, covering the south coast from Weymouth to Worthing. The aims and objectives of this group stand testimony to the growing recognition in England and Wales for cooperation along adjacent stretches of coastline:

- to ensure a fully coordinated approach to all coastal engineering works and relate matters between neighbouring authorities;

- to reduce the risk of coastal engineering work carried out by one authority adversely affecting the coastline of a neighbouring authority;

- to provide a forum for the exchange of information on the success or failure of specific types of coastal engineering projects and on future proposals;

- to establish close liaison with Government and other bodies concerned with coastal engineering and related matters;

- to identify aspects of overall coastal management where further research is required and to promote such research.

3.44 That these groups have an important role in providing a much-needed regional context for coastal defence is certain. Their importance has been recognised by both the Welsh Office who initiated **The Welsh Coastal Groups Forum** and MAFF who initiated **The Coastal Defence Forum** through which individual groups can liaise on technical matters of common interest (Table 3.6). However, it remains unclear as to whether some of the current groupings are the most appropriate for considering coastal defence issues in a regional sediment cell context. For example, whereas the composition of SCOPAC reflects the known pattern of sediment movement between Weymouth and Worthing, the neighbouring coastal groups merely reflect county boundaries (Devon and East Sussex). Indeed, the Devon group contains local authorities from the county's unconnected north and south coasts. It is likely that the most effective groupings of maritime authorities will only be determined as a result of regional studies of sediment transport such as that undertaken by SCOPAC (Bray et al. 1991) and the Anglian Sea Defence Management Study (Halcrow, 1991; see Table 3.7).

3.45 In this context, it is worth noting the recently completed research on the mapping of coastal cells carried out by HR Wallingford (1993). This study has involved the compilation a series of maps covering the coast of England and Wales, identifying the boundaries of major sediment cells (Figure 3.5).

3.46 In Scotland, the island and regional councils have strategic planning functions and, hence, there is the opportunity to plan overall coastal defence on a regional basis. However, it should be noted that much of the Scottish coast is undeveloped and of a different character to the problematic soft rock and low lying areas of England and Wales. Coastal defence issues are, hence, generally less severe than in England and Wales.

(iii) Shoreline management

3.47 Nowadays, the idea that coastal processes do not operate conveniently within fixed administrative boundaries is central to modern approaches to **shoreline management** such as the Anglian Sea Defence Management Study recently undertaken for the NRA (Fleming, 1989; Townend & Fleming, 1990). This pioneering study (Table 3.7) should enable NRA Anglian Region to:

- develop environmentally acceptable soft engineering solutions;

- consider long term strategic solutions rather than piecemeal approaches;

- take account of the possible impacts of sea level rise.

3.48 Much of the pioneering work in this field, however, has been undertaken by Canterbury City Council who, in the 1980s, developed a management system for the London Clay cliffs of the north Kent coast based on a **coastal process unit** (Roberts & McGown, 1987).

3.49 For management purposes a coastal process unit can be considered to be a discrete system, largely independent from processes operating along adjacent sections of the coastline. The extent of the unit managed by Canterbury City Council is shown in Figure 3.6. The western boundary, in the Swale estuary at Seasalter, marks the point where littoral processes are halted by shallowing water, whereas the eastern boundary is defined by a natural headland at Reculver Towers which acts as a terminal groyne preventing littoral transport from the east. The seaward boundary has yet to be defined but should coincide with the limit of offshore–onshore sediment transport. The landward boundary is defined by the limit of surface or subsurface drainage affecting coastal slopes or, in low lying areas, the extent of the 1953 flooding. By using such process units as a management tool the interactions between the various sections of coastline may be taken into account when considering the potential impacts of proposed works. The lack of this broader perspective or strategic view on dynamics of coastal systems has led to many problems in the past. For example, the construction of Hampton Pier, Herne Bay, in 1864 resulted in major erosion problems on the beach and cliffs at Studd Hill to the west. Similar stories can be told for many parts of the UK coast.

3.50 The basis for successful shoreline management is a combination of:

- an appreciation of coastal sediment cells or systems; management decisions need to be based on policies which relate to an appreciation of both **site conditions** and the **broader setting**.

- an understanding of the processes occurring along a stretch of coast.

Table 3.6 The coastal groups in England and Wales (as of March 1993)

- West Cumbria Coastal Group
- River Ribble to Morecambe Bay Coastal Group
- Llandudno to Mersey Estuary Coastal Group (The Liverpool Bay Group)
- Tidal Dee User Group
- Ynys Enlli to Llandudno Coastal Group
- Cardigan Bay Group
- Carmarthen Bay Coastal Engineering Study Group
- Swansea Bay Coastal Group
- Severn Estuary Coastal Group
- Somerset and Avon Coastal Group
- Devon Coast Protection Advisory Group
- Cornwall Countryside Coast Protection Group
- Standing Conference on Problems Associated with the Coastline (SCOPAC)
- East Sussex Coastal Liaison Group
- Kent Coastal Group
- Anglian Coast Authorities Group
- Holderness Coast Protection Project
- North East Coastal Authorities Group

A MAFF/Welsh Office Coastal Defence Forum was established in 1991, involving representatives of the coastal groups and spokesmen from the NRA and English Nature. The Forum's terms of reference are:

"To provide a national forum on coastal defence, including sea defence and coast protection matters, for government officials, representatives of Coastal Groups and others with an interest in England and Wales".

The Forum aims to assist authorities in their coastal defence functions by:

- furthering cooperation between parties with responsibility for coastal defence;
- sharing experience, data etc;
- identifying best practice;
- identifying research needs and possibilities;
- promoting strategic planning of coastal defence management;
- identifying obstacles to progressing planned works;
- keeping abreast of policy developments, R&D results and new initiatives.

3.51 The recently formed regional coastal groups certainly provide a forum for a broader awareness of coastal systems. However around much of the UK coast there is general lack of reliable and useful data on which policy decisions can be made. Indeed, a recent Institution of Civil Engineers working party report (CERAC, 1991) concluded that:

"there is an urgent need for experimental facilities and field stations coupled with high

Figure 3.4 The composition of coastal defence groups in England and Wales and extent of NRA regions (as of 1992)

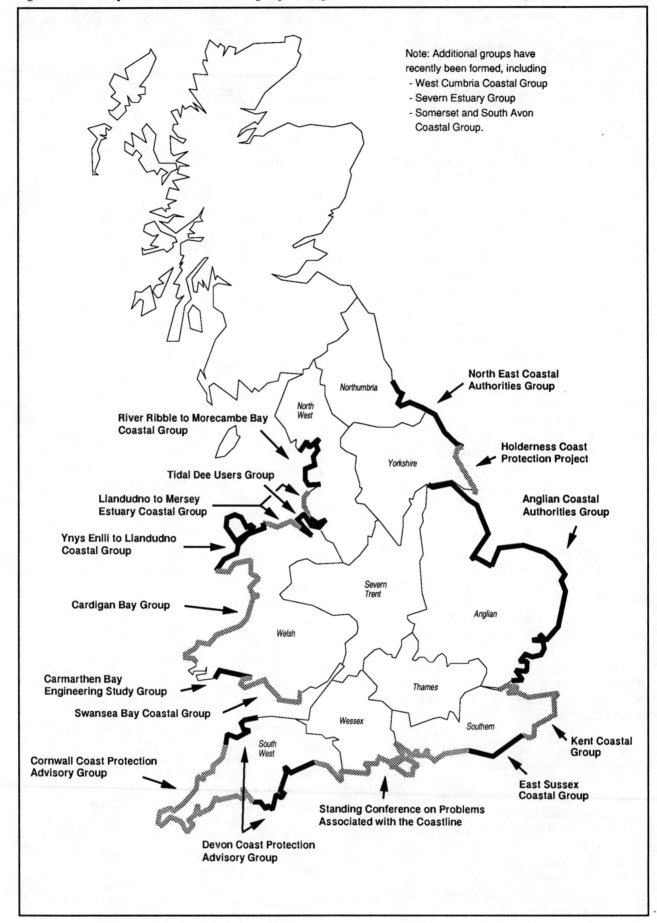

Note: Additional groups have recently been formed, including
- West Cumbria Coastal Group
- Severn Estuary Group
- Somerset and South Avon Coastal Group.

North East Coastal Authorities Group

Holderness Coast Protection Project

River Ribble to Morecambe Bay Coastal Group

Tidal Dee Users Group

Llandudno to Mersey Estuary Coastal Group

Ynys Enlli to Llandudno Coastal Group

Anglian Coastal Authorities Group

Cardigan Bay Group

Carmarthen Bay Engineering Study Group

Swansea Bay Coastal Group

Cornwall Coast Protection Advisory Group

Kent Coastal Group

East Sussex Coastal Group

Standing Conference on Problems Associated with the Coastline

Devon Coast Protection Advisory Group

Northumbria

North West

Yorkshire

Severn Trent

Welsh

Anglian

Thames

Wessex

Southern

South West

Figure 3.5 Boundaries of major Coastal Cells (after HR Wallingford 1993)

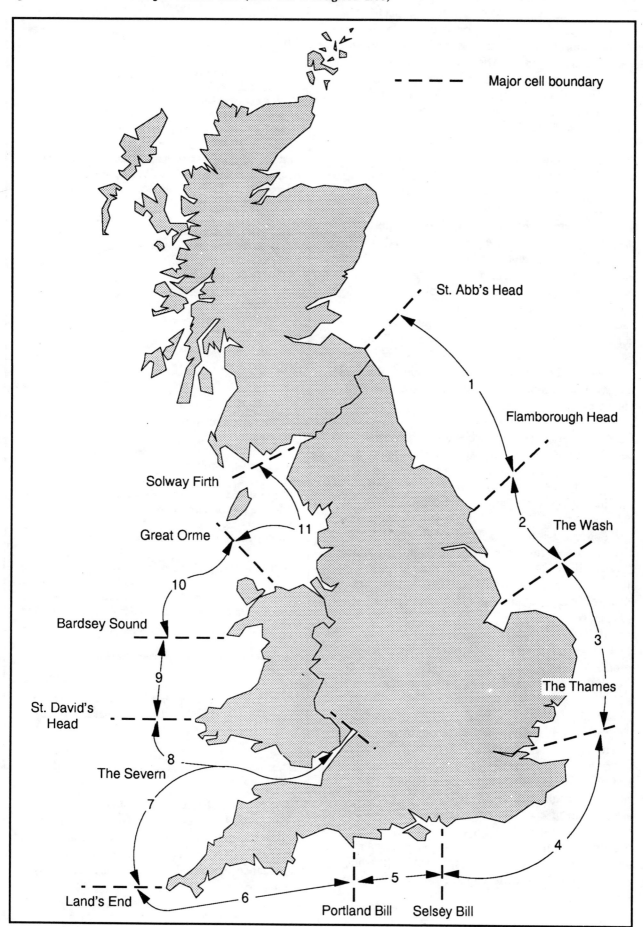

Major cell boundary

St. Abb's Head

Flamborough Head

Solway Firth

Great Orme

The Wash

Bardsey Sound

St. David's
Head

The Thames

The Severn

Land's End

Portland Bill

Selsey Bill

resolution computer models capable of predicting inshore wave conditions. Such facilities should be integrated into both short and long term programmes designed to provide the basis for more efficient and cost effective designs and coastal management systems. This is especially true in the light of the continuing need to replace or refurbish existing structures", (CERAC, 1991).

3.52 An exception to this pattern is Canterbury City Council which has recognised the need for a planned maintenance policy in order to ensure that the coastal defences are performing efficiently. This policy relies heavily on a broad monitoring programme which includes beach level and sea wall surveys, instrumentation of coastal slopes, tide and wave data collection, meteorological observations and the use of aerial photography. A total of 50 beach survey stations have been established at specific locations along their coastline (Figure 3.6), with surveys carried out every 3 months and after every major storm. These surveys provide data on littoral drift along the coast and help determine whether erosion or accretion is taking place at specific locations.

3.53 Providing fixed defences through coastal engineering is, of course, only one of a range of policy options available for a coastal defence strategy. These options are: do nothing, maintain the line, advance the line and retreat to a more defendable line (Payne, 1991). It is only the first two options that have been widely practised in the UK. In Wales, for example, some 850km of about 1200km has no artificial defences and along much of the remaining coast the "maintain" option has been selected at some time in the past (Payne, 1991).

3.54 The choice of policy option for a particular stretch of coast should depend on the nature of the coastline (whether is it eroding or accreting), whether the coast is developed, land use policies, conservation needs, benefits, costs and resources. It is clear, therefore, that the decision to proceed with an engineering solution needs to be made within the framework of a range of planning policies. However, perhaps the most serious failure of coastal management, in England and Wales, has been a lack of coordination between land use planning and decisions over coastal defence strategy. This has led to development proceeding, for example, in low–lying areas prone to flooding or cliffs vulnerable to landslide activity or erosion (see Chapter 6).

Table 3.7 The Anglian Sea Defence Management Study (prepared from Child, 1992)

The Anglian coastal area comprises:

- areas of high risk of flooding;
- a geomorphologically complex and diverse coast;
- areas of environmental sensitivity.

The Region is protected by around 1500 km of sea defences, ranging from sea walls and embankments to natural defences such as dunes and beaches. The overall objective of the Sea Defence Management Study was to develop a regional management strategy and a sound basis for investment plans for flood defence.

The study, undertaken by Sir William Halcrow and Partners, involved 5 main tasks:

Field Measurement of:
- nearshore bathymetric survey
- nearshore geological survey
- estuary sediment trends

Studies of:
- Nearshore currents
- Sediment modelling
- Offshore banks
- Impact of climatic change
- Impact of sea level rise
- Estuary studies

Monitoring
Geographic Information System
Management Strategy

The total study cost was £1.65M and was funded by the 5 local Flood Defence Committees in the Anglian Region with grant aid from MAFF. The benefits of the study involve **cost savings** and improved **effectiveness**:

Savings arise from 2 areas of project development:

- information; improved quality and reliability;
- investment; investment options are more robust and varied.

The effectiveness of flood defences will be improved in 2 areas:

- technical; improved knowledge and understanding;
- political; improved management approach, contributing to broader coastal zone management issues.

3.55 The lack of reliable information on coastal processes must be seen to be a major factor in limiting the potential effectiveness of many aspects of coastal management, not just the design and maintenance of coastal defences (see especially Chapters 6 and 7). This may lead to difficulties in quantifying the level of risk posed to development

Figure 3.6 The North Kent coastal process unit (after Roberts and McGowan, 1987)

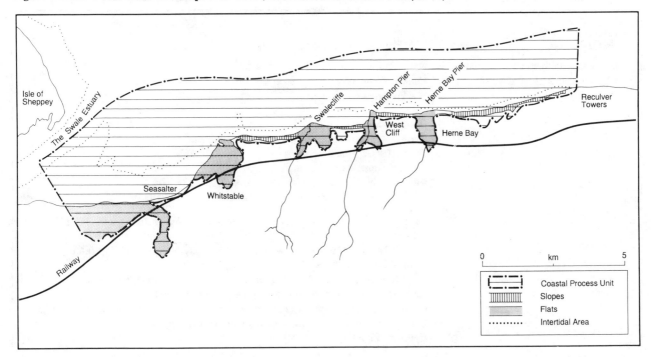

or the impact that a development may have on the coastal zone. These problems are further compounded by the uncertainty over the effects of future sea level rise. Indeed, an absence of a sound information base for much of the coastline means it is almost impossible to make anything other than vague generalisations about the changes that may occur at particular locations.

The extent to which the environmental implications of schemes are considered

3.56 Flood relief works (ie sea defence) are included in the list of Annex II projects that may require EA (see Chapter 2). New sea defence works require express planning permission and, hence, may require EA if the local planning authority considers the scheme as potentially having significant environmental effects. Sea defence improvements, however, are permitted development and thus do not require permission from the local planning authority (see Chapter 6; although appropriate consents would be required from, for example, the NRA if they are not the promoting body). In such instances the drainage authority is subject to the **Land Drainage Improvement Works (Assessment of Environmental Effects) Regulations 1988**, which provide for the advertising of proposals, consideration of representations, preparation of environmental statements where there is likely to be significant environmental effects and reference

to the Minister for decisions in cases of dispute.

3.57 Coast protection works do not appear in the list of Annex II projects and, hence, do not require formal EA. However, in recent evidence to the House of Commons Select Committee on the Environment, the Government indicated that it was considering whether to propose adding such works to the list of Annex II projects. This statement was reiterated in the Government's response to the Select Committee Report (DoE, 1992).

3.58 It can be argued that formal EA should be carried out for all such schemes because of possible extensive and long–term effects. These may include the disruption of sediment transport (eg Clayton, 1980), as well as effects on the local economy (degradation of tourist beaches), conservation interest (loss of access to important SSSIs and narrowing of the intertidal zone) and recreation (access to the foreshore).

The extent to which the system takes into account the interests of other groups

3.59 There are significant differences between the procedures for carrying out works under the 1991 Acts (in England and Wales), the 1961 Act (in Scotland) and the 1949 Act (Figures 3.7 and 3.8, Tables 3.2 and 3.8).

Table 3.8 Statutory consultees and consenting authorities for coast defence works, in England and Wales

Activity	Consultees
1. Coast Protection (by Coast Protection Authority)	Neighbouring maritime district councils; County Councils; Sea Fisheries Committee; NRA; Internal Drainage Board; Harbour, conservancy and navigation authorities; Crown Estate Commissioners; Country Conservancy Councils; Government Departments (eg DTp, MAFF); **(Coast Protection Act 1949 S.5; Regulations SI 124/1950).**
2. Sea Defence (by NRA)	Harbour, conservancy and navigation authorities **(Water Resources Act 1991 S.16 (4)).** English Nature/CCW (works within or which may affect an SSSI; **Water Resources Act 1991 S.17);** English Heritage/Cadw/Secretary of State (Scheduled monument consent; **Ancient Monuments & Archaeological Areas Act 1979 S.3);** Conservation organisations (advised by Conservation Guidelines; MAFF, 1991); Local planning authority (new works require planning permission; **Town & Country Planning Act 1990).**

(i) Sea Defence in England and Wales

3.60 Sea defence proposals do not have to be advertised and there is no right of objection. However, the 1988 environmental assessment regulations, which include advertising requirements, must be complied with (see above). Within the 1991 Acts there are limited requirements to consult with interested groups. Informal consultation with MAFF Regional Engineers (or their Welsh Office equivalents) generally occurs at an early stage, ensuring that the Ministry's requirements are understood.

3.61 **Conservation Guidelines for Drainage Authorities** have been produced jointly by MAFF/DoE and the Welsh Office (1991). These guidelines recommend that the NRA (and Internal Drainage Boards) should consult with a wide range of conservancy agencies and groups in the early stages of preparing proposals:

"Consultations should aim to find ways not only to avoid damage to sensitive features or wildlife but also consider how wildlife and landscape can be conserved and enhanced, and where appropriate, new wildlife features and habitats created including riparian buffer zones. They should also aim to find ways to avoid damage to important archaeological sites, or failing this consider arrangements for them to

be recorded before destruction"
(MAFF/DoE/WO, 1991).

3.62 New sea defence works above LWM require express planning permission and, therefore can proceed only after consultation with the local planning authority who will take a range of considerations into account (see Chapter 6). However, improvement and maintenance work on existing sea walls is permitted under **The General Development Order, 1988** (Schedule 2 Part 14). As sea defences in some form often exist at the site of a proposed scheme it is rare for planning approval to be needed, thus limiting the formal requirement for consultation.

3.63 **The Wildlife and Countryside Act, 1981** includes specific environmental obligations for bodies undertaking sea defence works; these were incorporated into **The Water Act, 1989** and reenacted in the 1991 Acts (Water Resources Act 1991 S. 16–17; Land Drainage Act 1991 S. 12–13). These requirements are also backed up by **The Land Drainage Improvement Works (Assessment of Environmental Effects) Regulations, 1988** (see above).

3.64 Drainage authorities also have specific recreational duties, as laid down in the 1991 Acts:

– to have regard to the desirability of preserving for the public any freedom of access to areas

Figure 3.7 Formal mechanisms by which drainage bodies take into account the interests of other coastal activities

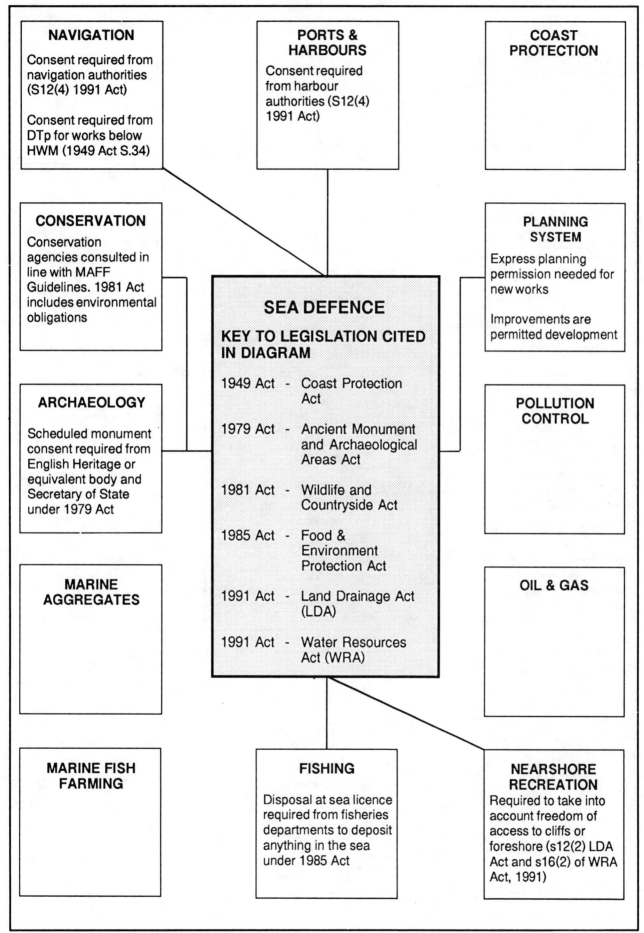

NAVIGATION

Consent required from navigation authorities (S12(4) 1991 Act)

Consent required from DTp for works below HWM (1949 Act S.34)

PORTS & HARBOURS

Consent required from harbour authorities (S12(4) 1991 Act)

COAST PROTECTION

CONSERVATION

Conservation agencies consulted in line with MAFF Guidelines. 1981 Act includes environmental obligations

ARCHAEOLOGY

Scheduled monument consent required from English Heritage or equivalent body and Secretary of State under 1979 Act

MARINE AGGREGATES

MARINE FISH FARMING

SEA DEFENCE

KEY TO LEGISLATION CITED IN DIAGRAM

1949 Act - Coast Protection Act

1979 Act - Ancient Monument and Archaeological Areas Act

1981 Act - Wildlife and Countryside Act

1985 Act - Food & Environment Protection Act

1991 Act - Land Drainage Act (LDA)

1991 Act - Water Resources Act (WRA)

PLANNING SYSTEM

Express planning permission needed for new works

Improvements are permitted development

POLLUTION CONTROL

OIL & GAS

FISHING

Disposal at sea licence required from fisheries departments to deposit anything in the sea under 1985 Act

NEARSHORE RECREATION

Required to take into account freedom of access to cliffs or foreshore (s12(2) LDA Act and s16(2) of WRA Act, 1991)

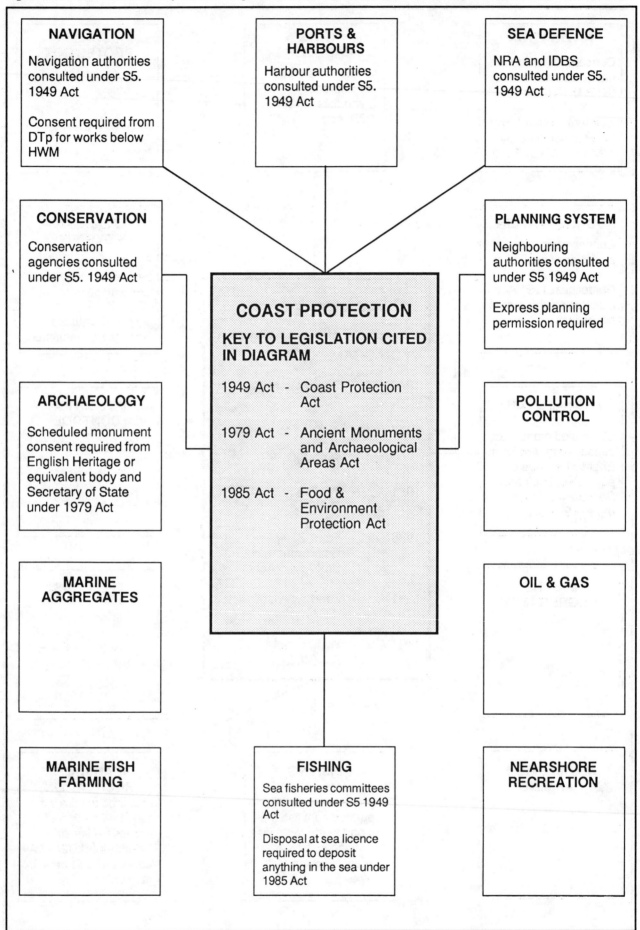

NAVIGATION

Navigation authorities consulted under S5. 1949 Act

Consent required from DTp for works below HWM

PORTS & HARBOURS

Harbour authorities consulted under S5. 1949 Act

SEA DEFENCE

NRA and IDBS consulted under S5. 1949 Act

CONSERVATION

Conservation agencies consulted under S5. 1949 Act

PLANNING SYSTEM

Neighbouring authorities consulted under S5 1949 Act

Express planning permission required

ARCHAEOLOGY

Scheduled monument consent required from English Heritage or equivalent body and Secretary of State under 1979 Act

COAST PROTECTION

KEY TO LEGISLATION CITED IN DIAGRAM

1949 Act - Coast Protection Act

1979 Act - Ancient Monuments and Archaeological Areas Act

1985 Act - Food & Environment Protection Act

POLLUTION CONTROL

MARINE AGGREGATES

OIL & GAS

MARINE FISH FARMING

FISHING

Sea fisheries committees consulted under S5 1949 Act

Disposal at sea licence required to deposit anything in the sea under 1985 Act

NEARSHORE RECREATION

of woodland, mountains, moor, heath, down, cliff or foreshore and other places of natural beauty;

- to have regard to the desirability of maintaining the availability to the public of any facility for visiting or inspecting any building, site or object of archaeological, architectural or historic interest; and

- to take into account any effect which the proposals would have on any such freedom of access or on the availability of any such facility. (Land Drainage Act 1991 S.12 (2) and the Water Resources Act 1991 S.16 (4)).

3.65 However, it is reported by the Royal Yachting Association (RYA) that, in the past, these duties have largely been seen in terms of bathing and walking interests rather than providing access for the launch of leisure boats. Indeed, concerns have been expressed by the RYA that the extensive sea defence works along the east coast, mainly built since the 1953 floods, have had the effect of bringing leisure boating and wildlife into increasing conflict. This is because the hard sea defence barriers generally do not provide access to the foreshore for leisure craft and, thus, have led to a concentration of moorings in sheltered estuaries where conservation interest is often considerable (Figure 3.9; Lankester, 1991).

3.66 Navigation interests have to be considered by drainage authorities. Indeed, consent needs to be obtained from navigation, harbour or conservancy authorities before a drainage authority may undertake works which could obstruct or interfere with navigation (Land Drainage Act 1991 S. 12(4) and the Water Resources Act 1991 S.16 (4)).

(ii) Sea Defence in Scotland

3.67 Flood prevention schemes are required to be advertised and notice served to all interested parties and statutory bodies whose functions may be affected by the operations (Schedule 2 of the 1961 Act). If any objections are not withdrawn, the proposals are considered at a public inquiry.

(iii) Coast protection in England, Wales and Scotland

3.68 For England and Wales, there are much broader statutory consultation requirements for coast protection than sea defence works, as outlined earlier (1949 Act S.5; Table 3.2). Coast protection works above LWM require express planning permission from the local planning authority, reinforcing the requirement for broad consultation with interested groups.

3.69 Consents may also be required from other authorities or bodies depending on the nature of the proposed scheme. Works below LWM, such as breakwaters and headlands, require:

- a lease for use of the sea bed from the Crown Estate Commissioners (see Chapter 7);

- a licence to deposit anything in the sea from the relevant fisheries department, under the Food and Environment Protection Act 1985 Part II (see Chapter 4).

3.70 In addition there are provisions within the 1949 Act (S.34) to ensure that any works in tidal waters do not affect navigation, with consent required from the Secretary of State for Transport for the following operations:

- the construction, alteration or improvement of any works on, under, or over any part of the seashore below spring HWM;

- the deposit or removal of any object or materials below the level of spring HWM.

3.71 Despite the broad consultation requirements, coast protection can become a very contentious issues, for example conflicts between interests of local property owners and national wildlife and landscape conservation priorities (see Chapter 5). Owners of vulnerable developments, such as properties in erosion-prone areas, naturally apply pressure on local authorities to provide coast protection measures to safeguard their investments. Such defences are, of course, funded by the public purse through MAFF grants and local authority contributions, with many schemes costing very large sums. Although cost/benefit analyses are undertaken to justify such expenditure the whole issue of coast defence is becoming increasingly politicised with local councillors and MPs often being drawn into debates over particular schemes as a result of lobbying by those whose house or livelihood is threatened (eg Luccombe, Isle of Wight; Lee, in press). In such circumstances, the choice of the engineering response has often led, in the past, to conflict with conservation agencies when for example, nationally or internationally important habitats or geological sites are affected in order to protect property. An example is the recent debate over a defence scheme proposed for Chewton Bunny, Christchurch (Tyhurst, 1991).

Figure 3.9 Distribution of major marinas and moorings around the UK

Isle of Wight

3.72 The former NCC observed:

"In the event of an objection being raised to coastal protection on geological grounds, the NCC is frequently berated, both privately and in public, by those promoting a particular scheme. Accusations of over-zealous behaviour and bureaucratic insensitivity abound in the one-sided war of words as local residents and their representatives promulgate their case", Earth Science Conservation (1988).

3.73 The balance between protecting vulnerable properties or communities and the need to preserve the character of the unspoilt coast also can lead to considerable conflict. For example, at Easton Bavents on the Suffolk coast, the Countryside Commission successfully opposed Waveney District Council's plans to protect a number of cliff top homes because of the possible effect of the proposed scheme on an Area of Outstanding Natural Beauty (McIlroy, 1990). Such decisions can be justified by the fact that a coast protection authority is not specifically required to protect all threatened development. However, there is no

mechanism to provide compensation for affected parties (see Chapter 6).

3.74 From the geological conservation perspective, the design of coast protection works should aim to control erosion sufficiently to protect the coast whilst allowing a small degree of erosion to maintain its exposure. For their part the former NCC commissioned **"A Guide to the Selection of Appropriate Coast Protection Works for Geological SSSIs"**, which was undertaken by Hydraulics Research Ltd (1991). This document considers appropriate engineering designs or alternative action, such as land purchase and compensation, for a variety of coastal environments (Leafe, 1991).

3.75 The need for environmental guidance in selecting appropriate coastal defence solutions was identified by MAFF in 1991. As a result they commissioned the Institute of Estuarine and Coastal Studies (Hull University) to prepare guidance to coastal engineers, planners, managers and environmental scientists. The manual (Pethick & Burd, 1993) provides the background to environmental issues in coastal defence, the natural physical and ecological processes involved and the engineering techniques available. It embraces the principle of **multiple sustainable use** of the coast which attempts to achieve the solution of coastal management problems through the use of environmentally sensitive schemes involving the use of natural coastal systems.

The extent to which the system allows coordinated decision making across the coastal zone

3.76 In England and Wales responsibility for coastal defence is split between the NRA (sea defence) and the maritime district councils (coast protection). This separation of roles does not occur in Scotland where both functions are the responsibility of the island and regional councils.

3.77 Although the NRA's powers (in England and Wales) to undertake works can be exercised above and below LWM (Water Resources Act 1991 S.165), there are no provisions in the sea defence legislation which allow a coordinated approach to managing related coastal activity. In contrast, the 1949 Act contains a number of important provisions which have the effect of linking different elements of coastal management. These are:

- the coast protection authority's ability to control the removal of materials from the sea shore and sea bed (see Chapter 7);

- the power of the Secretary of State for Transport to control works in tidal waters that may obstruct or endanger navigation (see Chapters 7 & 8).

3.78 However, schemes which involve works around LWM require consent from more than one authority: from the local planning authority for elements above MLWM such as sea walls; from the appropriate fisheries department and the DTp for elements below HWM such as offshore breakwaters.

3.79 There has been a long standing debate over the responsibility for and funding of, coastal defence works, especially in England and Wales. Indeed, a 1985 Green Paper entitled "**Financing and administration of land drainage, flood prevention and coast protection in England and Wales**" proposed an integrated approach with the then water authorities (now the NRA) to be responsible for all coastal works. Coast protection authorities would be relegated to a subsidiary role as "designated" coastal works authorities for particular areas. Although these proposals have not been implemented, it is not surprising that many of the groups and authorities interviewed expressed a desire to see their own roles strengthened.

3.80 One of the issues which were seen by many of those interviewed to diminish the effectiveness of the existing system in England and Wales was the split responsibility between NRA, Internal Drainage Boards, maritime district and borough councils, harbour authorities and private owners. A number of local authorities saw the distinction in responsibility as artificial, confusing and illogical. There was broad agreement over the value of a single authority to be responsible, although there was much divergence over whether this should be at the local, regional or national level.

Summary

3.81 Defending the UK's coastline from erosion and flooding involves a combination of:

- coast protection carried out by maritime district councils (in England and Wales) and island and regional councils (Scotland) under the Coast Protection Act 1949. In Northern Ireland there

is no specific legislation, although responsibility for coast protection is split between the Departments of Economic Development, Agriculture and Environment.

- sea defence carried out (in England and Wales) by NRA, Internal Drainage Boards, and maritime district councils under the Water Resources Act 1991 and the Land Drainage Act 1991. In Scotland regional and island councils have powers to carry out flood defence works. These powers are contained in the Flood Prevention (Scotland) Act 1961, although the Act is chiefly used for prevention of river floods in urban areas.

3.82 Schemes below HWM must also comply with provisions in the Food and Environment Protection Act 1985 for dumping materials in the sea, and S.34 of the Coast Protection Act 1949 for the safety of navigation.

3.83 It is clear that the sea defences around the UK have been very successful in preventing a repeat of the 1953 East Coast disaster in which over 300 people were killed. Indeed, in 1978 storm surge levels exceeded the 1953 level along parts of the east coast but resulted in only minimal damage. However, recent flooding at Towyn, North Wales, serve to emphasise the potential risks associated with storm surge events. Elsewhere, coast protection schemes have reduced the rates of coastal erosion and contributed to improvements to the overall stability of many coastal slopes as at Whitby, North Yorkshire (Clark & Guest, 1991).

3.84 These obvious benefits from coast defence have been achieved through close cooperation between local authorities, water authorities (and now the NRA) and Government. Indeed, many of the authorities contacted during this study remarked on the effectiveness of coast defence arrangements at the local level. However, it is also clear that many local authorities had not fully exploited their responsibilities and powers, especially those under the 1949 Act. Notably there was a lack of appreciation of the powers contained within S.18 of the Act which enables coast protection authorities to control the removal of materials from the sea bed, subject to confirmation from the Minister.

3.85 In the past coastal defence works have often led to problems elsewhere, because of the disruption to sediment transport along the coast. In many places around the coast this has resulted in a variety of problems from the depletion of tourist beaches to accelerated erosion and increased vulnerability to storm damage (eg at Happisburgh and Cromer; Clayton, 1990). This has been a long-term problem, highlighted by the changes in the coastal zone since the Royal Commission on Coast Erosion and Afforestation sat from 1906-1911:

> (In the Royal Commission Final Report) "it is reported that the area gained in estuaries and embayments over the preceding 35 years was seven times greater than that lost through erosion ...
> This situation has since reversed, although whether as a result of persistent sea-level rise or the activities of coastal engineers is open to question", Clayton (1990).

3.86 In England and Wales, MAFF/Welsh Office and most local authorities now recognise that many of the problems that arose in the past were a direct result of a piecemeal, uncoordinated approach to coastal defence in a manner that ignores the natural coastal process boundaries. These problems were exacerbated where a large number of bodies are involved, such as the MOD, National Trust, British Rail and private land owners. Often each body has its own interests and concerns which may not be in accordance with those of its neighbours.

3.87 Because of the variety of public and private bodies involved, sea defences have been constructed to a range of standards of protection. Some of these standards are no longer considered appropriate, particularly where the use of land in the protected area has changed. In this context, the NRA has recently carried out a Sea Defence Survey to assess the condition and effectiveness of all sea defences in England and Wales. The results of this survey highlighted areas where the standard of defence would need improvement, especially in the light of predicted sea level changes. The study concluded:

> "the capital and revenue spending over the years has resulted in a reasonably adequate standard of defence. Of course, records and newspaper reports do show that defences are at times overtopped by large storm waves, often bringing with them significant quantities of beach material, but defences are only built to a standard which limits damage. They cannot exclude totally all storms, however severe. Nature must never be underestimated. The survey confirms the need for a continuing programme of investment" (NRA Sea Defence Survey, 1992).

3.88 The recognition of the need to consider coastal engineering in the context of coastal systems or sediment cells can help develop a clearer understanding of the problems of managing the dynamic coast. Informal groups of coastal authorities such as the Carmarthen Bay Group and SCOPAC have, to an extent, provided the foundations for more effective **shoreline management** by creating the framework within which the broader implications of coastal dynamics can be considered. The momentum has been sustained by the establishment of national level coordination groups by MAFF and the Welsh Office to provide a forum for strategic thinking and technical cooperation between regions. However, it remains unclear whether the current groupings of authorities are the most appropriate in terms of managing problems within sediment cells. For example, along the south east coast of England groups have been established that reflect the existing administrative framework (Kent and East Sussex) and not the likely extent of coastal systems.

3.89 Although traditional, hard engineering schemes have been very successful in limiting the damage caused by coastal processes, it is now recognised that they can have adverse effects on the coastal environment. As a consequence, **soft engineering** solutions designed to work with rather than oppose natural processes are beginning to be considered as serious options in particular settings. This approach forms a central theme in English Nature's Campaign for a Living Coast.

3.90 Effective shoreline management is limited, however, by a general lack of reliable and useful data about processes operating around the coast. This also has lead to difficulties in quantifying the level of risk posed to development or the impact development may have on the coastal zone. These problems are compounded by the uncertainties over the effects of rising sea levels. Indeed, an absence of a sound information base for much of the coastline makes it almost impossible to predict the nature of changes that may occur at particular locations.

3.91 The condition of sea defences in England and Wales is likely to be of increasing concern in the future, with the threat of rising sea levels contributing to increased maintenance costs to prevent sea defences being overtopped or undercut. The maintenance of some sea walls, the only purpose of which is to protect areas of low lying farmland, may become uneconomic. Retreat to a more easily defensible line, combined with measures to maintain a buffer zone seaward of this line may become an increasingly economic alternative. Retreat or setback could also offer a means of avoiding the losses of intertidal habitats.

3.92 The need for coastal defence works have often led to conflict with conservation interests, especially the preservation of important geological sites (eg Chewton Bunny; Tyhurst, 1991). Decisions not to defend land on conservation or other grounds highlight the absence of a mechanism to provide compensation for affected parties (eg McIlroy, 1990). Some sea defence schemes have been the cause of conflict between leisure sailing and conservation interests as the hard barriers along stretches of coast have led to a concentration of moorings in sheltered estuaries of conservation value.

3.93 In Scotland, the island and regional councils have strategic planning functions and, hence, there is the opportunity to plan overall coastal defence on a regional basis. However, it should be noted that much of the Scottish coast is undeveloped and of a different character to the problematic soft rock and low lying areas of England and Wales. In general, coastal defence issues are less severe than in England and Wales.

References: Chapter 3

Brampton, A.H., 1992 Beaches – the natural way to coastal defence. In M.G.Barrett (ed) Coastal zone planning and management. Thomas Telford, 221–229.

Bray, M.J., Carter, D.J., & Hooke, J.M., 1991, Coastal Sediment Transport Study. Reports to SCOPAC, Department of Geography, Portsmouth Poly.

Brunsden, D., 1991 Coastal and landslide problems in Dorset. Proceedings of the SCOPAC conference on Coastal Instability and Development Planning, Southsea.

Child, M.W., 1992, The Anglian Management Study. In M.G.Barrett (ed) Coastal zone planning and management. Thomas Telford, 253–267.

Clark, A.R. & Guest, S., 1991, The Whitby Cliff stabilisation and coast protection scheme. In R.J. Chandler (ed), Slope stability engineering developments and applications, Thomas Telford, 263–270.

Clayton, K.M., 1980, Coastal protection along the East Anglian coast, UK. Zeit. fur Geom. Suppl. Bd. 34, 165–172.

Clayton, K. M., 1989, The implications of climatic change. In Coastal Management, Thomas Telford, 165–176.

Clayton K.M., 1990, Sea level rise and coastal defences in the UK. Q. J. Eng. Geol. 23, 283–287.

Coastal Engineering Research Advisory Committee (CERAC), 1991, Coastal engineering research requirements. Institution of Civil Engineers.

Department of the Environment, 1992, Coastal zone protection and planning. The Government's response to the Second Report from the House of Commons Select Committee on the Environment. HMSO.

Earth Science Conservation, 1988, No. 24, March 1988.

Fleming, C.A., 1989, The Anglian Sea Defence Management Study. In Coastal Management, 153–164, Thomas Telford.

Grampian Regional Council, 1990, Minerals Policy Review.

Sir William Halcrow and Partners, 1991 Sea Defence Management Study for Anglian Region.

Hampshire County Council, 1991 A Strategy for Hampshire's Coast. County Planning Department.

Hydraulics Research Ltd, 1991, A Guide to the Selection of Appropriate Coast Protection Works for Geological SSSIs. Nature Conservancy Council.

HR Wallingford, 1993, Coastal management: mapping of littoral cells. Report SR 328.

Keay, T.B., 1941, Coastal erosion. The Dock and Harbour Authority, Oct 1941.

Lankester, R., 1991 Response to the Countryside Commissions paper "Visitors to the Countryside", relating to coastal leisure sailing.

Leafe R., 1991, The English Nature View. Proceedings of the SCOPAC conference on Coastal Instability and Development Planning, Southsea.

Lee, E.M., in press, Landsliding and insurance: the problems of Luccombe Village, Isle of Wight. Paper presented to the Geological Society, 1991.

McIlroy, A.J., 1990, Clifftop families admit defeat in battle with the advancing sea. Daily Telegraph 8.10.90.

McNichol, J., 1990, Coastal horizons. Surveyor 19 April, 1990, 8–11.

MAFF, 1989, Caring for the Future: Flood and Coastal Defence. HMSO.

MAFF, DoE & Welsh Office, 1991 Conservation guidelines for drainage authorities.

National Audit Office, 1992, Coastal defences in England. HMSO.

Payne, H.R., 1991, Coastal and shoreline management. Paper presented at the CIRIA Meeting on Coastal Engineering, Llandrindod Wells, October 1991.

Parker, T., 1989, Brainstorming on the coast. Surveyor 18 May, 1989, 13–15.

Pethick, J., & Burd, F., 1993, Coastal defence and the environment: a guide to good practice. MAFF.

Roberts, A.G. & McGown, A., 1987, A coastal area management system as developed for Seasalter–Reculver, North Kent, Proc. Instit. Civ. Engrs., 1, 82, 777–797.

Townend, I.H., & Fleming, C.A., 1990, The Anglian Sea Defence Management Study. Proc. of Flood Plain Management Conference, Ontario, Canada.

Tyhurst, M.F., 1991 Planning aspects of the Chewton Bunny planning inquiry. Proceedings of the SCOPAC Conference on Coastal Instability and Development Planning, Southsea.

West G.M., 1992, Engineering the beaches. In M.G.Barrett (ed) Coastal zone planning and management. Thomas Telford, 231–236.

Wildlife Link, 1991, A selection of case studies illustrating the need for coastal zone management in the UK.

4 Pollution Control

Introduction

4.1 Control of pollution involves a combination of **international collaboration** and a **national** approach involving control of both **sea-based** and **land-based** polluting activities (Figure 4.1). This has arisen because management of pollution of coastal waters cannot be separated from the control of pollution of the open sea or river basins. The main sources of localised contaminants in the North Sea, for example, are rivers flowing from continental Europe, with catchments extending as far as Czechoslovakia (Reid, 1991).

International Collaboration

4.2 Over the last decade the UK has been taking positive action with its neighbours to improve the environment of the North Sea. These efforts have been focused through a sequence of **Ministerial Conferences** on the health of the North Sea, involving the 8 maritime states surrounding the sea. These conferences have provided a focus for the development of international cooperation over marine pollution:

- the Bremen Conference in 1984 (NSC1) recognised the limited nature of earlier attempts to control pollution;

- the London Conference in 1987 (NSC2) resulted in the decision to reduce inputs of the most hazardous pollutants and nutrients to affected areas by around 50% and the termination of disposal of industrial waste and marine incineration. The conference also established a **North Sea Task Force**, comprising the 8 maritime states of the North Sea, the Commission of the European Communities, the International Council for the Exploration of the Sea and the Oslo and Paris Commissions;

The Task Force is responsible for producing a comprehensive statement on contaminant sources and sinks, ecological conditions and the impact of human activity on the North Sea;

- the Hague Conference in 1990 (NSC3) agreed the complete phase out and destruction of equipment with PCBs by 1999. The conference also agreed a standard North Sea list of 35 dangerous substances and produced a separate "Memorandum of understanding on small cetaceans";

4.3 The DoE have produced **Guidance notes** on the implementation of the Ministerial decisions made at the 1987 and 1990 conferences (DoE, 1988, 1990). Of importance is that decisions made at the Ministerial Conferences are to be applied equally to all UK marine and estuarine waters.

Sea-based activities

Disposal of waste at sea

4.4 The disposal of waste at sea (sewage sludge, industrial waste, dredged material, inorganic mine and particulate waste and spoil) is carried out under licence from the relevant fisheries department (MAFF who also act as agents for the Secretary of State in Wales, the Scottish Office Agriculture and Fisheries Department (SOAFD) or DoE (Northern Ireland)) under powers in the **Food and Environment Protection Act, 1985, Part II** (as amended by the Environmental Protection Act 1990). The location of licensed disposal sites around Great Britain (as of 1991) are shown on Figure 4.2. Under the same legislation, MAFF is also responsible for granting licences for the

Figure 4.1 Control of pollution: A summary of the legal and administrative framework

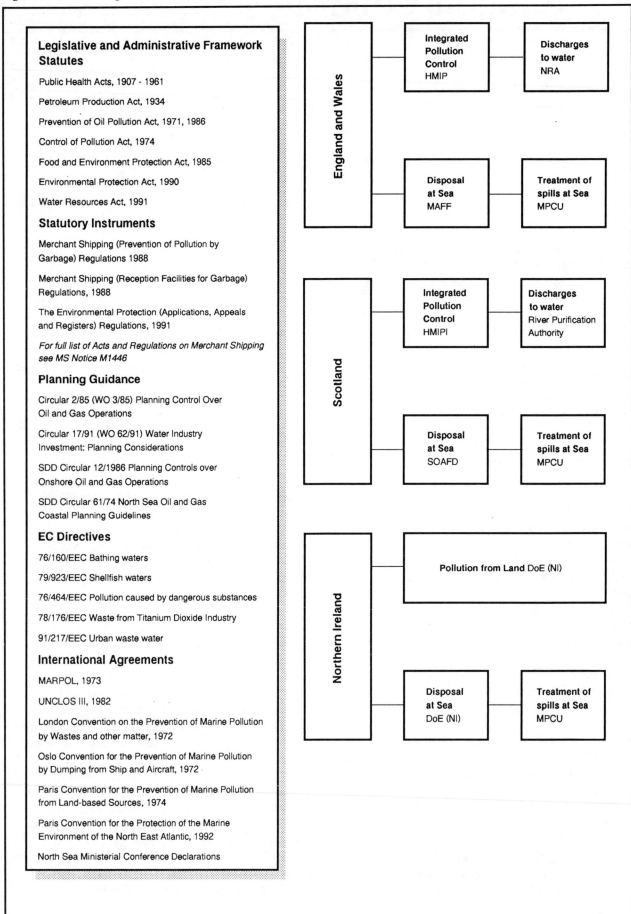

Legislative and Administrative Framework

Statutes

Public Health Acts, 1907 - 1961

Petroleum Production Act, 1934

Prevention of Oil Pollution Act, 1971, 1986

Control of Pollution Act, 1974

Food and Environment Protection Act, 1985

Environmental Protection Act, 1990

Water Resources Act, 1991

Statutory Instruments

Merchant Shipping (Prevention of Pollution by Garbage) Regulations 1988

Merchant Shipping (Reception Facilities for Garbage) Regulations, 1988

The Environmental Protection (Applications, Appeals and Registers) Regulations, 1991

For full list of Acts and Regulations on Merchant Shipping see MS Notice M1446

Planning Guidance

Circular 2/85 (WO 3/85) Planning Control Over Oil and Gas Operations

Circular 17/91 (WO 62/91) Water Industry Investment: Planning Considerations

SDD Circular 12/1986 Planning Controls over Onshore Oil and Gas Operations

SDD Circular 61/74 North Sea Oil and Gas Coastal Planning Guidelines

EC Directives

76/160/EEC Bathing waters

79/923/EEC Shellfish waters

76/464/EEC Pollution caused by dangerous substances

78/176/EEC Waste from Titanium Dioxide Industry

91/217/EEC Urban waste water

International Agreements

MARPOL, 1973

UNCLOS III, 1982

London Convention on the Prevention of Marine Pollution by Wastes and other matter, 1972

Oslo Convention for the Prevention of Marine Pollution by Dumping from Ship and Aircraft, 1972

Paris Convention for the Prevention of Marine Pollution from Land-based Sources, 1974

Paris Convention for the Protection of the Marine Environment of the North East Atlantic, 1992

North Sea Ministerial Conference Declarations

England and Wales

Integrated Pollution Control HMIP — Discharges to water NRA

Disposal at Sea MAFF — Treatment of spills at Sea MPCU

Scotland

Integrated Pollution Control HMIPI — Discharges to water River Purification Authority

Disposal at Sea SOAFD — Treatment of spills at Sea MPCU

Northern Ireland

Pollution from Land DoE (NI)

Disposal at Sea DoE (NI) — Treatment of spills at Sea MPCU

Figure 4.2 Licensed waste disposal sites (after Davidson et al, 1991)

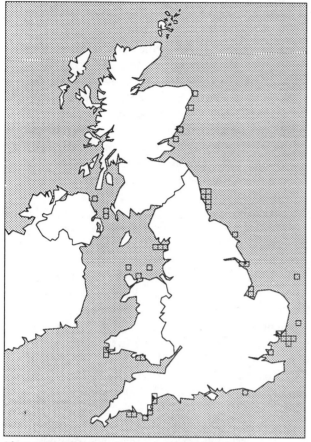

Licensed spoil dump sites around Great Britain

Licensed industrial dump sites around Great Britain

Sewage sludge dump sites around the UK

disposal of waste stone from coal mines on the shoreline.

4.5 The Government participates actively in the London Dumping Convention of 1972 and the Paris and Oslo Commissions (currently under revision) to adopt measures to protect the marine environment and has announced that:

- the issuing of licences for disposal of liquid industrial waste at sea will cease at the end of 1992 or early 1993 at the latest;

- disposal of waste stone from coal mines on beaches or at sea is to be phased out by 1995 and 1997, respectively, so long as practicable options for disposal on land can be found;

- disposal of sewage sludge at sea will cease by the end of 1998.

4.6 The discharge of garbage to sea can lead to marine wildlife becoming entangled in litter and unsightly pollution of beaches. In addition, the Keep Britain Tidy Group (now the Tidy Britain Group) reported that between 1977 and 1986 at least 100 people were advised to seek medical attention following exposure to the contents of chemical packages washed ashore (Dixon & Dixon, 1985).

4.7 The main source of marine litter is believed to be from ships, although holiday–makers are also likely to have contributed significant quantities (Dixon, 1990). Prevention of pollution from vessels is regulated under the **International Convention for the Prevention of Pollution from Ships 1973 (MARPOL)**. MARPOL consists of a Convention modified by a Protocol with 5 Annexes which contain regulations intended to control pollution of the sea by the discharge of oil, noxious liquid substances, packaged dangerous goods, sewage and garbage from ships.

4.8 This convention is implemented in the UK by various **Merchant Shipping Regulations**. For example Annex 1 (Oil Pollution) is implemented through:

- **Merchant Shipping (Prevention of Oil Pollution) Regulations 1983;**

- **Merchant Shipping (Prevention of Pollution) (Reception Facilities) Order 1984;**

- **Merchant Shipping (Prevention of Pollution) (Amendment) Regulations 1985.**

4.9 These and other Regulations set discharge requirements for ships between the baseline for measuring territorial waters and the territorial limit. The **Prevention of Oil Pollution Act 1971** and the **Prevention of Oil Pollution Act 1986** contain, amongst other things, discharge requirements for ships when they are landward of the baseline for measuring territorial waters.

4.10 The **Merchant Shipping (Prevention of Pollution by Garbage) Regulations 1988** apply to all UK ships and all ships in UK territorial waters. A two–tier approach to regulating garbage has been adopted:

- in **Special Areas** (the North Sea has recently been established as such an area by the

Secretary of State) it is prohibited to dispose of any garbage, although food waste may be dumped over 12nm from shore;

- outside Special Areas the disposal of plastics is prohibited. Disposal of other garbage is also prohibited except where it is made as far from land as practicable. Examples include: floating material such as biodegradable packing at least 25 nm offshore; food waste, paper, glass and metal at least 12nm offshore unless it has been ground or comminuted (3nm). However, these provisions have caused concern with conservation agencies and groups as many packaging materials include non–biodegradable plastics which may have a lasting effect on the coastal zone (Clare, 1991).

4.11 Although **The Tidy Britain Group** have reported that litter is widely distributed throughout the North Sea (Dixon, 1990), they note that the problem is expected to decline as these wastes are increasingly disposed of at port reception facilities required by the **Merchant Shipping (Reception Facilities for Garbage) Regulations 1988** (also implementing the MARPOL convention).

4.12 These regulations apply to harbour authorities and other terminal operators (eg piers, marinas, wharves and jetties). These authorities are given powers to provide reception facilities for garbage from ships (all vessels except hovercraft). If the facilities are not adequate to receive the garbage without causing delay or according to the needs of the users the Secretary of State may direct such facilities to be provided. Provision is also included to enable the authorities or operators to make reasonable charges for the use of the facilities.

Land–based pollution

4.13 As for many activities the coastal zone marks a change in the administrative framework for pollution control. In England and Wales, responsibility for control of **land–based** pollution of coastal waters rests with the NRA and Her Majesty's Inspectorate of Pollution (HMIP). Local authorities and HMIP are responsible for the regulation of pollutants for land and air. The relationship between NRA and HMIP is detailed in DoE Guidance note "Integrated Pollution Control – A practical guide", Annex C: Memorandum of understanding between HMIP and NRA.

4.14 In Scotland, river purification authorities (7 River Purification Boards and the 3 Island Councils) are responsible for water pollution control under the **Control of Pollution Act, 1974** (Figure 4.1). Her Majesty's Industrial Pollution Inspectorate (HMIPI) and the river purification authorities are jointly responsible for integrated pollution control of prescribed processes (see below).

4.15 In Northern Ireland water pollution control and integrated pollution control functions are the responsibility of DoE (NI).

4.16 The Government's approach to pollution control is based on a **precautionary approach** and is guided by a number of principles (HMSO, 1990):

- prevention of pollution at the source;

- minimising the risk of harm to human health and the environment;

- encouraging and applying the most advanced technical solutions, while recognising the integrated nature of the environment and the need to achieve the best practicable option for the environment as a whole;

- applying a "critical loads" approach which involves an assessment of the tolerance of an area to pollution;

- ensuring that the polluter pays for the necessary controls.

Integrated Pollution Control

4.17 HMIP (England and Wales) and HMIPI (Scotland) have the responsibility of implementing the **integrated pollution control** (IPC) procedures introduced under The **Environmental Protection Act 1990** (Part 1). These procedures control and regulate pollution from certain releases to air, land and water prescribed by the Secretary of State. It has been estimated that there are around 105 types of industrial process that will be covered by integrated pollution control (Morris, 1991).

4.18 Central to the IPC system is the principal that potential polluters must adopt the **best available techniques not entailing excessive cost** (BATNEEC). In England and Wales, HMIP is responsible for granting authorisation before such

processes can operate, although it is required to consult with MAFF, the Health and Safety Executive and the NRA (Table 4.1). English Nature (or its Welsh equivalent, CCW) must be consulted in cases where a release may affect an SSSI. Specific conditions are set down which the operator must meet in order to:

- prevent or minimise the release of the most polluting substances;

- render harmless all substances released;

- control releases in whatever way is best for the environment as a whole.

4.19 Much of the costs of operating IPC are recovered from potential polluters through charges for authorisations. Such authorisations are also likely to contain conditions which address environmental quality objectives and it is intended that HMIP (and HMIPI in Scotland) will set higher environmental standards as the available technology improves (HMSO, 1990).

Water Quality: England and Wales

4.20 Under **The Water Resources Act 1991**, (Part III), the NRA (Figure 4.3) is specifically responsible for water quality in controlled waters. In this context controlled waters include **territorial waters** within 3nm of their baseline (ie the shore) and **coastal waters** between the baseline of territorial waters and the landward limit of high tides. Of interest, the limit of NRA's responsibility, 3nm offshore, corresponds to a distance at which a cannon ball could still penetrate the hull of an enemy vessel.

4.21 NRA's responsibilities include the determination and issuing of consents for discharges of waste into these waters (except those discharges subject to integrated pollution control); monitoring of the extent of pollution; control of diffuse pollution; specification and achievement of **Statutory Water Quality Objectives** and classification requirements, as determined by the Secretary of State.

4.22 The **Environmental Protection Act, 1990** enables the NRA to specify discharge consent conditions to HMIP in order to achieve water quality objectives (Table 4.1). Indeed, HMIP can only set standards that meet or exceed NRA standards.

Table 4.1 Pollution control: consultation and notification for consents and other activities, in England and Wales. Note: similar procedures apply in Scotland

Activity	Authorising Body	Consultees and Notification
1. Discharge of prescribed process	Consents authorised by HMIP (Environmental Protection Act 1990)	Where discharge is into controlled waters NRA is consulted (EP Act 1990 S.28). Under 1991 Regulations English Nature/CCW consulted where discharge could affect an SSSI; harbour authority when discharge is into a harbour.
2. Control of pollution in controlled waters	NRA authorises discharge consents (Water Resources Act 1991)	Notice in national and local press, to local authority and (in coastal waters) Minister (WR Act 1991 S.10). NRA must consult English Nature/CCW before carrying out or authorising works etc that may affect an SSSI. (WR Act 1991 S.17)
3. Disposal of waste at sea	Fisheries Departments (eg MAFF, SOAFD) authorises licences (Food and Environment Protection Act 1985 Pt II)	Licencing authority has to have regard to protect marine environment, prevent interference with sea uses and other considerations (FEP Act 1985 Pt II S.8)
4. Discharges of litter from ships	Discharges at sea controlled by Merchant Shipping Regulations (see text). Garbage reception facilities required at all harbours and terminals.	

Water Quality: Scotland

4.23 Scotland has benefited from a system of independent control over pollution of the water environment since the 1950s. The river purification authorities (RPAs; Figure 4.3) are derived from the **Control of Pollution Act 1974** (as amended by the Water Act 1989, S.23). They have the responsibility of maintaining and improving river and coastal water quality and conserving the water resources of their areas.

Bathing Waters

4.24 Under the 1991 Act the NRA (England and Wales) and the RPAs (Scotland) are the "competent authority" responsible for achieving the requirements of EC Directives which impact upon aspects of coastal water quality. The **EC Bathing Waters Directive (76/160/EEC)** has the dual objectives of raising and maintaining bathing water quality and protecting public health. Whilst, for example, the NRA is not responsible for the public health aspects, it is concerned that standards are scientifically based and that compliance can be measured in a meaningful way (NRA 1991). Achieving the standards set in the directive is done by controlling the quality of discharges by granting consents with conditions.

4.25 The EC Directive defines bathing waters as those waters where bathing is either:

– **authorised** by a competent authority; or

– **not prohibited** and traditionally practised by large numbers.

4.26 In the UK the entitlement to bathe has derived from custom and although bathing may be limited by local authority byelaws (see Chapter 8) it does not require authorisation. As a result the Government identified bathing waters according to the second criterion above. Initially only 27 waters were identified in the UK on the basis of strict criteria (see NRA, 1991); a list which excluded premier resorts such as Blackpool and Brighton. However, using a more relaxed set of criteria 455 bathing waters had been identified by 1992, throughout the UK. This number compares with figures of over 600 beaches where bathing is traditionally practised (the Coastal Anti–Pollution League, 1983; Haigh, 1987). **Blue Flag** awards are made by the Foundation for Environmental Education in Europe to beaches which have passed the EC Directive's mandatory water quality standards, plus a level of beach management.

4.27 The major source of pollution of coastal waters is sewage effluent, which enters the sea through a variety of outfalls. It has been estimated that 17% of Britain's sewage is disposed of at sea

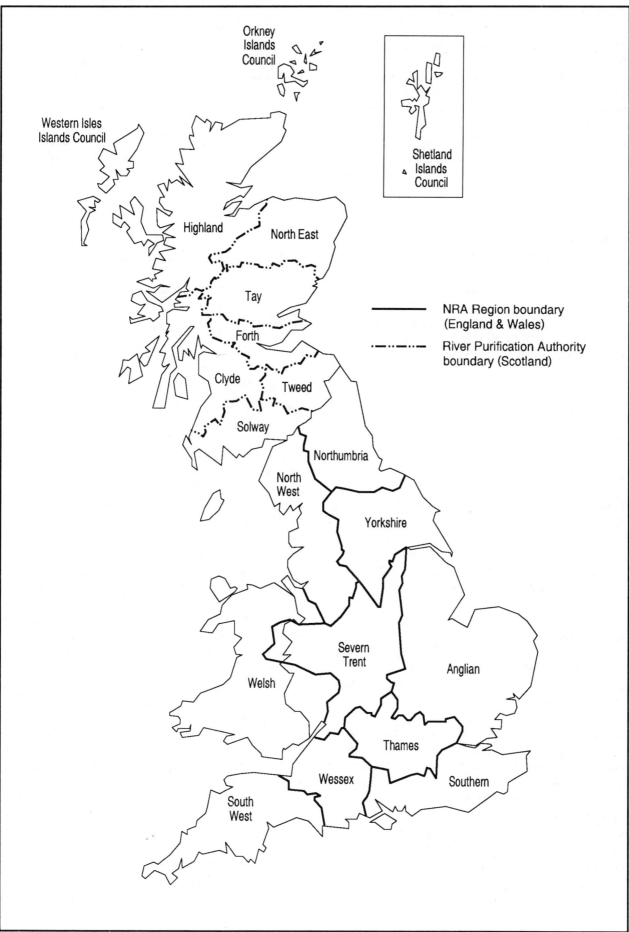

(HMSO, 1990), the vast majority of which is largely untreated. The most problematic discharges are those from short sea outfalls and stormwater overflows, many of which are too short to provide adequate dispersal of sewage (NRA, 1991). The pollution from these sources has often involved the gross fouling of recreation beaches with faecal solids and other debris; microbial contamination and occasional fouling of extensive lengths of shoreline by floating sewage debris (NRA, 1991). Sewage can also lower oxygen concentrations and increase nutrient levels, adversely affecting marine plant and animal communities.

4.28 In recognition of the unsatisfactory state of many beaches, the Government, in 1989, announced a £1.4b capital investment programme to bring all identified bathing waters into compliance with the directive (DoE, 1989). In 1990 the Government announced that all significant discharges of sewage to coastal and estuarine waters should receive treatment leading to the investment programme being increased by £1.5b.

4.29 Data from the NRA's 1990 survey indicate recent improvements n water quality, with 78% of bathing waters passing the terms of the directive (NRA, 1991). However, much concern was expressed in the summer of 1991 when it was reported in **Holiday Which** that many beaches failed "virus tests". This issue has raised doubts about the value of the standards, with the DoE defending its approach, under which compliance was:

> "...based on bacterial standards and not on virus content, mainly because it is impossible for any beach to guarantee that it will have a zero rating for viruses. They are introduced into the sea from a variety of sources, including bird droppings, and all member states are agreed that the present standards are unattainable", DoE spokesman quoted in The Times (14.8.91).

4.30 The **EC Urban Waste Water Treatment Directive (91/271/EEC)** requires member states to adopt a consistent approach to sewage treatment facilities, setting standards for discharges into waters. The UK Government has welcomed this directive and intends to act quickly on its implementation, although the additional requirements could add £2.2b to the estimated cost of improving bathing water quality (DoE, 1991).

The role of the local authorities

4.31 Under the 1990 Act certain local authorities are responsible for the regulation of waste disposal on land (above HWM) and some forms of air pollution. This Act also requires local authorities and landowners (except the Crown Estate Commissioners) to keep public access land free of litter. This duty is seen to require a daily sweep of all coastal parks and public beaches and has caused concern over the financial implications to authorities (Association of County Councils et al, 1991).

The effectiveness of the approach to pollution control

The extent to which coastal dynamics are considered

4.32 Marine pollution can arise from several sources – vessels, oil and gas rigs and from land based activities – and in several forms – mishaps, deliberate acts and the effect of discharge controls. Much of the UK's approach to pollution control is directed towards preventing or controlling pollution at source. This is done by ship and equipment design, operational controls and progressively enhanced licence regimes, often based on international conventions.

4.33 However, risks of accidental spillages cannot be eliminated. Oil spillages are amongst the most serious hazards to the coastal zone. The Amoco Cadiz accident, for example, involved the spillage of 230,000 tonnes of light crude oil off the coast of Brittany in 1978 (CNEXO, 1978). Over 80,000 tonnes of oil was washed onto the beaches and into estuaries where many wildlife communities were devastated (Laubier, 1982). Problems were greatest in the estuaries where initial sedimentation of oil residues was followed by months of remobilisation of degrading products causing persistently high toxicity and, consequently the collapse of the local oyster industry. Sorensen (1982) estimated that the disaster cost the equivalent of up to £170M, including losses to fishing, tourism and seaweed harvesting on the Brittany coast.

4.34 In polluting incidents the dynamic nature of the coastal environment, with 2 tides a day potentially washing oil or other dangerous substances onshore, makes it is essential that there is a fast and effective emergency response. The

Marine Pollution Control Unit (MPCU), set up in 1979 as part of the DTp, is on permanent standby to deal with incidents and constantly monitors all spills. The unit has 9 aircraft available at short notice, stocks of dispersants at strategically placed sites around the coast and special equipment for recovering oil from both at sea and on beaches. The unit also has the responsibility for the national contingency plan for such incidents.

4.35 Small scale incidents are likely to be dealt with by port or terminal operators under local contingency plans, while the NRA (England and Wales) and the RPAs (Scotland) have responsibility for dealing with incidents caused by industrial discharges or other land based sources. Local authorities have responsibility for shoreline clean-up operations and stockpiles of equipment for their use are maintained by MPCU, who, in the event of a major incident can assist and direct beach clean up operations.

4.36 In 1990 alone 791 oil spills were recorded around the coast, involving 136 clean–up operations (Advisory Committee on the Protection of the Sea, quoted in The Guardian, 1991). Close cooperation is needed between the emergency planning services to minimise the damaged caused by an oil spill. This was recently demonstrated by the response to the spillage of 1,000 tonnes of oil following the collision of a 250,000 tonne tanker and a trawler off the south Devon coast in May 1990. Contingency plans, developed by Devon County, involved alerting a wide range of groups including the MPCU, NRA, the (then) Nature Conservancy Council, the county emergency services, local harbourmasters and fishermen (Edwards, 1991).

4.37 As polluting processes become more strictly regulated, the main problems facing pollution control in the coming years will be resources to deal with major accidents. However, in response to the publication of the Department of Transport's plans for dealing with large oil spills (DTp, 1991), the National Audit Office suggested that not enough money and resources is allocated to deal with accidents and was critical of the apparent acceptance that some beaches were bound to get polluted (quoted in The Guardian, 22.2.91). At the same time, however, the Audit Office praised the Government for its record in inspecting tankers to see they met pollution standards and increasing aerial surveillance of the coast.

The extent to which environmental implications are considered

4.38 Environmental assessment is not required before granting or refusing consents or licences but, as described above, particular attention is paid to adopting a **precautionary principle** to balancing the risks and the scale of effort required to control a polluting activity (HMSO, 1990). This involves applying the **critical loads** approach by assessing the levels of a pollutant which local environments can tolerate without significant damage in order to focus protection on the most vulnerable locations. In essence the identification of activities which may have a significant effect is very similar to the approach adopted for identifying the need for EA (see Chapter 2).

The extent to which the systems takes into account the interests of other groups

4.39 In recent years pollution issues have tended to dominate the coastal agenda, from public fears of the dangers from bathing in affected waters (eg Bell, 1991) to growing international concerns for the health of the North Sea (eg Brodie–Cooper et al, 1990; Reid, 1991). The North Sea, for example, supports a closely connected ecosystem and is one of the richest wildlife habitats in the world. Besides providing breeding grounds and wintering areas for millions of seabirds, the sea yields around 2.6 million tons of fish a year (Brodie–Cooper et al, 1990). However, because it is a largely enclosed sea it is particularly vulnerable to potentially polluting activities such as exploitation of oil and gas, industrial waste discharges, transportation, the disposal and incineration of waste and dredged spoil contaminated by pollutants. Indeed, the effects of oil pollution, together with eutrophication and spills of industrial pollutants, are probably the greatest threats to coastal tourism, recreation, fishing and conservation. In general, however, the damaging effects of pollution have been shown to be concentrated in industrialised estuaries and some sections of the coast, with many areas remaining largely unaffected (North Sea Quality Status Report, 1987).

4.40 For hundreds of years estuaries have been the sink for chemicals and other wastes. For example, during the 19th century enormous volumes of toxic alkali waste from the soda industry in St Helens and Widnes were simply dumped into streams and rivers (Doornkamp and Lee, 1992). This can have lasting effects within coastal ecosystems as more than 90% of all materials entering the coastal zone remain in sediments, mudflats or marshes. For instance, there have been repeated cases of serious organic lead poisoning in the Mersey Estuary since 1979, killing hundreds of birds (Brodie-Cooper et al, 1990). Head et al (1980) have suggested that this lead is likely to have come from one of the petrochemical works that line the south bank of the river.

4.41 For brevity, the following sections examine the consultation arrangements in England and Wales. Similar procedures are relevant in Scotland.

(i) Consultation by HMIP

4.42 In the light of these concerns it is interesting to note that there is only limited public, interested party cr NGO participation in the decision to grant or refuse discharge licences or consents (Figure 4.4). For example, in issuing consents for discharge of substances from prescribed processes HMIP is only required to consult a limited number of bodies (**The Environmental Protection (Applications, Appeals and Registers) Regulations 1991**; Table 4.1):

- the NRA must be consulted over whether the consent may affect the achievement of water quality objectives and HMIP must apply standards at least as stringent as the NRA require;

- a harbour authority, if the discharge is to be into the harbour waters;

- English Nature or CCW, if the discharge may affect an SSSI.

- MAFF or the Secretary of State for Wales who, amongst other things, will consider the interests of the fisheries industry.

(ii) Consultation by NRA

4.43 The NRA is required to give notice of consents for discharges to controlled waters in the national and local press, and the appropriate Minister. Objections may be made within 28 days and can lead to the Secretary of State causing a local inquiry or hearing to be held (Water Resources Act 1991 Schedule 10). Local inquiries may also be ordered by the Secretary of State in connection with any matter relating to pollution control in controlled waters (1991 Act S.213).

4.44 Concerns have been expressed, however, that the bathing water improvements apply to only a limited part of the coastline (eg RSPB, 1991). Indeed, bathing is only one of a range of water sports and recreations that may take place throughout near shore waters. In areas such as the Solent, for example, windsurfing, water skiing and boating may take place in near shore waters that are not covered by existing water quality standards (Hampshire County Council, 1991). As described earlier, there is also continuing debate about the adequacy of the standards used to designate Blue Flag awards to bathing beaches, especially the concentration on bacterial standards.

4.45 A provision in the 1991 Act requires NRA to consult English Nature or CCW before carrying out or authorising any works, operations or activity that may affect an SSSI (S.17). NRA must also consult the Scottish river purification authorities for monitoring the extent of pollution in controlled waters (S.84).

(iii) Fisheries departments' environmental responsibilities

4.46 Although MAFF is not specifically required to consult interested groups over the issue of a disposal at sea licence (but see the Kimya example described below), it has to have regard for the need to:

- protect the marine environment, the living resources which it supports and human health;

- prevent interference with legitimate uses of the sea. (Food and Environment Protection Act 1985 S.8).

4.47 The granting of licences is sometimes criticised by conservation groups or other interests. For example, the recent extension of British Coal's licence to dump colliery waste on beaches at Dawdon and Easington in County Durham has been widely criticised by local MPs, Durham County Council and environmental groups (SCEC, 1986; Glegg & Horsman, 1990). The decision to extend licensing highlights a recurrent dilemma for coastal management; environmental improvement at the expense of local employment. Restoration of the beaches could be a factor in promoting tourist-related employment (ECOTEC Research & Consulting Ltd, quoted in Planning, 1988b). Ceasing the practice (note: the Government has now announced its intention not to extend licences) may, however, lead to closure of the colliery and loss of local employment as disposal in landfill

Figure 4.4 Formal mechanisms by which pollution control activity takes into account the interests of other groups

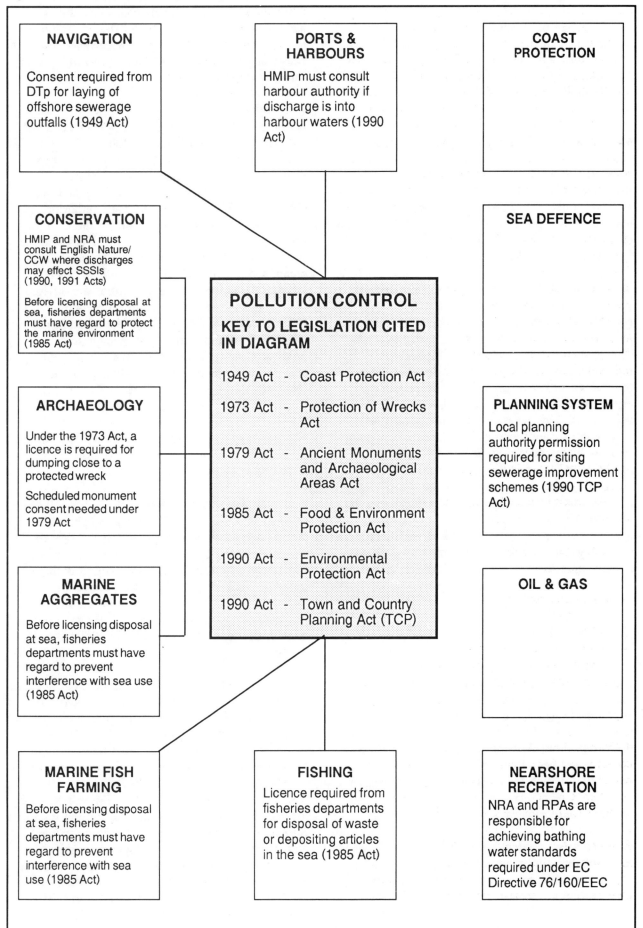

NAVIGATION

Consent required from DTp for laying of offshore sewerage outfalls (1949 Act)

PORTS & HARBOURS

HMIP must consult harbour authority if discharge is into harbour waters (1990 Act)

COAST PROTECTION

CONSERVATION

HMIP and NRA must consult English Nature/CCW where discharges may effect SSSIs (1990, 1991 Acts)

Before licensing disposal at sea, fisheries departments must have regard to protect the marine environment (1985 Act)

SEA DEFENCE

POLLUTION CONTROL

KEY TO LEGISLATION CITED IN DIAGRAM

1949 Act - Coast Protection Act

1973 Act - Protection of Wrecks Act

1979 Act - Ancient Monuments and Archaeological Areas Act

1985 Act - Food & Environment Protection Act

1990 Act - Environmental Protection Act

1990 Act - Town and Country Planning Act (TCP)

ARCHAEOLOGY

Under the 1973 Act, a licence is required for dumping close to a protected wreck

Scheduled monument consent needed under 1979 Act

PLANNING SYSTEM

Local planning authority permission required for siting sewerage improvement schemes (1990 TCP Act)

MARINE AGGREGATES

Before licensing disposal at sea, fisheries departments must have regard to prevent interference with sea use (1985 Act)

OIL & GAS

MARINE FISH FARMING

Before licensing disposal at sea, fisheries departments must have regard to prevent interference with sea use (1985 Act)

FISHING

Licence required from fisheries departments for disposal of waste or depositing articles in the sea (1985 Act)

NEARSHORE RECREATION

NRA and RPAs are responsible for achieving bathing water standards required under EC Directive 76/160/EEC

sites would probably be more expensive:

> "The cost of disposal will affect jobs in the mining industry, so Government must assess the alternative disposal options with proper concern for the full implications", John Gummer, Minister of State at MAFF quoted in Planning (1988).

4.48 The disposal of wastes at sea also promotes objections from environmental groups. Sludge disposal, for example, is reported to cause reduction of oxygen in the water column, reduction in the productivity of fisheries, an accumulation of toxic materials in fish and birds (SCEC, 1986) and claims of increases in the incidence of disease in fish (Dethlefsen, 1980).

4.49 Material dredged from ports, harbours and some estuaries and dumped at sea may be contaminated with heavy metals derived from industrial or domestic wastes dumped in the past. This is seen by Greenpeace as a method of transferring pollutants from estuaries into the open sea (Glegg & Horsman, 1990). However, the Government rejects allegations that damage is being caused by licensed disposal, noting that it's strict controls are specifically designed to prevent such problems occurring. Indeed, studies by MAFF/SOAFD scientists indicate that sewage sludge disposal, for example, has no significant adverse impact on marine life. It is likely that the different views are a reflection of a lack of agreement over cause and effects of incidents in an extremely complex natural system. However, there is agreement that the disposal of wastes at sea should be stopped (see for example Glegg & Housden, 1990; HMSO, 1990).

(iv) Harbour authority interests

4.50 Although most interested groups have applauded the implementation of the MARPOL convention, the requirement to provide reception facilities for garbage in harbours and other moorings has led to complaints over the cost from the British Ports Federation (BPF, 1991). These concerns are heightened by the availability of subsidies for such facilities in other EC states.

(v) Local authority interests

4.51 To a large extent the pollution control system does not formally require consultation with local authorities, although the latter undoubtedly benefit from the environmental improvements. However, local planning authorities have a key role in facilitating the planned water industry investment programme to improve, amongst other things, bathing water quality by 1995. This programme involves the construction of new sewage treatment works and extensive sewerage schemes to collect waste water, and outfalls.

4.52 Although provision of underground sewers is permitted development (GDO, 1988; Schedule 2 Parts 15 & 16; see Chapter 6) the above-ground headworks and treatment plans require express planning permission from the local planning authority. In a recent circular the DoE and Welsh Office have advised local planning authorities to give "sympathetic consideration" to such programmes and work closely with NRA and the water companies in order that the schemes are completed on time (DoE Circular 17/91; see Chapter 6). However, the authorities are advised that designated sites of wildlife importance (Ramsar sites, SPAs, National Nature Reserves; see Chapter 5) should normally outweigh such proposals and that care should be taken in siting such works in landscapes of national importance (National Parks and AONBs; see Chapter 5).

The extent to which the system allows coordinated decision making across the coastal zone

4.53 The Environmental Protection Act 1990 has resulted in a significant change in emphasis in pollution control from the traditional approach where land, air and water pollution were regulated separately. The current system recognises that pollution from one medium can have major implications in another, an essential requirement for managing pollution problems in the coastal zone where land and sea are in such close proximity.

4.54 Some recent publications have suggested that confusion over the responsibilities of HMIP and NRA have arisen because of the complexity of the existing legislation (eg Morris, 1991). These complexities have led to the need for informal working arrangements between the two bodies.

4.55 The relationships between HMIP, NRA and local authorities may be simplified by the proposed formation of an **Environment Agency**, in England and Wales which would be responsible for several of the pollution control functions. An environment agency is also proposed for Scotland which would assume the responsibilities of HMIPI, the river purification authorities, the waste regulation functions of the district and Island councils and the local authority air quality powers (Scottish Office, 1992).

4.56 There remains the potential for confusion between the aims of NRA, who have responsibility for water quality within 3nm of the shore, the MPCU who are responsible for dealing with clean-up of accidents, the fisheries departments and other interested bodies such as the local authorities. The widely cited example of the wreck of the Kimya, which sank in Caernarfon Bay in January 1990 carrying 1,500 tons of sunflower oil, illustrates this problem. The local authority, Countryside Council for Wales and the NRA were concerned about the possible impact on the coast. However, the MPCU felt there was no need to pump out the oil and favoured a "controlled leak" (Wildlife Link, 1991). The final decision in such cases lies with the relevant fisheries department who are responsible for issuing a licence for disposal the oil at sea.

Summary

4.57 Control of pollution involves a variety of legislation designed to regulate discharges into the sea from land and offshore sources:

- disposal of waste at sea requires a licence from the relevant fisheries department under the Food and Environment Protection Act 1985 Part II;

- discharge of litter from ships is prohibited or strictly controlled by Merchant Shipping Regulations. Further regulations require harbour authorities or terminal operators to provide reception facilities for garbage from users;

- the discharge of products from prescribed processes requires consent from HMIP (in England and Wales), HMIPI or the relevant RPA (in Scotland) under the Environmental Protection Act 1990;

- the discharge of other pollutants, including sewage, requires consent from NRA under the Water Resources Act 1991, or from the relevant RPA in Scotland under the Control of Pollution Act 1974;

- the disposal of solid waste on land requires consent from the relevant local authority.

4.58 The UK is also required to comply with EC directives, a number of which are of direct relevance to pollution control:

- 76/160/EEC Bathing Waters;

- 79/923/EEC Shellfish Waters;

- 78/176/EEC Waste from Titanium Dioxide Industry;

- 76/464/EEC Pollution caused by Dangerous Substances;

- 91/217/EEC Urban Waste Water.

4.59 Over the last decade there have been major developments in pollution control, which could lead to significant improvements in coastal water quality. The Ministerial Conferences on the health of the North Sea have led to decisions to end disposal of many waste materials at sea. The 1990 Act radically overhauled the traditional approach to pollution control with separately regulated systems for air, land and water. The current system recognises that pollution from one medium can have major implications in another. Through the introduction of integrated pollution control Great Britain has gone further in addressing potential hazards than any other European country (HMSO, 1990). In addition, the commitment by the water companies (in England and Wales) and sewerage authorities (in Scotland) to investment in sewage treatment works, together with the EC Urban Waste Water Treatment Directive should lead to marked improvements in bathing water quality (NRA, 1991). The EC Bathing Water Directive has already had a major impact on attitudes to improving water quality throughout Europe:

> "Identification of a bathing water as falling under the terms of the Directive has the effect of increasing the profile of bathing water quality in that area, and is often the precursor to the provision of large amounts of money to facilitate improving bathing water quality at the site" (NRA, 1991).

4.60 It is clear, however, that the effectiveness of these recent, and proposed, changes will only emerge over the next decade. It is important to recognise that measures of effectiveness will change over this period as public perception alters. Pollution control is concerned with the setting of standards and their enforcement. However, the standards that are set in legislation or directives are dependent on scientific understanding and public attitudes towards the environment at that time.

4.61 In 1980, for example, Parker & Penning-Rowsell wrote:

> "The public at large seems not to be interested in promoting higher pollution prevention standards", Parker & Penning-Rowsell (1980).

4.62 Headlines from August 1991 such as "Beaches of Shame" and "The Health-Risk Resorts the Government Didn't Want You to Know About" (The Daily Mirror, 14.8.91) are probably indicative of greater public concerns over water quality issues a decade later.

4.63 What was acceptable practice 50 years ago may be considered a major health risk today; it follows that what is acceptable today will not necessarily be acceptable in the future.

References: Chapter 4

Association of County Councils and others, 1991, Coastal Zone Protection and Planning. Memorandum of Evidence to the House of Commons Environment Committee.

Bell J, 1991, Swimming to safe shores. Surveyor 31 Jan. 1991, 12–14.

British Ports Federation, 1991, Evidence to the House of Commons Environment Committee.

Brodie-Cooper, S.A., Gubbay, S., Vijfvinkel, J., & van der Zwiep, K., 1990, Coastal zone management. Memorandum to the Seas at Risk Federation, Amsterdam, 1990.

Clare, N. (ed), 1991, Marine conservation handbook. Nature Conservancy Council/English Nature.

CNEXO, 1978, Amoco Cadiz: Premieres Observations sur la Pollution par des Hydrocarbures. Act Coll No.6 Brest.

Coastal Anti-Pollution League, 1983, The golden list of clean beaches in England and Wales. Coastal Anti-Pollution League, Bath.

Daily Mirror 1991, Beaches of shame. 14 August 1991.

Delthefsen, V., 1980, Observations of fish diseases in the German Bight and their possible relation to pollution. Rapp. P.v. Reun. Cons. Int. Explor. Mer. 179, 110–117.

Department of the Environment, 1988, Guidance note on the ministerial declaration.

Department of the Environment, 1989 The quality of UK bathing water improves. Environmental news release No.96.

Department of the Environment, 1990 Guidance note on ministerial declaration. 3rd International Conference on the Protection of the North Sea.

Department of the Environment, 1991 Environmental news release No. 183.

Department of Transport, 1991 Oil and chemical pollution at sea. HMSO.

Dixon, T.R., 1990, Operational discharges from ships and platforms (garbage, packed dangerous or harmful goods and pyrotechnics). In The Marine Forum North Sea Report 45–47.

Dixon, T.R., & Dixon, T.J., 1985, A report on a survey of packages dangerous goods, munitions and pyrotechnics recovered on beaches and in the nearshore waters of the British Isles. Stage 6. Marine Litter Research Programme. Keep Britain Tidy Group and the Advisory Committee on Pollution of the Sea.

Doornkamp J.C. & Lee E.M., 1991, Geology and Land use planning: St Helens, Merseyside. DoE.

Edwards, J., 1991, A slick response. Heritage Coast, 5.

Glegg, G. & Horsman, 1990, Inputs of inorganic and organic contaminants from sea disposal (dumping) by the UK. In The Marine Forum North Sea Report 37–44.

The Guardian, 1991, Coastal spills of oil reach record total of 791 in year. 13 August 1991.

Haigh, N., 1987, EEC Environmental policy and Britain. Longman.

Hampshire County Council, 1991 A Strategy for Hampshire's Coast. County Planning Department.

Head, P.C., D'Arcy, B.J. & Osbaldeston, P.J., 1980, The Mersey Estuary Bird Mortality, Autumn-Winter 1979. Report DSS-Est-80-1 NWWA Warrington.

Her Majesty's Stationary Office, 1990 This common inheritance. Britain's Environmental Strategy. Government White Paper.

Laubier, L., 1982, In Tippie, V.K. and Kester D.R. (eds) Impact of Marine Pollution on Society 93–105.

Morris, H., 1991, New-style watchdog. Surveyor 4 April 1991, 9–10.

National Rivers Authority, 1991 Bathing water quality in England and Wales – 1990. Water Quality Series No. 3 August 1991.

North Sea Quality Status Report, 1987, Report by the scientific and technical working group.

Parker D.J. & Penning-Rowsell, E.C., 1980, Water planning in Britain. The Resource Management Series, 1. George Allen & Unwin.

Planning, 1988a, Beach cleaning vital for coalfield recovery. 27 May 1988, 8.

Planning, 1988b, Coastal waste must go. 8 June 1988, 32.

Reid, P., 1991 Action for a healthier North Sea. Ecos 12(2), 41–45.

Royal Society for the Protection of Birds, 1991, Evidence to the House of Commons Environment Committee.

Scottish Office, 1992 Improving Scotlands environment. Scottish Environment Protection Agency: a consultation paper.

Sorensen, P., 1982, In Tippie V K & Kester D R (eds) Impact of Marine Pollution on Society, 106–112.

SCEC, 1986, Dumping of waste at sea. House of Lords Select Committee on the European Communities, 17th Report. HMSO.

The Times, 1991, Resorts beaches fail the test for viruses. 14 August 1991.

5 Conservation

Introduction

5.1 Conservation in the UK has been traditionally sub-divided into **landscape**, **nature** and **archaeological** areas of interest, a distinction which reflects the historical development of environmental and preservation interests by different disciplines; planning, biological sciences and archaeology. In addition, the conservation of areas of architectural or historic interest is an integral part of the planning system (see Chapter 6). Sea fisheries and salmon conservation measures are considered in Chapter 8.

5.2 This separation is gradually becoming blurred as "green" issues promote broader concerns over the environment as a whole. However, the traditional divisions are reflected in the different legislative and administrative frameworks which have been developed to achieve conservation objectives and, therefore, these form the basis for the following discussion of the numerous designations and their effectiveness (Figure 5.1).

5.3 It would be wrong, however, to imply that conservation begins and ends with the designation of important sites. Indeed, a number of bodies and authorities with a keen interest in the coastal zone have formal environmental duties which require them to make provision for conservation interests when carrying out their responsibilities (Table 5.1). Numerous voluntary bodies, operating at national and local level, have become particularly important in protecting the countryside, often through purchase of areas of conservation value, and making these accessible for the public. Of particular significance is the involvement and active management role played by a wide range of non-government organisations such as The World Wide Fund for Nature (WWF), The Marine Conservation Society, The Royal Society for the Protection of Birds (RSPB), The Royal Society for Nature Conservation (The Wildlife Trust Partnership) and The National Trust. Indeed, the efforts of many of these voluntary bodies have influenced the development of Government conservation policies (HMSO, 1990).

Landscape Conservation

National Parks and Areas of Outstanding Natural Beauty: England and Wales

5.4 Concerns about the effects of urban expansion and coastal development have had a significant influence on attitudes about the coastline over the last 100 years. The National Trust, for example, was established in 1895 in response to calls for countryside and coastal preservation. Throughout the early decades of this century much was achieved by voluntary and charitable organisations such as the National Trust, the Council for the Preservation of Rural England and the Council for the Protection of Rural Wales (Williams, 1987).

5.5 The first positive legislation was introduced in 1949 as the **National Parks and Access to the Countryside Act** through which stretches of coast in England and Wales were included within **National Parks** and **Areas of Outstanding Natural Beauty** (AONBs). Both designations are proposed by the Countryside Commission (and its successor in Wales, CCW) and confirmed by the appropriate Secretary of State.

5.6 National Parks are "the jewel in the countryside's crown and contain some of our most wild and beautiful landscapes" (HMSO, 1990). Their protection is given the highest priority by the Government. AONBs are "areas where the landscape is of such beauty and quality as to be of national significance but which are not suitable for designation as National Parks because they do not have sufficient open space suitable for recreation" (HMSO, 1990).

G

Figure 5.1 Conservation: A summary of the legal and administrative framework

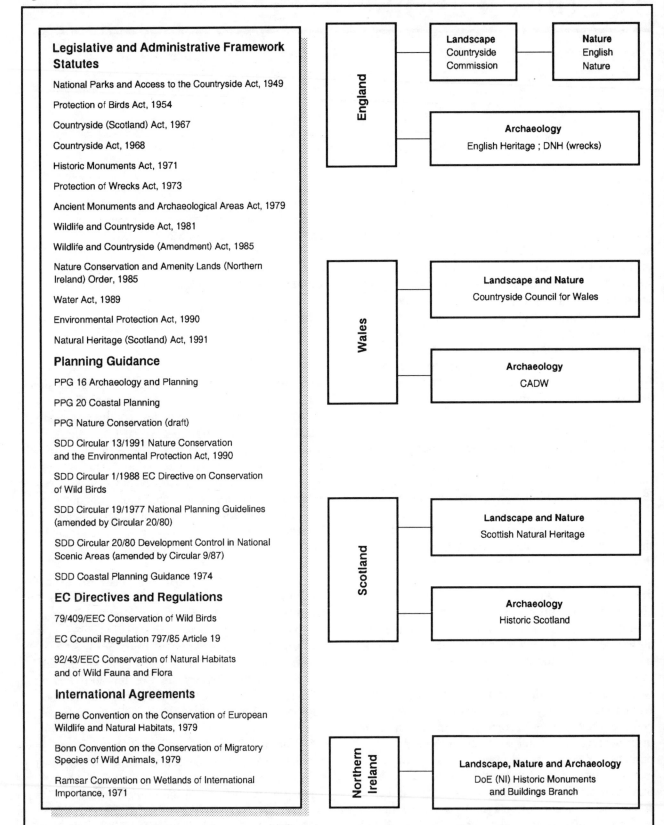

Legislative and Administrative Framework Statutes

National Parks and Access to the Countryside Act, 1949

Protection of Birds Act, 1954

Countryside (Scotland) Act, 1967

Countryside Act, 1968

Historic Monuments Act, 1971

Protection of Wrecks Act, 1973

Ancient Monuments and Archaeological Areas Act, 1979

Wildlife and Countryside Act, 1981

Wildlife and Countryside (Amendment) Act, 1985

Nature Conservation and Amenity Lands (Northern Ireland) Order, 1985

Water Act, 1989

Environmental Protection Act, 1990

Natural Heritage (Scotland) Act, 1991

Planning Guidance

PPG 16 Archaeology and Planning

PPG 20 Coastal Planning

PPG Nature Conservation (draft)

SDD Circular 13/1991 Nature Conservation
and the Environmental Protection Act, 1990

SDD Circular 1/1988 EC Directive on Conservation
of Wild Birds

SDD Circular 19/1977 National Planning Guidelines
(amended by Circular 20/80)

SDD Circular 20/80 Development Control in National
Scenic Areas (amended by Circular 9/87)

SDD Coastal Planning Guidance 1974

EC Directives and Regulations

79/409/EEC Conservation of Wild Birds

EC Council Regulation 797/85 Article 19

92/43/EEC Conservation of Natural Habitats
and of Wild Fauna and Flora

International Agreements

Berne Convention on the Conservation of European
Wildlife and Natural Habitats, 1979

Bonn Convention on the Conservation of Migratory
Species of Wild Animals, 1979

Ramsar Convention on Wetlands of International
Importance, 1971

England

Landscape
Countryside Commission

Nature
English Nature

Archaeology
English Heritage ; DNH (wrecks)

Wales

Landscape and Nature
Countryside Council for Wales

Archaeology
CADW

Scotland

Landscape and Nature
Scottish Natural Heritage

Archaeology
Historic Scotland

Northern Ireland

Landscape, Nature and Archaeology
DoE (NI) Historic Monuments
and Buildings Branch

Note : Attention is drawn to the various salmon, freshwater and sea fisheries legislation eg. the Sea Fisheries (Wildlife Conservation) Act 1992, and the role of the Fisheries Departments and Sea Fisheries Committees in conservation of this resource

Table 5.1 Environmental duties of authorities other than nature conservancy bodies

Authority	Environmental duty
NRA and Internal Drainage Boards	– to further the conservation and enhancement of natural beauty and the conservation of flora, fauna and geological or physiographical features of special interest. – to have regard to the desirability of protecting and conserving buildings, sites and objects of archaeological, architectural or historic interest. – to take into account any effect which the proposals would have on the beauty or amenity of any rural or urban area or on any such flora, fauna, features, buildings, sites or objects. (Land Drainage Act 1991 S.12). Note: The NRA's environmental duties are also defined by the Water Resources Act 1991 S.2 (duty to promote conservation) and S.16(1) (duty to further conservation).
Fisheries Departments (with regard to determining dumping at sea licences)	Licensing authorities must have regard to the need to: – protect the marine environment, the living resources which it supports and human health. (Food and Environment Protection Act 1985 S.8)
Harbour Authorities	Harbour authorities must have regard to: – the conservation of natural beauty of the countryside, flora, fauna and geological and physiographical features of special interest. – preserving freedom of access to places of natural beauty – maintaining the availability to the public to visit or inspect buildings, sites or objects of interest. (Harbours Act 1964 S.48A, as amended in 1992)
Crown Estate Commissioners	To maintain and enhance the value of the estate and the return obtained from it, but with due regard to the requirements of good management. (Crown Estate Act 1961)
Sea Fisheries Committees	Endeavour to achieve a reasonable balance between environmental considerations (the conservation of marine flora and fauna) and the other factors which are to be taken into account for the purposes of sea fisheries measures (Sea Fisheries Wildlife (Conservation) Act 1992)

5.7 Protection of the coastline was not the focus of these designations, although 5 of the 10 National Parks and 20 out of 38 AONBs have coastal frontages (Figure 5.2). The statutory protection afforded to these areas (eg restrictions on permitted development rights under the GDO) and byelaw-making provisions (Table 5.2) have ensured that the designations were considered by many bodies interviewed during the course of this study as a very effective approach to landscape conservation.

Areas of Outstanding Natural Beauty: Northern Ireland

5.8 The Department of the Environment for Northern Ireland (DoE (NI)) is both the legislative and administrative body for landscape conservation. It is advised by the Ulster Countryside Committee. The only landscape designation is the AONB, which applies to 73% of the coastline (Figure 5.2), although the Department also has the power to establish national parks.

National Scenic Areas: Scotland

5.9 The legislation for National Parks and AONBs does not extend to Scotland, where National Scenic Areas have been designated by the Scottish Development Department (SDD Circular 20/1980; see Chapter 6). These areas were selected by the Countryside Commission for Scotland (CCS; now Scottish Natural Heritage) as the best examples of Scotland's landscape and part of the natural heritage of Scotland (Figure 5.2). However, CCS recently concluded that additional protection, including designation of some areas along the lines of national parks, was necessary.

5.10 The **Natural Heritage (Scotland) Act 1991** created a new designation, the **Natural Heritage Area**, intended to safeguard and enhance areas combining high nature conservation value and landscape qualities. Such areas will designated by Scottish Natural Heritage (SNH) which will be responsible for managing and advising on both landscape and nature conservation interests.

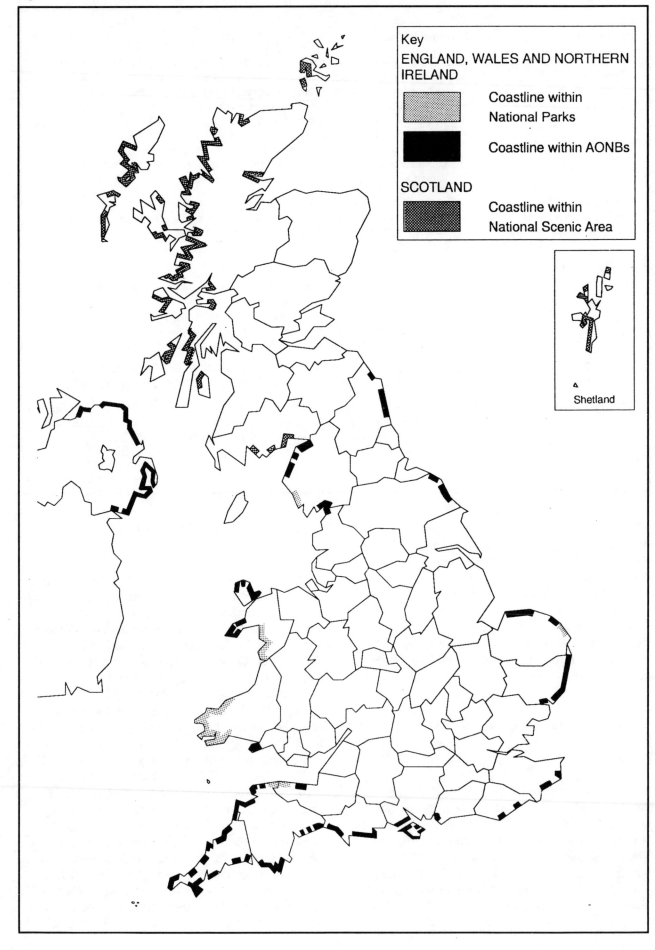

Table 5.2 Byelaws for control of activity within landscape and nature conservation areas

Location and activities	Byelaw–making powers and means of notification
Control of activity in **National Parks** and AONB's by prohibiting or restricting: – the use of land and water – depositing rubbish or litter – lighting of fires Control of parking places	Byelaws made by local authorities under 1949 Act S.90; confirmed by appropriate Secretary of State. Consultation required with CC/CCW/SNH. Byelaws must not interfere with public rights or functions of relevant authorities.
Control of activity in **National or Local Nature Reserves,** by prohibiting or restricting: – entry or movement within by persons, vehicles, boats and animals – damage to the reserve – shooting of birds – depositing of rubbish – lighting of fires	Byelaws made by the relevant CCC or local authorities for National and Local reserves, respectively (under 1949 Act S.20); confirmed by appropriate Secretary of State. Byelaws must not interfere with owner, lessee or occupiers rights or functions of relevant authorities.
Control of activity in **Marine Nature Reserves** by prohibiting or restricting: – entry into or movement within by persons or vessels – damage to marine life or sea bed – deposit of rubbish	Byelaws made by the relevant CCC under 1981 Act S.37; confirmed by appropriate Secretary of State. Notices required in national and local press, to all affected parties, local authorities and bodies. Byelaws should not interfere with the exercise of any functions of relevant authorities or bodies.

Heritage Coasts: England and Wales

5.11 In 1970 the Countryside Commission proposed the **Heritage Coast** concept, recommending that:

> "selected stretches of undeveloped coastline of high scenic quality should be given a special designation in order to protect their use for informal recreation" (Countryside Commission, 1970).

5.12 The original concept recognised that coastal sites are essential to some forms of development and that more satisfactory conservation measures could be achieved in restricted zones of particular beauty or scientific interest (Williams, 1987). The Government endorsed the Commission's basic objective but determined that there should be no new statutory designation procedure (DoE Circular 12/72; WO 36/72). It was recommended that the local planning authorities consider, in conjunction with the Commission, which areas should become heritage coasts. The policies to be pursued within these areas would then be contained within structure plans and local plans (see Chapter 6).

5.13 As many stretches of potential heritage coast lay within National Parks or AONBs the Commission were instructed to consider whether those heritage coasts without such statutory designation should be made AONBs. DoE Circular 12/72 also advised that an important factor in the safeguard of the unspoilt coast was the preparation of both planning and management policies that reflect the local needs, but within the context of a regional strategy. Policies should combine development control (see Chapter 6) and positive management in the interests of coastal conservation. Amongst the most important management aspects were seen to be:

– the encouragement of owners and occupiers to participate in the formulation and implementation of planning policies;

– provision of adequate access along the coast for walkers, but consulting with interested parties to limit the use of cars in certain areas;

– considering the possibility of diverting the need for additional holiday and recreational facilities to inland sites.

5.14 In England and Wales the Commission (and its successor in Wales, CCW) has identified around 1525km of the coastline as of heritage coast status (Figure 5.3). The majority (38 out of 45) receive some protection through inclusion in National Park or AONBs and around 30% is under the protective ownership of the National Trust (see below). All

Figure 5.3 Distribution of Heritage Coasts in England and Wales

are protected through policies included within development plans (see Chapter 6).

Nature Conservation

Introduction

5.15 The **Environmental Protection Act 1990** brought about the reorganisation of both the Nature Conservancy Council (NCC) and the Countryside Commission. Separate bodies now exist for dealing with landscape and wildlife issues in England, Scotland and Wales (Figure 5.1). DoE (Northern Ireland) has remained responsible for these functions in Northern Ireland. Under the 1990 Act, the separate councils are responsible for the establishment of a committee with a UK–wide remit for nature conservation (The Joint Nature Conservation Committee, JNCC).

5.16 The main legislation governing nature conservation (**The Wildlife and Countryside Act 1981** and **The Wildlife and Countryside (Amendment) Act 1985**) is unusual in the UK context in that it addresses protection of both land and marine sites. However, there are different types of designation procedures and consultation requirements on land and sea.

5.17 There are currently 3 main elements within the strategy for inland nature conservation in Great Britain (NCC, 1984):

- **the management of key sites** as National Nature Reserves;

- the **notification of sites** as Sites of Special Scientific Interest (SSSIs);

- the **maintenance of wildlife** in the wider countryside.

5.18 In addition to a variety of other wildlife conservation designations, both statutory and voluntary, the UK is party to a number of international conventions and EC Directives which are important for safeguarding habitats. Many of these designations can apply to the same location. For example, an estuary may be declared a Ramsar site, notified as an SSSI with part or all designated as a National Nature Reserve; areas of the reserve be leased and operated as a Local Nature Reserve.

5.19 Important sites can be either:

- **Nature Conservation Review Sites** (NCR sites); recognised for their biological interest. Prior to the 1981 Act, NCC had intended to designate all NCR sites as National Nature Reserves. However, this approach has been superseded by the Nature Conservation Review SSSI series;

- **Geological Conservation Review Sites** (GCR Sites); recognised for their geological or geomorphological value. All GCR sites are regarded as of national importance and, hence, have been designated SSSIs or are potential SSSIs.

National Nature Reserves

5.20 Under the **National Parks and Access to the Countryside Act 1949** (S.15), the NCC (and its successors, the 3 Country Conservation Councils)

has power to enter into agreement with landowners and tenants for the purpose of establishing a **National Nature Reserve**. These Reserves are managed by the introduction of byelaws restricting the use of the land by the public (S.20, 1949 Act; see Table 5.2). Statutory backing to the reserves was provided by the 1981 Act (S.35), which extended the designation to areas where there was no agreement with the relevant Country Conservation Council (CCC) or not in CCC ownership.

5.21 National Nature Reserves are also designated under the **Nature Conservation and Amenity Lands (Northern Ireland) Order 1985** under provisions which are similar to those which apply in Great Britain.

5.22 National Nature Reserves serve a variety of purposes: the conservation and preservation of sites, the maintenance of sites for research and study, the provision of advice on and the demonstration of conservation management, education and for recreation and amenity usages (Davidson et al, 1991). Since such reserves are managed specifically for nature conservation purposes and are owned or leased by the relevant CCC, or are managed on their behalf, they provide a powerful safeguard for protecting important habitats.

5.23 Local authorities have analogous powers under the 1949 Act (S.21) to establish **Local Nature Reserves**, many of which relate to the coast, such as Berry Head in Torbay. The Act gives local authorities powers to make byelaws, subject to confirmation by the relevant Secretary of State, to protect the reserves (Table 5.2). Davidson et al (1991) report that these powers are significant in securing the effectiveness of reserves, especially in Scotland where byelaws can provide for some of the few intertidal waterfowl refuge areas, since there is a general public right of access for shooting below HWM. In addition, Local Nature Reserves are effective in controlling further development which may be damaging to wildlife in an area, since the planning applications usually are considered by the same local authority that designated the reserve.

Sites of Special Scientific Interest

5.24 **Sites of Special Scientific Interest** (SSSIs) are widely considered to be the cornerstone of nature conservation in Great Britain. Even where there are additional international or European provisions, these have generally been implemented through the SSSI system.

5.25 Under the 1981 Act and its 1985 amendments English Nature (and its counterparts CCW and SNH) is required to notify the Secretary of State, the local planning authority, and the landowner or occupier that a site is of special interest (under the Water Resources Act 1989 S.17 the NRA and under the Land Drainage Act 1991 S.13 internal drainage boards must be notified). The notification to owners and occupiers must specify the nature of the special interest, which could include:

- outstanding examples of semi–natural habitats;

- areas supporting large populations of birds and other animals;

- areas supporting endangered plant and animal species, or outstanding assemblages;

- features of national geological or physiographic interest.

5.26 The notification must also specify those operations likely to damage the special interest. Once notified, owners and occupiers must give the relevant CCC written notice before carrying out a potentially damaging operation (PDO). The operation can be carried out if the relevant CCC give written consent or if it is carried out in accordance with a management agreement with the CCC or if 3 months have elapsed from the giving of the notice of the operations (**Countryside Act 1968** S.15). If the CCC considers the operation unsuitable, they will either persuade the owner or occupier not to proceed or negotiate a management agreement. Should this approach fail, it may be appropriate for the CCC to apply to the Secretary of State for a **Nature Conservancy Order** under the 1981 Act S.29. In exceptional cases the site may be compulsory purchased. There are 2 exceptions to the requirement for consultation over PDOs:

- in emergencies;

- where the operation is authorised by planning permission.

5.27 To date over 5,600 SSSIs have been designated, many of which have a coastal element. These range from the internationally important stratigraphic marker horizons such as the Barton

Beds at Chewton Bunny, Christchurch; to raised beach deposits at Hopes Nose, Torbay; and rare bird breeding grounds on mudflats and marshes in estuaries such as the Orwell and Medway. The existing network of SSSIs goes a long way towards achieving the objective of conserving the variety and geographical range of plant and animal communities and earth science sites.

5.28 Guidelines for the selection of biological SSSIs are described in NCC (1989). Sites are chosen on the basis of their importance as habitats including: sand dunes, saltmarshes, sea cliffs, shingle, coastal grazing marsh, lagoons and estuaries. The criteria are complex and are used in different combinations or with different emphasis for different wildlife features. Two important principles underlie NCR site selection: the **exemplary site** principle used for selecting the best examples of ecosystem types and the **minimum standards** principle which applies chiefly to species populations (Davidson et al, 1991). However, not all important sites are included within this network, a problem noted by Rothwell & Housden (1990).

5.29 Earth science SSSIs are selected on the basis of national or international importance to research. The **Geological Conservation Review** has selected sites by scientific discipline producing a national network of sites representing the geology and geomorphology of Great Britain.

5.30 The system of GCR sites is complemented by Regionally Important Geological and Geomorphological Sites (RIGS). These are selected locally, not by the relevant CCC, and are based on a blend of educational, research and historical importance.

5.31 In Northern Ireland, the equivalent DOE (NI) can designate **areas of special scientific interest** (ASSIs) which are virtually identical in substance to SSSIs.

Areas of Special Protection

5.32 These areas are designated by Statutory Instrument of the Secretary of State, with the agreement of the owner or occupier, under the 1981 Act (S.3). They were formerly designated as **Bird Sanctuaries** under the **Protection of Birds Act 1954**. There are currently 38 designated Bird Sanctuaries/AoSPs in Great Britain, such as at Berry Head in Torbay. The approach provides strong statutory protection for wildlife and has the additional advantage of conferring protection on open-water areas (Davidson et al, 1991).

Ramsar sites and Special Protection Areas

5.33 In total some 50 different areas in the UK have been designated as Ramsar Sites in accordance with the **Convention on Wetlands of International Importance especially as Wildfowl Habitat 1971**. Whilst this convention is widely interpreted as for bird conservation, it actually addresses broader issues of "wise use" of wetlands. The convention places an obligation on the signatories to carry out a management policies that balance economic development and ecological character (Wolff, 1988; van der Zwiep, 1991). Under the convention designated wetlands must be protected. This is achieved in Great Britain by their parallel status as SSSIs (or ASSIs in Northern Ireland). However, as SSSIs are confined to land under the control of local planning authorities (ie above LWM), the contiguous sub-tidal and marine areas vital to the integrity of the wetland ecosystem are not protected. In addition, the RSPB feel that there are many wetlands which meet the Ramsar criteria, but are not protected in the UK because they have not been designated SSSIs (Rothwell & Housden, 1990).

5.34 Similar problems have arisen over the designation of **Special Protection Areas** (SPA) under EC Directive 79/409/EEC to conserve certain bird habitats. In the UK protection is also afford through the parallel designation as SSSIs, leading to similar criticism from conservation groups (eg Rothwell & Housden, 1990).

The Habitats Directive: Special Areas of Conservation

5.35 EC Directive **92/43/EEC Conservation of Natural Habitats and of Wild Fauna and Flora** (the Habitats Directive) was agreed in December 1991. This requires Member States to take measures to maintain or restore natural habitats and wild species at a favourable conservation status in the Community, giving effect to both site and species protection objectives. The Government is required to put in place any necessary legislation and administrative provisions to implement the Directive within 2 years of its coming into effect.

Sites to be designated as **Special Areas of Conservation** must be agreed within 6 years.

Environmentally Sensitive Areas

5.36 **Environmentally Sensitive Areas** are designated by the Government with advice from the relevant CCC and the Countryside Commission in England. These are areas where traditional farming methods have helped create attractive landscapes and valuable habitats, as in the Norfolk Broads and the Machairs of the Uists, Benbecula and Barra. The approach was established by **Article 19 of EC Council Regulation 797/85 and the Agricultural Act 1986**. The EC regulation enables member states to make payments to farmers, in designated areas, who volunteer for the scheme, to encourage farming practices that are favourable to the environment.

Marine Nature Reserves

5.37 The need for site protection in the marine environment has been widely discussed by conservation groups since the Torrey Canyon disaster in March 1967. The designation of marine conservation sites has implications for other sea uses, such as fishing and transport; consequently there were initial reservations about including marine sites within conservation legislation (Warren, 1991). However, the opportunity for **Marine Nature Reserves** was introduced in the **Wildlife and Countryside Act 1981** (S.36).

5.38 Reserves may be designated by the appropriate Secretary of State on intertidal land below HWM and within territorial waters for the purpose of:

- conserving marine flora and fauna or geological or physiographical features of special interest;

- providing special opportunities for marine research.

5.39 Following the introduction of the Act the then NCC proposed 7 Reserves: the waters around Lundy Island, Skomer Island, the Isles of Scilly, Bardsey Island, Loch Sween, the Menai Straits and the coast off St Abbs. However, in the 12 years since the Act was introduced only the waters around Lundy Island (declared in 1986) and

Skomer Island (declared in 1990) have achieved Marine Nature Reserve status.

Archaeology

5.40 There are a number of national organisations directly or indirectly involved in protecting archaeological sites and objects. **English Heritage** has responsibilities and duties laid down under the **Heritage Act 1983**, with the objective of securing the long–term conservation and widespread understanding and enjoyment of the historic environment for the benefit of present and future generations. Similar responsibilities fall to **Cadw** (in Wales), **Historic Scotland** and DoE (Northern Ireland).

5.41 Under **The Ancient Monuments and Archaeological Areas Act 1979** English Heritage, Cadw and Historic Scotland are involved in statutory processes such as the scheduling of ancient monuments, some of which are in the coastal zone (such as Kents Cavern, Torbay), and in the respective consent procedures, providing advice and financial assistance for repair and management. The Act does not apply in Northern Ireland, although the **Historic Monuments Act 1971** provides equivalent protection.

5.42 The 1979 Act extends to monuments and areas on or under the sea–bed up to the limit of Territorial Waters. Under S.1 of the 1979 Act monuments can include the site or remains of a vessel, excluding sites designated under the **Protection of Wrecks Act 1973** (see below; S.61). However, there are no sites protected in this way in marine waters around the UK.

5.43 The consent of the Secretary of State is required before any work is carried out that will result in the demolition, destruction or damage, or involve removing, repairing, altering, adding to, flooding or covering up the monument (1979 Act, S.2).

5.44 The overwhelming majority of archaeological sites are not scheduled, although many may be of national or regional importance (Fairclough, undated). In such cases protection is provided through the planning system, as emphasised in the recent Planning Policy Guidance note on Archaeology and Planning (DoE, 1990) which stressed:

– development plans should reconcile the need for development with the interests of conservation including archaeology, and should provide policies for the protection, enhancement and preservation of sites of archaeological interest and their settings;

– that where nationally important remains are affected by proposed development there should be a presumption in favour of their preservation.

5.45 Under the **Protection of Wrecks Act 1973** the appropriate Secretary of State can, by order, designate **restricted** areas around the site of a vessel of historical, archaeological or artistic value (excluding areas above MHWM; S.1). In England, the responsibility for the administration of these areas lies with the Department of National Heritage (DNH). Cadw and Historic Scotland administer the heritage provisions of the Act in Wales and Scotland, respectively. In Northern Ireland, the Act is administered by DoE (NI) through the Historic Monuments and Buildings Branch.

5.46 It is an offence to undertake the following actions without a licence from the Secretary of State:

– tamper with, damage or remove any part of a vessel or object;

– carry out diving or salvage operations;

– deposit anything that may damage or obstruct access.

5.47 At present 34 wreck sites are protected under the 1973 Act. Isle of Wight County Council, however, have estimated that there may be up to 300 historic wrecks of importance in the Solent alone, many of which may already have been damaged by trawling and dredging. Submerged archaeological sites can also be of value in providing an indication of the nature of historic changes along a coast, giving an indication of dates of marine incursions and long term sea level changes and rates of coastal erosion (Raban, 1988; Tomalin, 1992).

5.48 The White Paper "This Common Inheritance" proposed to transfer the responsibility for maritime archaeology from the Department of Transport to the DoE (HMSO, 1990). This transfer has now taken place. However, bodies such as the Institute of Field Archaeologists, the Society of Nautical Research, the Nautical Archaeological Society and the Council for British Archaeology have called for protection equal to that for sites on land. In this context, the Joint Nautical Archaeology Policy Committee report in 1989 (JNAPC, 1989) recommended:

- new legislation for the protection of underwater sites and artifacts;

- allocation of resources to establish a national and local record, similar to the land based Sites and Monuments Record.

5.49 Progress has been made towards establishing a national record of marine sites. Following the publication of the White Paper "This Common Inheritance" the Royal Commission on the Historical Monuments of England was given the responsibility for compiling an inventory of known archaeological material in coastal waters around England and adding it to the National Archaeological Record. A 3 year programme to compile the inventory commenced in April 1992. However, this does not involve the identification of new sites. Equivalent responsibility has been given to the Scottish and Royal Welsh Commissions.

Protective Ownership

5.50 Despite the value of statutory protection to important sites, protective land ownership is widely viewed as the most effective way of achieving conservation objectives around the coastline. Many local authorities have been actively purchasing coastal land to secure public access for recreation or to protect sites of conservation interest. Sefton MBC, for example, has acquired land to give itself legal standing on coastal issues, including concerns over dredging within the Ribble estuary. The Council also owns sections of the coastal dunes which it manages in accordance with its **Coast Management Plan** (see Chapter 6).

5.51 The most important protective ownership scheme in the UK has been **Enterprise Neptune**, launched by **The National Trust for Places of Historic Interest or Natural Beauty** in 1965. The National Trust is a charity, reliant wholly on subscriptions from over 1.5M members, grants, gifts and legacies. Set up in 1895, the **National Trust Act 1907** empowered the Trust to declare its land and buildings inalienable (they cannot be sold or mortgaged), and subsequent legislation has given it the right to appeal to Parliament against any

compulsory purchase orders on its unalienable land.

5.52 Enterprise Neptune was launched in response to mounting development pressure on the coast, in England and Wales, and the need to protect unspoilt parts of the coastline for the benefit of the public. The original objectives were to:

- focus public attention on the problem of coastal development;

- acquire and preserve fine coastland;

- improve the quality of the Trusts existing coastline by careful management;

- raise an initial sum of £2M.

5.53 The Trust saw its powers to declare land inalienable as one of the few ways to ensure the preservation of parts of the coast for public benefit, for all time. The fund-raising campaign raised £2M by 1973, by which time the Trust ownership had increased from 187 to 338 miles of coast. Plans to acquire "the next hundred miles" were announced in 1973 and the target achieved by the early 1980s. The appeal was relaunched in 1985 enabling the Trust to purchase further land.

5.54 The Trust also owns and manages 100 ha of land for every kilometre of coastline. Management of this coastal strip has involved encouraging tenant farmers to preserve historic field patterns and use sympathetic building materials; unsightly buildings have been removed; sand dunes and salt marshes have been protected from erosion; and public access has been organised to maintain a balance between enjoyment of the coast and prevention of disturbance to wildlife habitats. In many of these activities the Trust acts closely with local authorities, the Countryside Commission, English Nature/CCW/SNH and other groups. The Trust now owns over 800km of coast of which 30% lies within Heritage Coast areas.

5.55 A number of other conservation groups have active policies for the acquisition, leasing or management of areas of conservation value, including **local wildlife trusts**, the **RSPB** and the **Wildfowl and Wetlands Trust**. The RSPB, for example, has a membership of over 400,000 and seeks to acquire land that is of high wildlife value, especially for breeding or migratory bird populations. The society has substantial holdings and manages over 56,000ha throughout Great Britain (RSPB, 1989).

5.56 The Ministry of Defence and the Territorial Army Volunteer Reserve are also major landowners, managing long stretches of coastline for defence purposes. Many MoD areas have their own conservation groups overseeing the management of the land, and some are managed by agreement with local wildlife trusts. The exclusion of other coastal activities from these areas has often been to the benefit of wildlife and landscape conservation interests:

> "The restrictions to public access imposed in the limitations to development in such places means that they can be amongst the most pristine areas of wildlife habitat", Davidson et al, (1991).

5.57 For example, at Penhale, Cornwall, a large holiday camp is set within an area of dunes which have been degraded by tourists, whereas the dunes within neighbouring MoD land have remained intact. Similar benefits have emerged in the tank over-fire area in Dorset which provides protection for a voluntary marine nature reserve off Purbeck.

5.58 In other cases landowners have been encouraged to manage their land in the interests of conservation. A current example is the **Countryside Stewardship Scheme**, initiated by the Countryside Commission in collaboration with English Nature and English Heritage. This scheme provides incentives and agreements for landowners to manage their land in the interests of wildlife, history and public access. The Countryside Council for Wales launched its own stewardship scheme, **Tir Cymen**, in July 1992.

5.59 Although protective ownership and acquisition have been very successful tools in managing a range of coastal zone activities there are important limitations, not least the cost of purchasing and management. However, schemes such as Enterprise Neptune have attracted world-wide interest not simply because of the acquisition of land or management approaches, but also for its ability to mobilise widespread public support for coastal management (Carter, 1988).

The effectiveness of conservation in the coastal zone

The extent to which coastal dynamics are considered

5.60 Coastal landforms, and the habitats which develop upon them, are ephemeral components of the coast. Attempts to protect them against erosion and flooding are likely to be counter to the processes that created them. For example, stabilisation of coastal dunes can lead to significant loss in conservation value, as it is their very instability that sustains their wildlife and geomorphological functions (Stevens, 1992). In such circumstances conservation should accept change as part of the natural evolution of coastal habitats and not be preoccupied by the preservation of selected sites of interest (Doody, 1989, 1992).

5.61 The impact of coastal defences on conservation interests has already been described in Chapter 3 which highlighted the problems of disruption of natural sediment transport systems and coastal squeeze. These concerns are central to the overall objective of English Nature's **Campaign for a Living Coast** (English Nature, 1992):

> "English Nature will seek to halt and reverse the loss of coastal habitats and natural features resulting from coastal squeeze and from the disruption of natural sedimentary systems. We shall try to establish a principle that new or replacement sea defence, coast protection or similar works should not exacerbate coastal squeeze or disruption of systems and **should reverse these whenever possible**, so as to maintain habitats and natural features **at least equivalent to their present distribution** (1992) and in a sustainable condition". (English Nature, 1992).

5.62 Available information about recent habitat loss is fragmentary and of variable quality. It has been estimated, however, that erosion has resulted in a 10–44% loss of saltmarsh area, in the estuaries of south east England, since 1973 (Burd, 1992). Losses of other habitats has been on a smaller scale and often related to human activities such as development, waste disposal and aggregate extraction (CERC, 1992).

5.63 Of equal concern to conservation interests are the possible effects of sea level rise on coastal sites. Amongst the likely impacts described by Doody (1990, 1991) are an accelerated loss of intertidal habitats on mudflats, sandflats and salt marshes. Where these habitats abut existing sea defences, it is likely that the habitats will be squeezed into even narrower areas, with a "consequent and perhaps catastrophic effect on coastal habitats and wintering bird populations" (Doody, 1991).

5.64 It has been recognised, however, that the landforms upon which these habitats have developed provide natural barriers which, if allowed to, can adjust to changes in sea level or wave climate. In this way the management of such features many provide a cost–effective strategy for dealing with the problem of sea level rise in undeveloped areas and restrict the decline in the coastal habitat resource. This approach to management of conservation interests is essentially the **soft engineering** approach described in Chapter 3 and may involve a number of scenarios (Table 5.3).

5.65 Experiments into the viability of one of these options, **managed retreat**, are currently being carried out at Northey Island in the Essex marshes by English Nature, NRA and the National Trust. In addition, Posford Duvivier Environment (1991) have recently undertaken a review of the opportunities for "managed retreat" as an option for restoring habitats and landscapes currently under threat from sea–level rise.

5.66 In this context the value of submerged archaeological sites can extend beyond the importance of preserving features of historic interest. The identification and interpretation of coastal sites allows greater understanding of long term sea level changes and can provide an indication of the pattern of past trends of erosion and deposition (Tomalin, 1992). This information is of particular value as it extends the historical evidence for coastal changes contained in early maps and records. However, the potential has yet to be realised in shoreline management.

The extent to which the environmental implications of conservation policies are considered

5.67 There is no formal mechanism for assessing the environmental effects of designating areas of conservation value. However, it is clear that the designation of sites or areas of conservation value has had a major impact on the UK countryside, usually for the better, improving the quality of the environment and, where appropriate, extending

public access to the countryside. It is important to recognise, however, that there have been less favourable effects, most notably the concentration of "unsuitable" development in landscapes which may be undervalued at present. This, together with other factors, has tended to increase pressures in estuaries, often to the detriment of internationally important wetland sites. The concentration of leisure boat marinas and new industrial development in these areas are examples of this pattern.

The extent to which conservation takes into account the interests of other groups

5.68 As stated in "This Common Inheritance" (HMSO, 1990), the aims of the Government's policies for the countryside are to:

- integrate environmental and economic activity in rural areas;

- conserve and improve the landscape and encourage opportunities for recreation;

- give extra protection to areas of special value;

- conserve the diversity of Britain's wildlife, particularly by protecting habitats;

- provide scientific monitoring and research to support these aims.

5.69 These aims are particularly significant in the coastal zone where development opportunities have to take account of some of the UK's most outstanding scenery and habitats of international importance. Indeed, they reflect a policy that involves balancing national or local conservation interest, with the need to sustain economic growth and to provide opportunities for recreation.

(i) Landowners, occupiers and local authorities

5.70 Many of the designations outlined above rely on a combination of:

- **management agreements** with landowners or occupiers to control land use and, if appropriate, allow public access (eg National Parks, AONBs, National Nature Reserves);

- **statutory restrictions** placed on owners or occupiers to limit what they may do with their land (eg SSSIs, Scheduled Ancient Monuments).

77

Table 5.3 Scenarios for coastal retreat and soft engineering (after English Nature, 1992)

Scenario 1 Managed retreat to a new defensible position:

- abandonment of the current line of sea defence protecting land in low value use;
- use of intervening land to recreate salt marsh habitats and reduce wave power.

Scenario 2 Partial set back onto land with existing conservation value:

- partial retreat allows landforms and habitats space to adjust to conditions;
- maintains existing conservation interests.

Scenario 3 Maintenance of existing defences on muddy coasts protecting low-lying land in high value use:

- sediment recharge encourages accretion of mudflats and saltmarshes and, hence, natural flood defences;
- maintenance of man-made sea defences ensures protection of coastal communities.

Scenario 4 Maintenance of existing defences on sandy coasts protecting low-lying land in high value use:

- recharge encourages accretion of beaches, dunes, spits or bars and, hence, natural coastal defences;
- maintenance of man-made defences ensures protection of coastal communities.

Scenario 5 Management of eroding soft cliffs fronting land in high value use:

- restricting rather than preventing erosion maintains geological interest in exposed cliffs;

- **compulsory purchase** of land, if necessary, to protect conservation interests.

5.71 These arrangements are complemented by national planning policies which are designed to ensure that, wherever possible, landscapes or sites of national and international importance are protected from damaging development (Table 6.1). However, despite clear national guidance on the importance of many conservation designations (eg through the draft PPG Nature Conservation and DoE Circular 15/88 (WO 23/88) Environmental Assessment; see Chapter 2) the reliance on the planning system to control potentially damaging development in or around SSSIs has led to criticism from many conservation groups (see Chapter 6).

5.72 The consultation and commenting arrangements which are required in the designation procedures for conservation sites reflects the need to reach agreement with landowners or occupiers and provide notice to the local planning authority (Table 5.4). However, the lack of formal consultation arrangements with other interested groups has, at times, created the impression that national conservation interests can take precedent over the local economy (Figure 5.4).

5.73 Difficulties have arisen in the coastal zone where common law rights and traditional activities such as bait-digging, cockling, access, permitted development rights and private Acts of Parliament, may affect the protection afforded by the SSSI designation (Rothwell & Housden, 1990). As a result lasting damage to SSSIs has occurred. Indeed, between 1986–1989 the NCC reported 146 instances of permanent or lasting damage to SSSIs throughout Great Britain (Davidson et al, 1991). Estuarine SSSIs appear to be particularly prone to loss and damage with 56 sites (17% of all estuarine sites) affected between 1986–1989, including parts of 27 sites which were considered to have been permanently destroyed or suffered long-term damage (Davidson et al, 1991). In the coastal zone the most important threats to SSSIs are perceived to be disturbance, recreation, marina development, barrages, land claim, port and industrial expansion, bait-digging, cockling, wildfowling and pollution (Rothwell & Housden, 1990).

(ii) Balancing interests on the unspoilt coast

5.74 The objective of the heritage coast definition is to provide for comprehensive conservation and management. This also involves facilitating and enhancing enjoyment by the public of such areas by the promotion and encouragement of recreational activities consistent with the conservation of their natural scenery and heritage features ie protection and management (Countryside Commission, 1992).

5.75 The heritage coast concept is viewed by many local authorities to have been a considerable success in preserving the unspoilt coastline (eg Association of County Councils et al 1991). On the Glamorgan coast, for example, the Commission successfully supported the local authorities refusal of a proposed large intrusive caravan site at a public inquiry in 1985, on Heritage Coast grounds (Phillips, 1990). Internationally, it is recognised as a model of its kind with potential for replication elsewhere.

Table 5.4 Consultation and commenting arrangements involved in the designation of nature, landscape and archaeological conservation areas in England and Wales

Designation	Statutory consultees	Invitation to comment
National Park	Local Authority (1949 Act S.7)	Notice in national and local press
AONB	Local Authority (1949 Act S.87)	Notice in national and local press
Heritage Coast	Countryside Commission/CCW (DoE C. 12/72)	Other bodies concerned
National Nature Reserve		Agreement with owner, lessee, occupier (1949 Act S.16). Notice published by English Nature/CCW (1949 Act S.19).
Local Nature Reserve	English Nature/CCW (1949 Act S.21)	Agreement with owner, lessee, occupier (1949 Act S.16). Notice published by local authority (1949 Act S.19).
SSSI	Owners and occupiers (1981 Act S.3(5))	Notice of intent to local planning authority, owner or occupier and the Secretary of State followed by formal notification after considering objections (1981 Act S.28). Notification to water companies and NRA (Water Act 1989 S.9; Water Resources Act 1991 S.17).
Areas of Special Protection (Birds)		Notice to owners and occupiers or in local press (1981 Act S.5(4)).
Ramsar sites and Special Protection Areas	Protection afforded by parallel status as SSSI's (see above)	
Marine Nature Reserves	Secretary of State shall consult with any appropriate groups (1981 Act Sch. 12). Extensive informal consultation by relevant CCC with all bodies etc with an interest in the proposed reserve.	Notice given to all interested organisations and authorities, national and local press and in council offices (1981 Act Sch.12).
Scheduled Ancient Monuments		Notification of schedule to owner, occupier and local authority (1979 Act S.1).
Protection of Wrecks: – restricted areas	Secretary of State shall consult with any appropriate bodies etc before making an order (1973 Act S.1).	Advisory Committee on Historic Wreck Sites and the Archaeological Diving Unit are invited to comment.

1949 Act – National Parks and Access to the Countryside Act
1973 Act – Protection of Wrecks Act
1979 Act – Ancient Monuments and Archaeological Areas Act
1981 Act – Wildlife and Countryside Act

5.76 The success can be attributed to a range of factors:

– Heritage Coasts are a management concept rather than a formal designation. Their protection and improvement, therefore, relies on positive action rather than just negative planning controls. For example, the management of the Suffolk Heritage Coast has involved the development of a Management Plan which has involved cooperation and participation from the whole community (Cross, 1983; see Table 5.5 for a list of Heritage Coast management plans prepared to date).

An important feature of the approach has been the focus given to the appointment of Heritage Coast Management Officers and specific Heritage Coast Management Services, who are primarily responsible for facilitating positive management. To date, there are 32

Figure 5.4 Formal mechanisms by which nature and landscape conservation takes into account the interests of other coastal activities

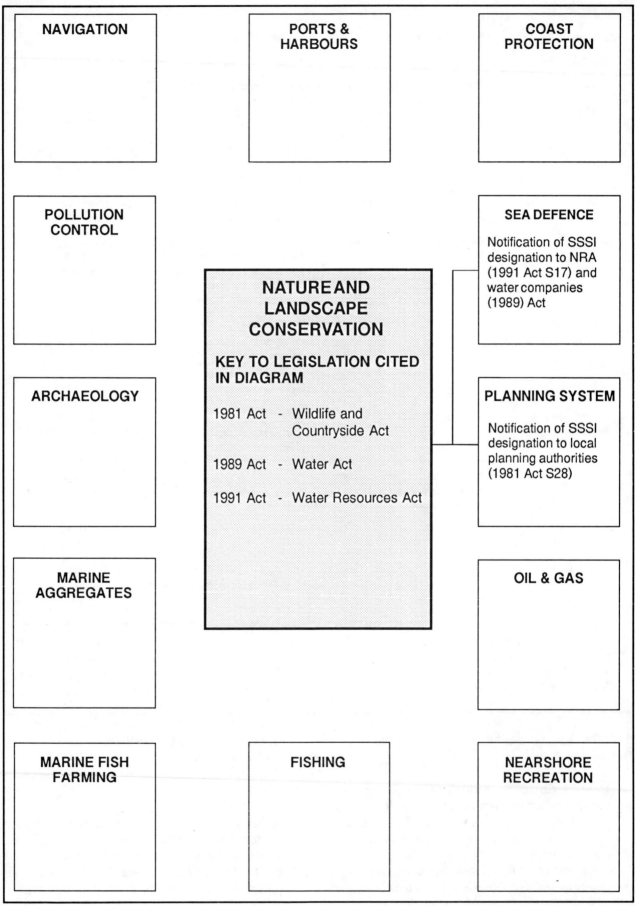

Table 5.5 Management plans prepared for Heritage Coasts around England and Wales.

Heritage Coast	Comment	Date
Anglesey	Whole Coast Plan	1982
Ceredigion		1989
East Devon	In preparation	1993
Exmoor	National Park Plan	1991
	Heritage Coast Plan	1993
Flamborough Head		1989
Glamorgan		1988
Gower		1990
Great Orme	Managed as a Country Park	
Isle of Wight		1987
Llyn	Draft Plan	1990
Lundy	Whole Island Plan	1990
North Cornwall		1988
North Norfolk		1989
North Northumberland	Consultation Draft	1991
North Yorks/Cleveland		1987
Pembrokeshire	National Park Plan	1985
Purbeck		1978
Spurn	Management brief	1988
Suffolk		1978
West Dorset		1982
White Cliffs	Country Park Draft Plan	1992

management services covering all but 2 Heritage Coasts and, in some instances, undertaking works on adjacent undefined coasts (eg around the coast of Anglesey);

- the definition of an area as a heritage coast has raised awareness of coastal issues, particularly in areas of greatest pressure;

- management is generally viewed as very cost effective, the prime responsibility being with local authorities working through small budget allocations. There is considerable reliance upon volunteer labour and practical support;

- they enjoy widespread support in the country, both from statutory bodies and non-governmental bodies and conservation groups. Indeed, the **Heritage Coast Forum** was established in 1987 to foster a sense of a "heritage coast community". This forum is organised and run separately from the Commission and CCW to emphasise the sense of shared ownership and purpose (Phillips, 1990).

5.77 The Countryside Commission's policy statement on heritage coast policies and priorities in England (Countryside Commission, 1992) has, however, prompted widespread reflection over the value of the concept to protect the coast in the future. Many authorities closely involved recognise that the increasing pressures on the coast require even more effective planning and management in the future (eg Association of County Councils et al, 1991). In this context, a number of the local authorities and other bodies contacted during the study expressed shortcomings of the way heritage coasts were addressed by the planning system (see Chapter 6).

5.78 The heritage coast concept has helped match the increasing demand for outdoor recreation. However, the benefits have been largely confined to informal recreation such as walking. Other forms of recreation, which require permanent facilities, such as leisure boating have tended to be diverted away from these stretches of coast and as a result have concentrated in estuary sites where they generate conflict with the protection of wetland sites.

(iii) Sea users: navigation and fisheries interests

5.79 The need to reach agreement with all users of the sea and sea bed has led to slow progress with the designation of Marine Nature Reserves; only 2 have been designated since 1981. This has generated severe criticism from marine conservation groups. Gubbay (1990, 1991) and

H

Warren (1990, 1991), for example, cite two main reasons for the slow progress:

- **the limited powers given to the relevant CCC to protect and manage the Reserves**; the principal method of protection is through byelaws. However, the CCC can only introduce byelaws if they do not interfere with rights of fishing and navigation or the functions of "relevant authorities" (eg NRA, local authorities, sea fisheries committees; Table 5.2). The CCC could persuade these authorities to make byelaws that would assist the management of the reserve. However, it has been reported that some authorities have stated that it was not in their remit to introduce byelaws for nature conservation (Gubbay, 1990). In addition, byelaws cannot be made which restrict the right of passage of vessels (other than pleasure boats in some circumstances) or restrict discharges from vessels.

The provision in the 1981 Act to preserve private rights renders owners of foreshores and fisheries substantially immune.

- **the procedure for implementing the legislation**; the procedures for designation are significantly more complex than those for a National Nature Reserve, reflecting the problems of controlling traditional rights of sea use. The relevant CCC is obliged to carry out an 11 stage informal consultation in order to obtain the agreement of **all relevant bodies** (from Government Departments to boating interests and local fishermen; Figure 5.5) before an area can be designated by order of the Secretary of State. Before an order is made, it is published in draft, and representations and objections invited. A local enquiry or hearing may be necessary if objections are raised.

The complex procedures arise from what are seen to be the very strict interpretation by the DoE and Welsh Office of undertakings made by ministers during the passage of the 1981 Act, rather than the legislation itself.

The procedures are in contrast to those required for the designation of SSSIs, where notification is made first, followed by the opportunity for representations and objections. In practice a single objection to a Marine Nature Reserve can halt the procedure indefinitely as the Secretary of State will not arbitrate (Gubbay, 1990). No application for Reserve status will proceed without agreement from all parties (Warren, 1991).

5.80 The Marine Nature Reserve concept has potential for safeguarding estuarine and intertidal habitats, as the designated area can extend from HWM to the limit of territorial waters. In the opinion of the former NCC, the linking of intertidal and subtidal parts of the coastline goes further, in principle, than is currently possible with the SSSI and National Nature Reserve designations (Davidson et al, 1991). However, the effectiveness of the approach is severely hampered by the time consuming procedures involved in their designation and the limited protection and management powers.

5.81 Although the White Paper on the Environment, "This Common Inheritance" (HMSO, 1990), emphasises the Government commitment to "work towards designating more Marine Nature Reserves", many marine conservation groups feel that the approach will never provide an adequate network of marine site protection (eg Warren, 1991). Indeed, in contrast to SSSIs and National Nature Reserves on land there is no obligation for owners or relevant bodies to consult the CCC prior to carrying out or authorising activities which may adversely affect a Marine Nature Reserve. However, licenses must be obtained from the relevant fisheries department for the deposit of materials in the sea or obtain discharge consents (from NRA or HMIP in England and Wales; see Chapter 4).

5.82 The White Paper also indicated that the Government was considering extending the **Marine Consultation Area** scheme. This scheme has been operating in Scotland since 1986 when the then NCC identified 14 marine sites to inform the Crown Estate Commissioners (CEC) of nature conservation interest. A further 15 sites have since been identified. These sites have no statutory protection, but their selection as consultation areas allows bodies which consult with the relevant CCC to be aware of marine conservation issues within particular areas.

5.83 The proposed extension of Marine Consultation Areas to England and Wales was outlined in a consultation paper issued in 1992. This paper includes a list of 16 new sites of marine conservation interest and government guidelines addressed to regulatory bodies. The scheme is intended to run on a voluntary basis with JNCC monitoring results in order to determine its effectiveness. However, the proposals have been criticised by conservation groups and sea fisheries

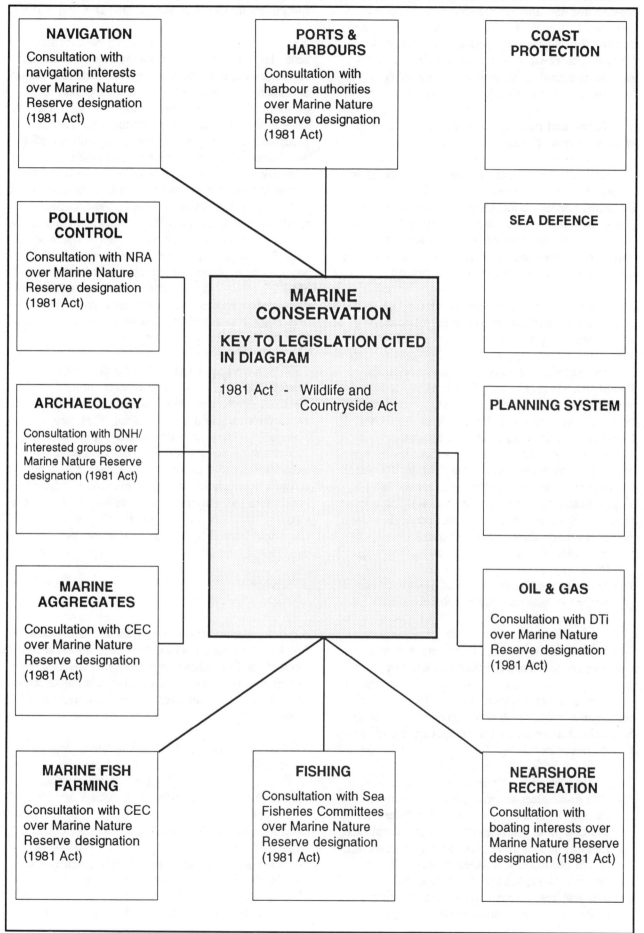

interests because of the non–statutory nature of the scheme and the limited consideration of sea fisheries. In this context, the Marine Conservation Society (MCS) has proposed the concept of **Marine Protected Areas** as an alternative approach to marine conservation (Table 5.6; Warren & Gubbay, 1991).

(iv) Marine archaeology interests in conflict with navigation and fishing

5.84 The problems faced by marine conservation are matched by the concerns expressed by interested parties about the ineffectiveness of the protection afforded marine archaeological sites. Indeed, the designation of restricted areas around important wrecks can be in direct conflict with the traditional rights of navigation and fishing.

5.85 The 1973 Act is hampered by the lack of a system for identifying and charting sites, relying on ad hoc reporting by finders. However, under the **Merchant Shipping Act 1894** all objects recovered from below MLWM have to be reported to the **Receiver of Wreck** who will normally retain possession for one year. Unclaimed objects are normally auctioned as a means of rewarding the finder. This route can, therefore, be a more attractive option than reporting wrecks under the 1973 Act. Further problems can arise as it is legal for salvers to destroy a wreck, by any method, to obtain materials. Damage may also arise as a result of trawling, diving, recreation and dredging (South Wight Borough Council pers. comm.).

The extent to which the system allows coordinated decision making across the coastal zone

5.86 The main legislation governing nature conservation is unusual in that it addresses protection of both land and sea sites. However, the different designation procedures and consultation requirements on land and sea have meant that there is no direct mechanism for integrating conservation in the coastal zone.

5.87 In the absence of management agreements over intertidal areas or protective ownership by bodies such as RSPB, it has proved difficult to provide complete protection for many coastal bird populations. For example, the landward element of the Minch coastline is covered by many conservation designations but there is no management regime for offshore waters. As a result the threats from pollution and fishing

practices are considered by many groups to undermine the areas conservation value (eg RSPB, 1991).

5.88 The difficulty in achieving conservation objectives for habitats covering the intertidal range has meant that many ecosystems, especially in estuaries, are only partially protected. This has led the RSPB to question whether the UK has adequately met its international obligations under the Ramsar Convention and EC Directive 79/409/EEC (Rothwell & Housden, 1990). At the centre of this problem is the fact that such sites are protected by the planning system through their parallel designation as SSSIs. As local planning authority jurisdiction generally ends at MLWM (see Chapter 6), no such protection is afforded below this level. Important sites or habitats below MLWM rely on the environmental assessment and consultation procedures that form part of the regulatory framework for sea bed activities (see Chapter 7).

5.89 It has been reported that South Wight Borough Council have used powers under S.18 of the Coast Protection Act 1949 to protect marine archaeological interests (Tomalin, 1992; see Chapter 3). The Coast Protection Order made in 1951 enables the council to control mineral extraction up to 3nm offshore (Figure 3.2). The council require archaeological evaluation of the sea bed before extraction licences are renewed, enabling them to adopt a "curation" policy consistent with that applied to sites on land.

Summary

5.90 The Government policy for the environment involves finding a balance between conservation interests and economic growth. There are a number of important conservation statutes relating to the protection of sites of national and international importance:

– National Parks and Access to the Countryside Act 1949;

– Countryside Act 1968;

– Protection of Wrecks Act 1973;

– Ancient Monuments and Archaeological Areas Act 1979;

– Wildlife and Countryside Act 1981;

Table 5.6 A summary of the Marine Protected Area concept for marine conservation (after Warren & Gubbay, 1991)

The Marine Conservation Society has proposed the concept of **Marine Protected Areas** as an alternative approach to marine conservation (Warren & Gubbay, 1991). This concept recognises that marine protection is relevant to many activities other than just conservation interests. It is argued that such a designation could be of relevance to protecting nursery grounds for fish stocks, safe waters for recreation, important nautical archaeological sites and "Areas to be Avoided" by shipping. Backed by a new system of legislation, a two-tier approach to Marine Protected Areas is envisaged giving different levels of protection (Gubbay, 1991):

Areas of lived in seascape; where activities are covered by a management plan to ensure that conservation interests are not damaged. Uses of these zones should not be restricted unless they were potentially harmful. The area would act as a buffer zone for the strictly protected area. This zone is seen to be similar in philosophy to National Parks on land.

Areas of strict protection; activities would be restricted unless given specific exemption. These areas would ideally lie within the larger areas of lived in seascape which would act as a buffer for protecting these most important sites.

– Wildlife and Countryside (Amendment) Act 1985;

– Natural Heritage (Scotland) Act 1991.

5.91 In addition the UK is required to comply with the conservation provisions in a number of EC directives and international agreements, the most important of which are:

– the Ramsar Convention on Wetlands, 1971;

– 79/409/EEC Conservation of Wild Birds;

– 92/43/EEC Conservation of Natural Habitats and of Wild Fauna and Flora (the Habitats Directive).

5.92 There are a wide variety of designations for landscape, nature and archaeological conservation which cover both the land and sea (see also Chapter 4 for description of Special Areas at Sea). The common theme is that protection is generally provided through a combination of management agreements with owners and occupiers, statutory protection or compulsory purchase.

5.93 Conservation policies can have three principal effects:

– they protect and enhance features or landscapes of national or international importance;

– they interfere with the rights of use by owners or occupiers of land, or sea users; and

– they divert development and other coastal activities towards less valued coastal environments.

5.94 Conservation policies can, therefore, affect many interests in the coastal zone, from coastal defence to fisheries and navigation interests. They are often the source of conflict between local economic interests and national environmental goals.

5.95 The planning system is an important source of protection for many of these designations through the inclusion of policies in development plans, with the DoE/Welsh Office/Scottish Office providing national guidance on the importance of conservation sites. However, concerns have been raised over the effectiveness of this approach in practice, especially in the context of protecting the unspoilt coast through the heritage coast concept and preventing damage to SSSIs (see Chapter 6).

5.96 Problems have arisen because the boundaries of conservation sites such as SSSIs are drawn along MLWM, coinciding with the normal limit of local authority jurisdiction. Adjacent areas, below this level, are often of equal scientific importance but are not afforded protection through the planning system. This has significant implications for bird communities, especially in estuaries, and has led conservation groups to doubt whether the UK can fulfil its international obligations under the Ramsar Convention and EC Directive 79/409/EEC.

5.97 Considerable difficulties have also been experienced in providing protection to wildlife and archaeological sites in the marine environment, where conservation may be in direct conflict with traditional rights of navigation and fishing. This has led to considerable concern from conservation groups such as the Marine Conservation Society.

References: Chapter 5

Association of County Councils and others, 1991, Coastal Zone Protection and Planning. Memorandum of Evidence to the House of Commons Environment Committee.

Burd, F., 1992, Erosion and vegetation change on the saltmarshes of Essex and north Kent between 1973 and 1988. Research 7 Survey in Nature Conservation No.42, NCC Peterborough.

Cambridge Environmental Research Consultants Ltd, 1992, Targets for coastal habitat recreation. English Nature Research Report No.35.

Carter, R.W.G., 1988 Coastal Environments : An introduction to Physical, Ecological and Cultural Systems of Coastlines. Academic Press.

Countryside Commission, 1970, The coastal heritage: a conservation policy for coasts of high quality scenery. HMSO.

Countryside Commission, 1992, Heritage Coast Policies and Priorities – Policy Statement.

Cross, F.L., 1983, Coastal planning– managing a heritage. In Shoreline protection, 31–37, Thomas Telford.

Davidson, N.C., d'A Laffoley, D., Doody, J.P., Way, L.S., Gordon, J., Drake, C.M., Pienkowski, M.W., Mitchell, R. and Duff, K.L., 1991 Nature conservation and estuaries in Great Britain. Nature Conservancy Council.

Department of the Environment, 1990, Archaeology and Planning. PPG 16. HMSO.

Doody, J.P., 1989, Management for nature conservation. In C.H. Gimmingham, W.Ritchie, B.B. Willetts & A.J. Willis (eds) Coastal sand dunes. Proceedings of the Royal Society of Edinburgh, 96B, 247–265.

Doody, J.P., 1990, Sea–level rise (coastal conservation). North Sea Report. The Marine Forum.

Doody, J.P., 1991 Global warming and sea–level change on British estuaries. In N C Davidson et al (eds) Nature conservation and estuaries in Great Britain 381–387. Nature Conservancy Council.

Doody, J.P., 1992, Sea defence and nature conservation: threat or opportunity. Aquatic Conservation: Marine and Freshwater Ecosystems, 2, 275–283.

English Nature, 1992, Campaign for a Living Coast. Peterborough.

Fairclough, G., undated, Archaeological Conservation–policy, procedure, planning.

Gubbay, S., 1990, Marine protected areas. European Workshop on Coastal Zone Management.

Gubbay, S., 1991, Protection of marine life around our shores. Presentation to the European Coastal Zone Management Workshop.

Her Majesty's Stationary Office, 1990 This common inheritance. Britain's Environmental Strategy. Government White Paper.

Joint Nautical Archaeology Policy Committee, 1989, Heritage at sea: proposals for the better treatment of archaeological sites underwater.

Nature Conservancy Council, 1984, Nature conservation in Great Britain. Peterborough.

Nature Conservancy Council, 1989, Guidelines for selection of biological SSSIs. Peterborough.

Phillips, A., 1990, Keynote Address – The Coastal Heritage. In Houston J & Jones C (eds) Planning and management of the coastal heritage, Symposium Proceedings, Southport, 1989, 11–15.

Posford Duvivier Environment, 1991. Environmental opportunities in low lying coastal areas under a scenario of climatic change. Report to NRA, DoE, NCC and Countryside Commission.

Raban, A., 1988, Archaeology of coastal change. Proceedings of the 1st International Symposium, Cities and the Sea, Haifa, 1986. British Archaeological Reports No.404.

Rothwell P & Housden, S, 1990 Turning the Tide : A Future for Estuaries. RSPB.

Royal Society for the Protection of Birds, 1989, RSPB; where to go birdwatching. A guide to RSPB reserves. London, BBC books.

Royal Society for the Protection of Birds, 1991, Evidence to the House of Commons Environment Committee.

Stevens, C., 1992, The open coastline. In M.G. Barrett (ed) Coastal zone planning and management. Thomas Telford, 91–99.

Tomalin, D., 1992 Maritime archaeology as a coastal management issue: a Solent case study from the SCOPAC coast. In Proceedings of the SCOPAC seminar The Regional Coastal Groups: After the House of Commons Report, 93–112.

Warren, L., 1990 Statutory Marine Nature Reserves in Great Britain. A progress report 1989. WWF (UK).

Warren, L., 1991 Marine Nature Reserves: Fact or Fiction. Ecos 12(2), 35–39.

Warren, L. & Gubbay, S., (eds) 1991 Marine protected areas: a discussion document. Marine Protected Areas Working Group, WWF (UK).

Williams, A.T., 1987, Coastal conservation policy development in England and Wales with specific reference to the Heritage Coast concept. J. Coastal Research, 3(1), 99–106.

Wolff, W.J. 1988, Management of wetlands case study: The Wadden Sea. In Nature Management and Sustainable Management. Proc. Int. Conf. Foundation for Nature Management and Sustainable development, Groningen Univ.

van der Zwiep, K., 1991, The Ramsar Convention and coastal planning. Ecos 12(2), 27–30.

6 Control of Development on Land

Introduction

6.1 The principal control over land in the UK is through the operation of the **planning system**. However, this system does not control all development or activity on land. Some projects such as the planning and construction of trunk roads and motorways or power stations are the responsibility of the relevant Government department. Most **harbour authorities** have a significant degree of autonomy to operate under statutory powers set out in local Acts of Parliament or by means of orders made under the **Harbours Act 1964**. In other instances private Acts may provide a method of giving developers the authorisation for activities outside the scope of the planning system (see Chapter 2).

The Planning System

6.2 The town and country planning system is designed to regulate the development and use of land in the public interest. It is an important instrument for protecting and enhancing the environment, and reconciling the interests of conservation and development

6.3 The principal planning legislation is contained in the **Town and Country Planning Act 1990** (the equivalent legislation for Scotland is the **Town and Country Planning (Scotland) Act 1972**). Important amendments are contained in the **Planning and Compensation Act 1991**. Although the legislation does not specifically address development in the coastal zone, its various provisions are applicable in coastal areas.

6.4 Development is defined, as:

"the carrying out of building, engineering, mining or other operations in, on, over or under land, or the making of any material change in the use of any building or other land". The Town and Country Planning Act, 1990 (S.55), (and also the Town and Country Planning (Scotland) Act 1972 S.19).

6.5 The powers provided by the 1990 Act are exercised by **local planning authorities**. The two most important functions of planning authorities are the preparation of **development plans**, and **control of development** through the determination of **planning applications** (Figures 6.1 and 6.2). In shire counties the planning responsibilities are shared between the county council and district councils. Elsewhere, London borough councils, some Scottish regions and metropolitan boroughs are the sole planning authorities. In certain circumstances planning powers can be vested in other bodies, such as in National Parks (under provisions in the **Local Government Act, 1972**) and in the Broads (under the **Norfolk and Suffolk Broads Act, 1988**).

6.6 The planning system should not normally be used to secure objectives achievable under other legislation. This principle of **non-duplication** should be maintained even though the powers and duties resulting from the other legislation may also be the concern of local authorities (PPG 1, DoE 1992).

6.7 For maritime local planning authorities in England and Wales the administrative area, and hence the limits of control, normally ends at MLWM. In Scotland, the limit of jurisdiction is normally spring LWM, although there are notable exceptions such as Shetland whose administrative area extends to the limit of territorial waters.

Development Plans

6.8 Planning decisions must be in accordance with the development plan unless other material

Figure 6.1 The Planning System: A summary of the legal and administrative framework

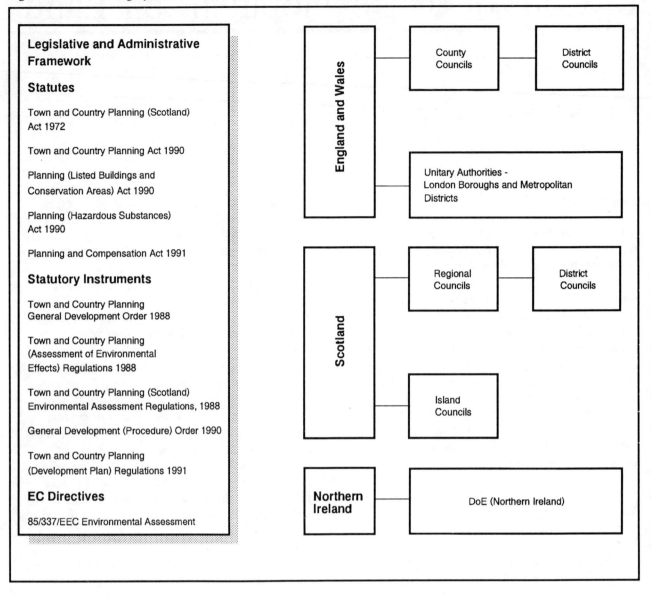

considerations indicate otherwise. Such plans set out the land use policies and proposals that will apply in an area. There are three main types of development plan:

(i) **Structure plans**, in which shire counties set out key strategic policies as a framework for local planning. They have to have regard, inter alia, to national and regional policies. These plans will have to include policies on conservation of the natural beauty and amenity of the land, the improvement of the physical environment and management of traffic. They are also advised to include policies on: new housing, Green Belts and conservation, the rural economy, the urban economy including employment generating and wealth creating development, strategic

transport and highways, minerals, waste disposal, tourism, recreation and leisure and energy generation, including renewable energy.

Authorities are advised to ensure that the interactions between policies are fully considered and that policies form an integrated whole by forming an overall strategy (PPG 12, DoE 1992). Such a strategy could, for example, address coastal issues.

Structure plans must have regard to environmental as well as social and economic considerations. Authorities are also advised that they should take all these considerations into account when preparing detailed development plans.

Figure 6.2 The Planning System: A summary of the relationship between national policy advice, development plans and development control in England

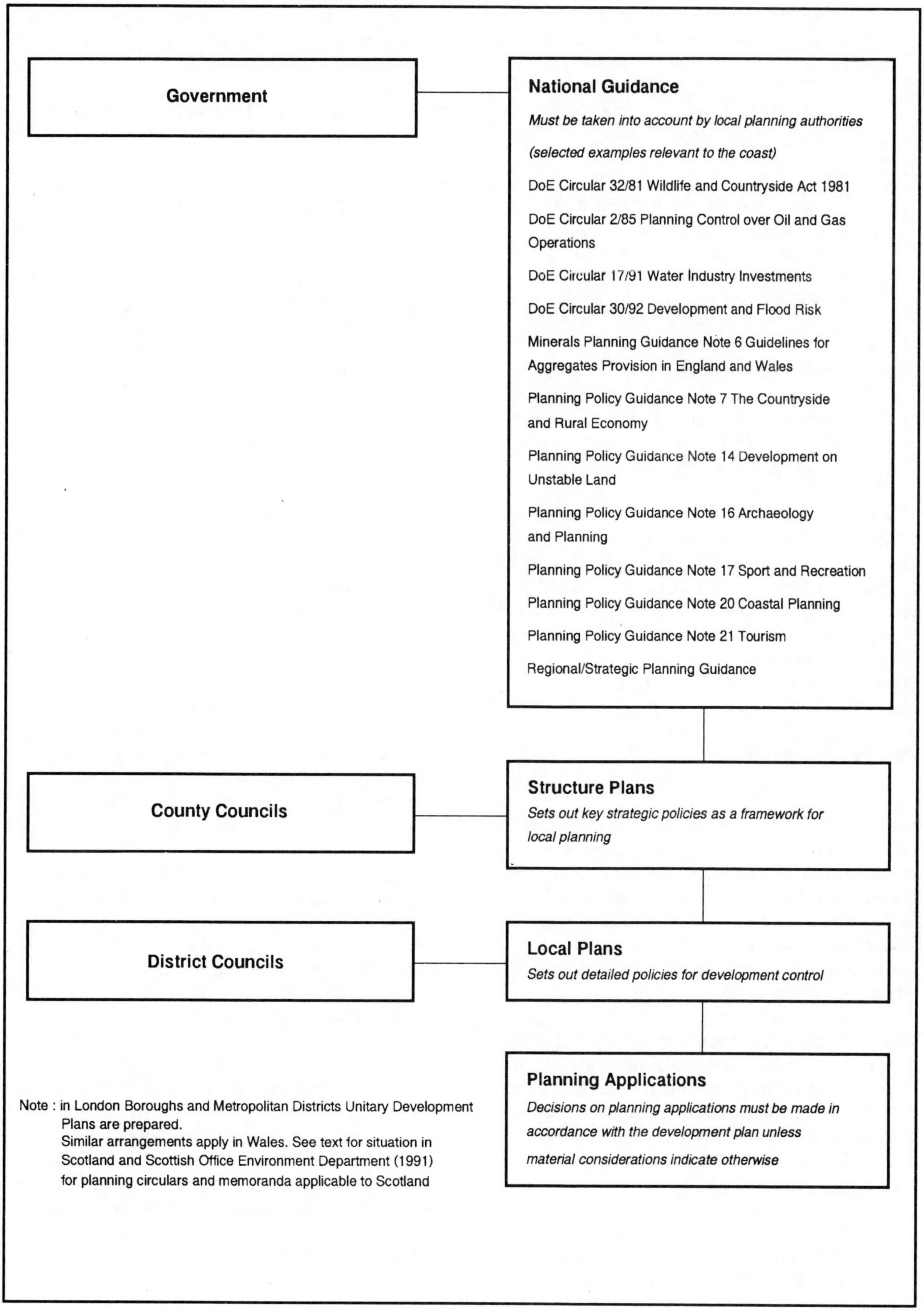

```
┌─────────────────────────────┐      ┌──────────────────────────────────────────────┐
│                             │      │ National Guidance                            │
│        Government           │──────│                                              │
│                             │      │ Must be taken into account by local planning │
└─────────────────────────────┘      │ authorities                                  │
                                     │ (selected examples relevant to the coast)    │
                                     │                                              │
                                     │ DoE Circular 32/81 Wildlife and Countryside  │
                                     │ Act 1981                                     │
                                     │                                              │
                                     │ DoE Circular 2/85 Planning Control over Oil  │
                                     │ and Gas Operations                           │
                                     │                                              │
                                     │ DoE Circular 17/91 Water Industry Investments│
                                     │                                              │
                                     │ DoE Circular 30/92 Development and Flood Risk │
                                     │                                              │
                                     │ Minerals Planning Guidance Note 6 Guidelines │
                                     │ for Aggregates Provision in England and Wales│
                                     │                                              │
                                     │ Planning Policy Guidance Note 7 The          │
                                     │ Countryside and Rural Economy                │
                                     │                                              │
                                     │ Planning Policy Guidance Note 14 Development │
                                     │ on Unstable Land                             │
                                     │                                              │
                                     │ Planning Policy Guidance Note 16 Archaeology │
                                     │ and Planning                                 │
                                     │                                              │
                                     │ Planning Policy Guidance Note 17 Sport and   │
                                     │ Recreation                                   │
                                     │                                              │
                                     │ Planning Policy Guidance Note 20 Coastal     │
                                     │ Planning                                     │
                                     │                                              │
                                     │ Planning Policy Guidance Note 21 Tourism     │
                                     │                                              │
                                     │ Regional/Strategic Planning Guidance         │
                                     └──────────────────────────────────────────────┘
                                                          │
┌─────────────────────────────┐      ┌──────────────────────────────────────────────┐
│                             │      │ Structure Plans                              │
│       County Councils       │──────│ Sets out key strategic policies as a         │
│                             │      │ framework for local planning                 │
└─────────────────────────────┘      └──────────────────────────────────────────────┘
                                                          │
┌─────────────────────────────┐      ┌──────────────────────────────────────────────┐
│                             │      │ Local Plans                                  │
│      District Councils      │──────│ Sets out detailed policies for development   │
│                             │      │ control                                      │
└─────────────────────────────┘      └──────────────────────────────────────────────┘
                                                          │
                                     ┌──────────────────────────────────────────────┐
                                     │ Planning Applications                        │
                                     │ Decisions on planning applications must be   │
                                     │ made in accordance with the development plan │
                                     │ unless material considerations indicate      │
                                     │ otherwise                                    │
                                     └──────────────────────────────────────────────┘
```

Note : in London Boroughs and Metropolitan Districts Unitary Development
Plans are prepared.
Similar arrangements apply in Wales. See text for situation in
Scotland and Scottish Office Environment Department (1991)
for planning circulars and memoranda applicable to Scotland

(ii) **Local plans**; district councils and National Park authorities have to prepare plans covering the whole of their areas. These local plans set out more detailed policies for development control and proposals for specific sites. Local plans are required to be in general conformity with the structure plan.

County Councils and National Parks authorities are required to produce a minerals local plan and a waste disposal local plan, with the exception of counties in Wales where the districts include waste policies in local plans.

(iii) **Unitary development plans** (UDPs), prepared by London and metropolitan boroughs and combining the functions of both structure and local plans. UDPs include minerals and waste policies.

6.9 In Scotland, structure plans are prepared by regional and island councils and, unlike England and Wales, continue to require the approval of the Secretary of State. Local plans are prepared by district councils, except in Borders, Dumfries and Galloway and Highland where they are prepared by the regional councils and in Orkney, Shetland and Western Isles by the islands council.

Development control

6.10 A primary aim of the planning system is to facilitate acceptable and appropriate development and to strike the right balance between that development and the environment (PPG 1, DoE 1992). The planning system can be important instrument in achieving sustainable growth and development, especially through policies included within development plans.

6.11 A fundamental feature is that development may not take place without **planning permission**. In most circumstances express (specific) planning permission is required upon application to the local planning authority, usually the district council. The decision whether or not to grant planning permission must be made:

"in accordance with the plan unless material considerations indicate otherwise" The Town and Country Planning Act, 1990 (S.54A).

6.12 Any consideration which relates to the use and physical development of land may be a planning consideration. Whether a particular consideration is material will depend on the circumstances of the case.

6.13 Permission may be granted subject to such **conditions** as the local planning authority or the Secretary of State may think fit, provided the conditions are necessary, relevant to planning, relevant to the development, enforceable, precise and reasonable in all other respects. Where matters which are necessary in planning terms cannot be dealt with by way of conditions, such as where the action is not reasonably within the power of the applicant to secure, legal agreements under the 1990 Act may be a necessary precursor to the granting of planning permission.

National Guidance: England and Wales

6.14 National guidance on relevant planning considerations, in England and Wales, is issued by the Government in a variety of ways. Until 1988 the most frequent and influential forms of policy guidance were **Circulars** and **Development Control Policy Notes** (DCPN). Since then, however, the Government has been issuing national guidance in the form of **Regional Planning Guidance** (RPG), **Planning Policy Guidance** (PPG) and **Minerals Planning Guidance** (MPG). These are progressively replacing the guidance given in earlier Circulars and DCPNs and are intended to provide clearer, more accessible and more systematic policy guidance.

6.15 These documents are an important factor in defining "material considerations" and influencing the way in which the planning system operates. Indeed, the Courts have held that these policy statements must be taken into account, where relevant, in decisions on planning applications (EC Gransden and Co Ltd v SSE and Gillingham BC 1985).

6.16 **Regional planning guidance** is given by the Government where issues apply across regions or parts of regions and need to be considered on a scale wider than a single county or district. The primary function of such guidance is to provide the framework for the preparation of structure plans. **Strategic guidance** is provided for metropolitan areas.

6.17 Within England and Wales there are 9 planning regions (Figure 6.3), of which 8 have a coastline. The way the guidance is prepared varies from region to region. The guidance for East Anglia (RPG6, DoE, 1991), for example, follows the regional strategy which the Standing Conference of the East Anglian Local Authorities (SCEALA) submitted to the Secretary of State. The note addresses a range of topics of relevance to forward planning in the region. These include: environment and conservation (including the need to take into account sea-level rise); economic development; transportation; population and housing land; the development framework; retail development; land resources; sport and recreation; minerals and waste disposal.

6.18 Most Government Circulars, PPGs and MPGs are relevant to planning in the coastal zone because of the enormous variety of land uses and activities which take place along the coastline. However, amongst the most relevant are summarised in Table 6.1, and address the following broad issues:

- **opportunities for development, redevelopment and urban renewal**; PPG 20 Coastal Planning; PPG 21 Tourism;

- **management of coastal hazards**; PPG 14 Development on Unstable Land; PPG 20 Coastal Planning; DoE Circular 30/92 Development and Flood Risk;

- **protection of conservation interests**; PPG 7 The Countryside and Rural Economy; PPG 16 Archaeology and Planning; PPG 20 Coastal Planning; PPG Nature Conservation (draft); DoE Circular 15/88 Environmental Assessment; DoE Circular 8/87 (WO 61/87) Historic Buildings and Conservation Areas – Policy and Procedures;

- **consideration of issues related to sea use**; DoE Circular 2/85 Planning Control over Oil and Gas Operations; MPG 6 Guidelines for Aggregate Provision in England and Wales; DoE Circular 17/91 Water Industry Investment: Planning Considerations; PPG 17 Sport and Recreation; PPG 20 Coastal Planning.

National Guidance: Scotland

6.19 The Scottish Development Department (now the Environment Department) of the Scottish Office is responsible for promoting the proper operation of the land use planning system in Scotland. In contrast to England and Wales, strategic planning is carried out at a regional level by the regional and island councils (Figure 6.3). Various forms of advice and formal guidance has been issued, many of which have direct relevance to coastal planning (Table 6.2). The most significant include:

- **opportunities for development, redevelopment and urban renewal**; North Sea Oil and Gas: Coastal Planning Guidelines (1974); National Planning Guidelines: Aggregate Working (1977); National Planning Guidelines: Priorities for Development Planning (1981); National Planning Policy Guideline (NPPG) Land for Mineral Working (draft July 1992);

- **management of coastal hazards**; no specific advice;

- **protection of conservation interests**; North Sea Oil and Gas: Coastal Planning Guidelines (1974); SDD Circular 20/80 (as amended by 9/87) Development Control in National Scenic Areas; SDD Circular 1/88 EC Directive on the Conservation of Wild Birds (Directive 79/409/EEC); SDD Circular 13/88 Environmental Assessment Implementation of EC Directive; SDD Circular 13/91 Nature Conservation and Environmental Protection Act 1990;

- **consideration of issues related to sea use**; North Sea Oil and Gas: Coastal Planning Guidelines (1974); SDD Circular 51/74 Development affecting Fisheries Interests; National Planning Policy Guidance (NPPG) Land for Mineral Working (draft July 1992);

Permitted development

6.20 Not all development requires specific planning permission. In England and Wales, the **Town and Country Planning General Development Order 1988** (GDO; as amended) gives general planning permission in advance for certain defined classes of development set out in Schedule 2 to the Order. However, in National Parks, AONBs and the Broads some permitted development rights are reduced and others withdrawn completely.

6.21 Important examples of permitted development in the coastal zone include:

Figure 6.3 Planning regions in England and Wales, together with Administrative Regions in Scotland

Table 6.1 National planning guidance of relevance to coastal planning in England and Wales

DoE Circular 2/85 Planning Control over Oil and Gas Operations; Advises local planning authorities of their role in regulating the landward oil and gas exploration and development programme (see Chapter 7). The circular also contains details of the procedures for handling licence applications for landward areas that fall outside local authority jurisdiction (eg estuaries).

DoE Circular 15/88 (WO 23/88) Environmental Assessment; Consideration should be given to the need for EA where a Schedule 2 project is likely to affect an SSSI. Special EA considerations apply to both SPAs and Ramsar sites, where there is a particular obligation to avoid developments which could have a damaging effect on the nature conservation interest of the site. Before approving development proposals affecting an SFA the local planning authority is required to publicly demonstrate that it has fully addressed the international conservation aspects and that any significant disturbance to birds or damage to habitat is outweighed by economic or recreational requirements.

DoE Circular 17/91 (WO 62/91) Water Industry Investment: Planning Considerations; Guidance is given about the planning implications of the planned water industry investment programme to meet EC and national water quality standards (see Chapter 4). Local planning authorities are advised that they should handle applications for the proposed works expeditiously in order to enable the schemes to be completed on time.

DoE Circular 30/92 (MAFF FD 1/92; WO 68/92) Development and Flood Risk; provides guidance to local planning authorities and others on the arrangements for ensuring that planning decisions take account of any risk of flooding.

PPG 7 The Countryside and the Rural Economy; Provides advice on the preparation of planning policies for designated areas, including National Parks and AONBs.

PPG 14 Development on Unstable Land; Advises local planning authorities and developers of the need to take instability into account in the planning process. Advises that coastal authorities may need to consider a presumption against development in areas of coastal landslides or rapid coast erosion.

PPG 16 Archaeology and Planning; Advises that development plans should include policies for the protection, enhancement and preservation of sites of archaeological interest and their settings. Where nationally important remains occur, there should be a presumption in favour of their preservation.

PPG 17 Sport and Recreation; Describes the role of the planning system in assessing opportunities and needs for sport and recreation. Of significance to the coastal zone, the PPG includes advice on the use of redundant or disused land to alleviate the widespread shortage of leisure boat mooring facilities, without causing significant detriment to the natural environment. Planning authorities are advised that where conflict arises in designated areas of landscape value (eg National Parks and heritage coasts) the conservation and enhancement of natural beauty must prevail over encouragement of recreational activities.

PPG 20 Coastal Planning; Highlights issues that are particularly relevant to the coastal zone, including a endorsement of the heritage coast definition. Key policy issues addressed are: conservation of the natural environment; development on the coast; policies for risks; improving the environment. The document also draws attention to the strategic nature of many coastal issues, and the need for cooperation and coordination with other coastal managers.

PPG 21 Tourism; outlines the economic significance of tourism and its environmental impact. Emphasises that the planning system should facilitate and encourage development and improvement in tourist provision, while tackling any adverse effects of existing tourist attractions and activity in a constructive and positive manner.

PPG Nature Conservation (draft); Sets out the principles and policies that apply to the reflection of conservation priorities in land use planning. Draws to the attention of local planning authorities the need to give protection for designations such as SSSIs by refusing permission or minimising impacts through the imposition of planning conditions. The document also draws attention to the fact that development adjacent to SSSIs can be damaging and must be strictly controlled. Permitted development rights for certain temporary land uses within SSSIs are withdrawn. It states that the Secretary of State will normally call in planning applications which are likely to significantly affect sites of international importance (ie declared or potential SPA or Ramsar sites) as well as sites of recognised national importance. Also states that EA will often be required for Schedule 2 projects in sites of international and recognised national importance.

MPG6 Guidelines for Aggregates Provision in England and Wales; Advises local planning authorities of the need to make every effort to identify and safeguard, in their development plans, suitable locations for marine aggregate wharves.

Table 6.2 National guidance of relevance to coastal planning in Scotland

---

National Planning Guidelines; draw attention to types of development and uses of land likely to raise national issues, including:

North Sea Oil and Gas: Coastal Planning Guidelines 1974
Aggregate Working 1977
Priorities for Development Planning 1981

Circulars; provide statements of Government policy, contain guidance on policy implementation through legislative or procedural change, including:

Circular 51/74	Development affecting Fisheries Interests
Circular 20/80	Development Control In National Scenic Areas (amended by Circular 9/87)
Circular 1/88	EC Directive on the Conservation of Wild Birds (Directive 79/409/EEC)
Circular 13/88	Environmental Assessment Implementation of EC Directive
Circular 13/91	Nature Conservation and Part VII of the Environmental Protection Act 1990

NPPG Land for Mineral Working (draft July 1992)

Planning Advice Notes; advice to local authority planners on the preparation of development plans, including:

3. The Countryside
5. Sport, Outdoor Recreation and Tourism
9. Nature Conservation
12. Scottish Fishing Industry

Land Use Summary Sheets; prepared for nationally significant land uses or activities, including:

3. Nature Conservation
4. Landscape Resources
8. Aggregate Working
13. Recreation and Tourism

- the construction of a swimming pool or hard standing within the boundaries of a property (Part 1 Class E & F);

- temporary uses which are permitted for not more than a specified period in a calender year (eg war games, 28 days; motorcycle and 4-wheel drive events, 14 days; Part 4 Class B, but certain temporary recreational rights are not available within SSSIs (DoE Circular 1/92; WO 1/92);

- development under **Local or Private Acts**, or **Harbour Orders** (see below; Part 11 Class A);

- certain development by local authorities, highway authorities, drainage bodies, the NRA, sewerage undertakers and statutory undertakers (Parts 12–17). Statutory undertakers include dock, pier, harbour, or water transport undertakings. Part 17 Class B of Schedule 2 to the Order permits development on operation land required for the purposes of shipping (see below); Part 17 Class D authorises the use of any land for the spreading of any dredged material.

6.22 Such permitted development rights can be withdrawn by a direction under Article 4 of the GDO which normally requires the Secretary of States approval. However, it is intended that these rights should only be withdrawn in exceptional circumstances. In general, local planning authorities appear unwilling to seek such directions because of their liability to pay compensation if planning permission for the development was subsequently refused (1990 Act S.107–108).

Development outside planning control

6.23 Under the 1990 Act a number of activities are defined as not to constitute "development" of land and, therefore do not require planning permission (S.55). These include:

- maintenance, improvement or alteration of a building which does not materially affect its external appearance;

- the carrying out of road improvement or maintenance works on land within the boundary of the road;

- the carrying out of inspection, repair or renewal works (eg for sewers or water mains) by local authorities or statutory undertakers;

- the use of a building or land within its curtilage for any purpose incidental to the enjoyment of the dwelling;

- the use of land and existing buildings for agriculture and forestry.

6.24 Development by The Crown does not require planning permission, although there is a non-statutory authorisation procedure set down in DoE

Circular 18/84 whereby local planning authorities are consulted. These procedures are similar to the procedures outlined earlier, except that instead of granting or refusing planning permission the local planning authority indicates whether or not it objects to the proposal. Unresolved objections are referred to the Secretary of State, if necessary following a public inquiry.

Land Drainage Consents

6.25 In England and Wales, the NRA has the power to make byelaws for flood defence and land drainage purposes (see Table 3.3). As outlined in Chapter 3, these byelaws can be used to regulate excavation, construction or activity between MHWM and up to 200m inland of the landward side of any sea defence (the precise distances vary between NRA regions).

6.26 Developers, operators and landowners must obtain consent from the NRA before carrying out works which may affect watercourses or sea defences. On receipt of the application, the NRA is obliged to respond within 2 months. If no notification is provided within 2 months, the authority is deemed to have consented. The applicant has the right of appeal to an independent arbitrator or Government Minister if he believes that consent has been unreasonably withheld. The authority's consent is given solely on flood defence and environmental criteria and is not a substitute for planning permission or any other licences or consents that may be required.

6.27 If works are carried out without prior approval, the NRA can serve a notice requiring that the nuisance is abated within a specified time. The authority has the power to pull down, alter or remove any unauthorised works and recover the costs incurred in the process (Water Resources Act 1991 S.109).

Control of Harbour Development

6.28 As an island nation, ports and harbours have always been central for trade with overseas markets, transport, national security and the fishing industry. There are over 300 harbours around the coast ranging from the container terminal at Southampton to the ferry port of Harwich, the oil terminal at Milford Haven and the fishing port of Brixham.

6.29 There are 3 main types of statutory harbour authority: those which are privately owned (eg Mersey and Felixstowe); those which run as trust ports (eg Port of Tyne, Ipswich and Cromarty Firth); and those belonging to local authorities (eg Bristol). The structure of the industry has changed in recent years. The **Port Act 1991**, for example, provided for the transfer of trust ports into private ownership, thereby enabling the greater powers of a registered company to be used in connection with harbour development, its assets and facilities. Examples of ports which have changed their status from trust ports to registered company include Tees and Hartlepool, Clyde and Forth.

6.30 In contrast to most local planning authorities, harbour authorities' powers can extend below LWM and may involve the control of navigation or fishing within harbour waters. All have a significant degree of autonomy to operate under statutory powers set out in **local Acts** or **Orders** made under **The Harbours Act 1964**. Harbour authorities rely on **statutory powers** provided within local Acts for the construction and maintenance of harbour works below HWM to ensure that they are not open to challenge in the courts on the grounds that the works interfere with public rights of navigation. As a result of these statutory powers and the need to undertake operations within harbour waters, there is a range of methods to control or regulate activity, including the need for a licence to deposit materials or for construction below HWM from the relevant fisheries department (under the Food and Environment Protection Act 1985 Part II see Chapter 4; Table 6.3).

6.31 In the absence of sufficient statutory powers, harbour authorities can seek authority to carry out works by means of a **Harbour Order** under the 1964 Act. **Harbour revision orders** may be made by the appropriate Secretary of State to allow a range of activities, including (S.14 & Schedule 2):

- the improvement, maintenance or management of a harbour;

- marking or lighting and making safe for navigation;

- regulating harbour operations undertaken by other parties;

- the acquisition of land through agreement or compulsory purchase;

- the disposal of property no longer required.

Table 6.3 Control and regulation of various activities within ports and harbours

Activity	Local Planning Authority Consent	Government Authorisation
Above MLWM		
1. Development authorised under Local Acts	No – permitted development (GDO, 1988; Part 11 Class A).	
2. Development authorised under harbour orders	No	Authorised by appropriate Secretary of State (Harbours Act 1964 S. 14–17)
3. Development on operational land required for shipping or loading/unloading	No – permitted development (GDO, 1988; Part 17 Class B).	
4. Development requiring express planning permission	Yes – application determined in accordance with development plan unless material considerations indicate otherwise	
Below MLWM		
5. Deposit of substances or articles in the sea.	No	Licence required from fisheries dept. (1985 Act S.5).
6. Works on or below the shore below HWM.	No	Consent required from DTp under 1949 Act S.34
7. Deposit of any object or materials below HWM.	No	Consent required from DTp under 1949 Act S.34. Also see 5 above.
8. Dredging operations authorised under Local Acts	No	No – but see 5 above.
9. Removal of any object or materials from below LWM (not covered by 8 above).	No	Consent required from DTp under 1949 Act S.34.
Harbour Waters		
10. Control of movement of ships through byelaws	No	Byelaws are subject to confirmation by appropriate Minister etc.
11. Taking up, diverting or altering the level of harbour watercourses (1991 Act S.180).	No	No

1949 Act – Coast Protection Act
1985 Act – Food and Environment Protection Act
1991 Act – Water Resources Act

6.32 **Harbour empowerment orders** are used in cases where there is no statutory harbour authority. The orders may be made by the appropriate Secretary of State to provide the necessary powers for (S. 16):

- improvement, maintenance or management of a harbour, dock or estuary;

- construction of an artificial harbour or inland waterway.

6.33 The original 1964 Act restricted the use of harbour orders to shipping and passenger freight activities. However, the **Transport and Works Act 1992** includes important amendments to the 1964 Act, enabling harbour orders to be used in the case of matters relating to the recreational use of harbours such as marinas. The amended Act now exempts operations authorised by harbour orders from the requirement to obtain the consent of the Secretary of State under S.35 of the Coast Protection Act 1949 which provides for the safety of navigation.

6.34 The Secretary of State reviews applications for orders and decides whether the proposals are desirable for the improvement or efficient running of the harbour and can properly be made under the 1964 Act, taking into account the results of an environmental assessment (see below) and comments from bodies who have been consulted about it. If objections are raised then it is usual to resolve the dispute through a **public inquiry**.

6.35 Under the Harbours Act 1964 the appropriate of Secretary of State may, by order, prohibit a number of harbour activities including the construction, reconstruction, improvement or repair of a harbour or harbour buildings and structures (except dry docks). Authorisation for such works may be granted upon written application to the Secretary of State (S.9).

6.36 Port and Harbour authorities also benefit from significant **permitted development rights** under the 1988 GDO (Part 17 Class B) which permits:

"Development on operational land by statutory undertakers or their leasees in respect of dock, pier, harbour.... undertakings, required–

(a) for the purposes of shipping, or

(b) in connection with the embarking, disembarking, loading, discharging or transport of passengers, livestock or goods at a dock, pier or harbour..." (1988 GDO, Part 17 Class B).

6.37 Dredging operations to remove accumulated material from navigation channels and marina berths are generally authorised under local Acts. The dredged material may be spread on land or dumped at sea. Whilst the former is permitted development (see above) the latter requires a dumping at sea licence from the appropriate fisheries department (see Chapter 4). Hence, dredging is effectively controlled by the need to satisfy the relevant fisheries department that disposal of the dredged material at sea will not interfere with other interests or damage the marine environment.

6.38 Harbour authorities also have powers to take up, divert or alter the level of harbour watercourses to improve navigability, provided the result is an equally effective watercourse from the NRA's water management perspective (Water Resources Act 1991 S.180).

6.39 In estuaries the appropriate fisheries department may give harbour authorities the powers of a local fisheries committee (**Sea Fisheries Regulation Act 1966** S.18; see Chapter 8). With such powers the authority may make byelaws for restricting or prohibiting fishing or the deposit or discharge of any solid or liquid that may be detrimental to fishing or sea use (S.5). In this context the byelaws cannot conflict with byelaws made by the NRA and must be confirmed by the appropriate Minister or Secretary of State, who may call a local inquiry.

The effectiveness of the systems for the control of development on land in the coastal zone

The extent to which coastal dynamics are considered by the planning system

6.40 In the past, the planning system has not taken full account of the dynamic nature of the coastline. As a result developments have proceeded which have subsequently required protection from erosion or flooding, eg at Durlston Bay, Dorset (Earth Science Conservation, 1988) and at Downderry, Cornwall (Coard et al, 1987). This reflects a weakness in the operation of the planning system; namely that some authorities have taken the view that hazards such as erosion, flooding and landslides are not a planning issue.

6.41 In recent years Government has advised planning authorities that it is the purpose of the planning system is "to regulate the development and use of land in the public interest" and needs to take into account "whether the proposal would unacceptably affect amenities and the existing use of land and buildings which ought to be protected in the public interest" (PPG 1, DoE, 1992; see also PPG 12, DoE 1992). Brook (1989, 1991) has related these general principles to the instances where development has lead to a demand for expensive coast protection works and suggested that such development may not be in the public interest.

(i) Development on unstable coastal slopes

6.42 The existing planning system is entirely capable of taking account of coastal hazards. That it has always not done so to date reflects the prevailing view that the occurrence of hazards such as landsliding is a problem for the owner, developer or insurer rather than the planner; and the widespread, but false, view that instability problems are difficult to predict and therefore most easily and cheaply accommodated by maintenance and remedial measures in response to damaging events (Jones & Lee, in press).

6.43 These general conclusions were largely borne out by a survey of a sample of district and county planners (in inland as well as coastal areas) undertaken as part of the DoE commissioned **Review of Research in Landsliding in Great Britain**. The purpose of the survey was to ascertain how the problem of landsliding was perceived by planning officers, how the councils reacted to the issues raised and what kinds of decisions they made '(Geomorphological Services Ltd, 1987). A majority of the officers contacted either considered that landslides were not a problem, or did not appear to be a problem in the sense of restricting development options, despite the recorded occurrence of such problems in the area and the available published information. Of 24 planning officers contacted: 11 considered that, despite some ambiguity in the legislation, the spirit and intent of the Town and Country Planning Acts supported the consideration of landsliding as a relevant planning issue in policy and decisions; 5 officers were unsure of the situation; and 8 considered that landslides were not a legitimate planning issue.

6.44 The survey found that although some form of hazard map was in widespread use by local authorities, especially in mining areas or near industrial complexes, landsliding was recorded in only a small minority of instances. Indeed, only one district had landslide hazard maps for public inspection (limited to coastal landslides) and two others had landslide hazard maps for part of their areas, but not for public inspection. None of the county councils contacted included hazards as an issue in their structure plans. Out of 24 District Councils interviewed, only 4 had policies in Local Plans relating to hazards only 3 mapped the extent of hazards as a constraint and only one included landslide hazard in local plan policy. The principal development constraint factors were found to be considerations of landscape amenity and conservation, traditional planning constraints that are well understood by the profession and considered more easily defended than a constraint based on hazard.

6.45 This last point represents one of the major problems that has to be overcome if hazard assessments are to be incorporated within the planning system and embraced by planning practitioners (Jones & Lee, in press). Other problems include:

- the high degree of uncertainty which is associated with forecasting hazard events;

- the disparity between the time–scales applicable to geomorphological processes and the time frames of decision– makers which often leads to accusations that hazard assessments are "vague and uncertain predictions";

- the demarcation of zones on maps may cause problems such as adverse effects on property values (blight) and the potential for litigation if they are not prepared with great care.

6.46 The recent study of landslide problems at Ventnor, Isle of Wight (outlined below), which defined objectively the nature and scale of contemporary processes operating within different parts of the town and their impact on buildings and structures is likely to point the way forward in terms of development of hazard maps as management tools (Lee et al 1991b). This approach has proved much more understandable than hazard assessments in which zones are subjectively described as having "high", "medium" or "low" hazard; such terms have no meaning to the non–scientific community and may actually create a false impression of the real level of hazard in an area, as was the case following earlier attempts to define landslide hazard in Ventnor by Chandler & Hutchinson (1984).

6.47 The attitudes of local planning authorities has undoubtedly been influenced by the absence of unequivocal guidance from the Government. However, the position regarding the need to take instability into account in the planning process has been clarified in PPG 14 which states that:

"the stability of the ground, in so far as it affects land use, is a material consideration which should be taken into account when deciding a planning application". (DoE, 1990).

6.48 The document advises that coastal authorities may wish to consider the introduction of a **presumption against development** in areas of coastal landslides or rapid coastal erosion.

6.49 Implementation of this policy advice has been supported by a number of DoE commissioned research projects into the way such problems can be addressed by the planning system. As a result of one of these studies, the advice now forms an integral part of the **Undercliff Landslide Management Strategy** to tackle ground movement problems in Ventnor, Isle of Wight which lies within a major area of ancient landsliding (Lee & Moore, 1991; Lee et al, 1991a). This strategy was developed in response to the cumulative effects of slow and intermittent ground movement on property and services in the town. The local planning authority (South Wight Borough Council) is now able to incorporate a detailed awareness of ground behaviour into development plan preparation and control of development, aided by a 1:2,500 scale **Planning Guidance Map** of the town (Jordan, 1991).

6.50 It is felt that the proper consideration of landsliding in the planning process will assist in reducing the impact of ground movement on the community. Whilst the legacy of historical development in unsuitable areas will dictate that there will continue to be some problems, it should be possible to avoid future problems by appropriate control of new development and redevelopment.

(ii) Development in flood risk areas

6.51 A similar situation was revealed by a recent study of planning policies for development in flood and erosion risk areas along the central part of the south coast (Holt, 1991). Only 3 planning authorities (Hampshire CC, Bournemouth BC and West Sussex CC) were found to have specific policies concerning development in risk areas (Table 6.4), although a number of others have chosen to control development in risk areas through other restrictive policies such as Green Belt or Heritage Coast. Holt (1991) reported that there was some indication that planning authorities were:

> "reluctant to use specific policies because of the possibility of compensation claims where development is refused solely on grounds of flooding or erosion risk", Holt (1991).

6.52 Holt (1991) and Inder (1991) both noted that it was "surprising" that few planning authorities used the NRA to define flood risk areas, especially as NRA Regions had given sets of maps of flood risk areas to all local planning authorities. The study also demonstrated that the weight given to recommendations made by the NRA, when consulted on development proposals in flood risk areas, varied between authorities. Some authorities gave "considerable weight" to flood risk advice, in most cases overriding other considerations, (eg Fareham BC). Others took "account where applicable". This inconsistency was seen by Holt (1991) as reflecting a lack of clear guidance in the

Table 6.4 Examples of coastal hazard policies included within development plans

---

Structure Plan Policies

"When considering the allocation of land or granting of planning permission, account will be taken of land drainage and liability to flooding and to the stability of the ground" (Clwyd County Council).

"In order to minimise the effects of tidal flooding, there will be a presumption against development on land to the seaward side of sea defences including the siting of temporary holiday chalets and caravans. On the landward side of sea defences and behind embanked watercourses, there will be a presumption against development in areas liable to flood unless the standard of defence is appropriate to the development proposed" (Norfolk County Council).

"There will be a presumption against new building in areas likely to be affected by marine erosion within the expected lifetime of the development" (Norfolk County Council).

Local Plan Policies

"There will be a presumption against development in the coastal area which would:

(1) increase the risk of flooding or coastal erosion through its impact on natural coastal processes, or

(2) prejudice the capability of the coast to form a natural sea defence or adjust to changes in conditions without risk to life or property, or

(3) increase the need for additional sea walls or other civil engineering works for coastal protection purposes except where necessary to protect existing investment, or

(4) be likely to be subject to flooding by inundation by the sea" (Delyn District Council).

"Development in the flood plain of any water will not normally be permitted" (Bournemouth Borough Council).

---

original DoE Circular 17/82 (Development in Flood Risk Areas). This advised planning authorities to **seek the views** but does not advise what priority to give these views in relation to other factors.

6.53 However, the recently revised advice now contained in DoE Circular 30/92 (MAFF FD 1/92; WO 68/92) states that:

"Where flood defence considerations arise, they should always be taken into account by local planning authorities in preparing development plans and in determining planning applications."

6.54 As described in Chapter 3, the NRA is required to carry out surveys of areas with flood problems (Water Resources Act 1991 S.105(2)). Copies of these surveys should be sent to the appropriate local planning authority. The Circular states that the information provided should be taken into account in the preparation of development plans. In a number of instances the NRA Regions have prepared "model policies" to assist planning authorities in preparing flood protection policies (Table 6.5).

6.55 The Circular also advises local planning authorities that they will need to consult the NRA on individual applications before granting planning permission, where significant flood defence considerations arise.

6.56 The apparent reluctance of local planning authorities to address coastal hazards in their development plans has had significant implications for coastal defence strategy, (see below). However, it appears likely the publication of PPG 14 and Circular 30/92 will prove significant in encouraging planning authorities to include policies specifically addressing these issues in their development plans, (Table 6.4). Indeed, the advice on coastal hazards was reiterated in PPG 20:

"Due to the nature of coastal geology and landforms, there are risks, particularly from flooding; erosion by the sea; and land slips and falls or rock. The policy in these areas should be to avoid putting further development at risk".

(iii) Coastal hazard management in Scotland

6.57 The Scottish Office have not issued formal planning advice regarding matters of instability or flooding. Generally these are not considered to be national issues and the England and Wales approach to addressing the planning and legal issues raised by coastal hazard problems will not necessarily be taken by the Scottish Office in the future (Scottish Office pers. comm.).

(iv) Permitted development and development outside planning control

6.58 In the context of coastal management it is important to recognise that a number of activities that do not require express planning permission may increase the risk to adjacent property from hazards. For example, construction of swimming pools, terracing of gardens, open trench excavations, removal of vegetation from slopes and building improvements have all been demonstrated to contribute to slope instability problems in both Luccombe and Ventnor, Isle of Wight (Lee & Moore, 1989, 1991; Lee et al 1991b). This has led to South Wight Borough Council and the Joint Island Planning Unit to seek additional control over many such activities as part of their Undercliff Management Strategy (see above; Jordan, 1991).

The extent to which the environmental implications of schemes are considered

6.59 Certain types of development projects needing permission from local planning authorities or undertaken by harbour authorities are covered by the following Environmental Assessment regulations (see also Table 2.3):

- the **Town and Country Planning (Assessment of Environmental Effects) Regulations 1988**;

- the **Harbour Works (Assessment of Environmental Effects) Regulations 1988**; applications for revision or empowerment orders;

- the **Harbour Works (Assessment of Environmental Effects) (No. 2) Regulations 1988**; other harbour works.

6.60 As described in Chapter 2 the main criterion for determining whether an Annex II project requires an EA is if the project may have a significant environmental effect. However, it is possible to identify a range of smaller scale projects that could have a major impact on adjacent coastal development, conservation interests or coastal processes. Possible examples include:

- the maintenance dredging of navigation channels which may disrupt sediment transport and disturb estuarine or marine habitats;

Table 6.5 Model flood protection policies prepared by NRA Anglian Region.

> **Summary Policy Statement**
>
> Policy 1/1   There will be a presumption against development (including the raising of land) where, in the opinion of the Local Planning Authority after consultation with the NRA, such development would be likely to impede materially the flow of flood water, or increase the risk of flooding elsewhere, or increase the number of people or properties at risk.
>
> **Coastal and Estuarial Defences and Embanked Watercourses**
>
> Policy 1/6   Planning permission will not be granted for development which would adversely affect the integrity of tidal or fluvial defences.
>
> Policy 1/7   In order to minimise the effects of tidal flooding, there will be a presumption against development on land to the seaward side of sea defences, including the siting of temporary holiday chalets and caravans. On land between a first line sea defence and the main defence, the siting of holiday chalets, caravans and camping sites may be permitted following consultation with the NRA. Time–limited occupancy conditions will be imposed and enforced preventing occupation during the period from November–March inclusive when the risk of tidal inundation is greatest.
>
> Policy 1/8   On the landward side of sea defences and behind embanked watercourses, there will be a presumption against development in areas liable to flood unless the standard of defence is appropriate to the development proposed.
>
> Policy 1/9   Where development is permitted in areas having substandard protection, appropriate increased protection must be provided in advance of the development as defined by the local planning authority in consultation with the NRA and funded by the developer.

- coast protection works which may disrupt the supply or transport of sediment (see Chapter 3);

- engineering cut and fill operations or slope reprofiling for housing development which may have an adverse effect on slope stability;

- building of swimming pools or removal of vegetation from slopes in areas of unstable land which may cause landslide problems on adjacent slopes;

- spreading of dredged spoil which may affect intertidal habitats.

6.61 Whilst the environmental effects of any proposed development has always been a factor in considering whether planning permission should be granted, many of the activities above do not require express planning permission and, therefore, there is no formal mechanism for reviewing their potential effects. In some instances it may be necessary to consider the withdrawal of certain permitted development rights which may have an adverse effect on the coastal zone, as has been proposed in Ventnor (Lee et al, 1991a; Jordan, 1991).

6.62 In other instances, such as for coast protection schemes, the list of projects to which the Environmental Assessment regulations apply should be extended. In addition, it may be advisable to reevaluate the indicative criteria by which the requirement for an EA is determined. In the coastal zone, many landforms and habitats are particularly sensitive to the effects of even small-scale development, emphasising the need to take into account the **sensitivity of the environment** as well as the type of development when determining the need for an EA.

The extent to which the planning system takes into account the interests of other groups

6.63 The planning system aims to balance multiple land use demands made on an area. Through the preparation of development plans and the determination of planning applications, the local authorities plan for and manage change, organising the resources needed to implement and control agreed land use policies. Consultation, open discussion and the right of appeal against refusal or non determination of a planning application are central parts of the planning system. The need to discuss proposals runs right through from

Table 6.6 Consultation by local planning authorities in the preparation of development plans, in England and Wales

Statutory Consultees	Development plan policy or proposal
Secretary of State for the Environment	Every case
Secretary of State for Transport	
NRA	
Countryside Commission	
English Nature/CCW	
English Heritage/Cadw	

Advised to consult	
MAFF	Matters relating to agricultural land, sea defence, coast protection.
MOD	MOD holdings
Department of Employment	Tourism
Forestry Authority	Forestry Matters
Department of Trade and Industry	Industrial and mineral working policies
Crown Estate Commissioners	Matters affecting the Crown Estate
HMIP	Policies involving pollution control
Regional Tourist Board	Tourism
Sports Council	Sport and physical recreation
Water Company	Water and sewerage services

Other public bodies should be consulted where their interests appear to be affected or where they have requested consultation.

Adapted from the Town and Country Planning (Development Plan) Regulations 1991 and PPG 12.

Government to the review of an individual planning application.

6.64 Local authorities consult the public and interested bodies at an early stage of plan preparation. Certain consultees are prescribed (eg other local authorities, the Countryside Commission, NRA). People have an opportunity to object to policies in structure plans (which normally lead to an **Examination in Public** of issues arising) and in local plans and UDPs (where they have the right to have their objections heard at a **Public Inquiry**). Applicants may appeal against refusal of planning permission through the **written representation procedure**, a **hearing** or **public inquiry**. The requirements for statutory consultation by the local planning authority are detailed in the GDO 1988 (Article 18) and the **Town and Country Planning (Development Plan) Regulations 1991**. Selected examples of particular relevance to the coastal zone are listed in Tables 6.6 and 6.7.

6.65 In most planning authorities the determination of planning applications is carried out by a sub–committee of **elected members** who are advised by professional officers. As a result decision–making is **publicly accountable**, although this may lead to local economic issues taking preference over broader concerns. In the absence of strategic overviews of policies for a wide range of activities, this has led to coastal issues being addressed at the local level, without a regional or national perspective. Such an overview has, however, existed in Scotland since the preparation of **Coastal Planning Guidelines** in 1974 by the Scottish Development Department (SDD, 1974; these guidelines have been incorporated in the **1981 National Planning Guidelines**; Table 6.8).

6.66 The planning system has close links with each of the 3 mechanisms designed to protect the coastal environment (sea defence, pollution control and conservation; see Figure 6.4). These are described below.

(i) Coastal defence

6.67 The planning system has an important role in minimising the risks associated with rising sea levels, either through refusing permission to develop in vulnerable locations, or making permission conditional upon specified building measures such as floor heights in flood hazard areas or types of foundation on unstable land. In addition, the trends towards more efficient shoreline management through the regional coastal groups described in Chapter 3 can be reinforced by increased coordination between land use planning and coastal defence strategies. Recommendations on coastal defence strategy made in the context of

Table 6.7 Requirements for statutory consultation by local authorities, in England and Wales, before granting planning permission

Development	Consultee
Development likely to affect land in a National Park	County planning authority
Development likely to affect the site of a scheduled ancient monument	English Heritage or Secretary of State for Wales
Development on or adjacent to SSSIs	English Nature or Countryside Council for Wales
Development on high quality agricultural land (see PPG 7; The Countryside and the Rural Economy)	MAFF or Secretary of State for Wales
Development in the bed or on the banks of a river or stream	NRA (see also DoE Circular 30/92)

Selected examples; for full list see GDO, 1988 Article 18, as amended.

an understanding of the dynamic nature of the coast should be taken into account in development plans.

6.68 However, one of the most serious failings of coastal management in the past has been the lack of coordination between land use planning and decisions over coastal defence strategy. Many parts of the UK coast suffer from an inheritance of unplanned communities and developments, built before planning control was established in 1947. Often it is these cases which have resulted in the greatest conflict between private property owners and the local authorities when the effects of coast erosion or flooding take their toll on unprotected or vulnerable communities. In recent years, the plight of Fairlight on the Sussex coast, Luccombe on the Isle of Wight and Towyn in Clwyd have all caused considerable distress to local residents (eg Jones & Lee, in press; Lee & Moore 1989; Kay & Wilkinson, 1990). However, many properties now at risk also have been permitted under the planning system such as at Downderry in Cornwall (Coard et al, 1987), Lyme Regis (Conway, 1979; Lee 1992), Charmouth (Denness et al, 1975) and at

Durlston Bay, Dorset (Earth Science Conservation, 1988).

6.69 Despite guidance from Government (formerly DoE Circular 17/82 and now DoE Circular 30/92) many local authorities do not have specific planning policies concerning development in flood risk areas and are uncertain as to the importance they should place in NRA's recommendations (Holt, 1991). Examples of "set–back" policies to counter the problems of coastal erosion are also rare, Canterbury City Council's cliff top "coastal protection zones" where no permanent development is permitted are amongst only a few exceptions (Table 6.9). Few authorities have developed strategies that attempt to reduce risks through modifying building design or ensuring that development does not heighten existing problems (Table 6.9). Controlled abandonment of communities or property threatened by erosion or flooding are unheard of, except in historical times.

6.70 The unwillingness of local planning authorities to view landslides, erosion or flooding as anything other than a problem for the developer, has led a preference for managing the coastline through engineering options rather than planning control. Paradoxically, it may have been the clear success of engineered defences that has led to a lack of control of development in those areas at risks from natural hazards. For example, construction of sea defences often leads to increased pressure for development in what is now perceived to be a safe area. In reality, however, construction of sea defences only **reduces** the risk of damage. It **cannot eliminate** the risk. Increased investment and density of development behind the defences may only lead to higher losses when, inevitably, larger floods occur.

6.71 Similar problems have arisen over the use of planning controls and Building Regulations (Table 6.10). In Ventnor, Isle of Wight, for example, it appears that planning consent was given to buildings independently of the building control process. The past reliance on the Building Regulations to take account of unstable foundation conditions has led to a situation where attention has been focussed on **site problems** rather than appreciating the interrelationships between different parts of the landslide complex. As a result certain building practices, such as the use of soakaway drains, have contributed to the ground movement problems on adjacent slopes. In addition, it was found that many properties, including many modern buildings, were unsuited to accommodate the ground movement that could be anticipated at a

Table 6.8 Coastal Planning Guidelines for Scotland

Guidelines were produced in 1974 as planning advice on the location of North Sea oil and gas developments. The guidelines take into account the demand arising from the basic activities (eg supply and servicing, platform fabrication, oil and gas transport and storage), the results of the **Coastal Survey** (see below), and the need to site new development in a way that makes the best use of existing labour and infrastructure or minimises the effect of subsequent decline.

The main policy guidelines are:

Preferred development zones; within which sites for oil and gas related development seem likely to be appropriate and within which such developments should be encouraged.

Preferred conservation zones; areas of particular national scenic, environmental or ecological importance in which new oil and gas related developments would be inappropriate and could be justified only in exceptional circumstances.

The significance of these zones to coastal planning in Scotland was restated in the National Planning Guidelines, 1981.

The Coastal Survey

This survey drew together existing information in support of the preparation of the 1974 Coastal Planning Guidelines. The results were published as an atlas of nine 30 mile:1" scale maps with extended legends:

Map 1 Central Government Ownership of the Coast
Map 2 Coastal Planning Policy as stated in statutory County Development Plans
Map 3 Interim Assessment of the Nature Conservation Interest of the Coast
Map 4 Inshore Fishing
Map 5 Underground Oil Storage Capacity
Map 6 Coastal Topography
Map 7 The Countryside Commission for Scotland Coastal Survey
Map 8 Air Photography Programme
Map 9 Gazetteer of the Coast (10 mile:1" scale)

site. The most widely used foundation and building types (traditional strip footings and non-framed structures) are particularly vulnerable to ground movement.

6.72 Consequently the Ventnor study recommended closer cooperation between planning and building control, outlining the most appropriate building styles that should be used in different parts of the town (Lee & Moore, 1991; Lee et al 1991a). For this purpose an Advisory Code of Practice is being prepared by the local authority, which is aimed at improving overall standards of design and construction. In addition, revised procedures should ensure that the decision whether to grant planning permission for future development in vulnerable locations takes into account the views of the Building Control Department.

6.73 There are indications that coastal hazards are beginning to be addressed in structure plans and local plans (Tables 6.4 & 6.9). As the pressure for development on more vulnerable sites increases and the implications of sea level rise become clearer, it is important that more local planning authorities attempt to reduce the risks to public safety and property by producing and implementing strong planning policies. However, as Owens & Cope (1991) note, stricter development control in areas of coastal hazards is likely to lead to calls for compensation by affected property owners. To provide compensation in such circumstances would require new legislation:

"Currently there are institutional mechanisms to **stop** the coast retreating, but not to **allow** it to retreat while compensating those who might otherwise be protected", (Owens & Cope 1991).

(ii) Pollution control

6.74 Concern has been expressed by the NRA (1991) that a number of local planning authorities have not taken on board their advice on water quality implications when determining planning applications. Indeed, in some instances the advice is reported to have been disregarded to the potential detriment of coastal waters. At Pontardulais in South Wales, for example, a housing development was permitted with what the NRA felt was an inadequate storm sewerage system. As a result overflows operate more frequently than desirable and, thus, poor quality water is discharged onto the beach or into a nearby stream (NRA pers. comm.).

6.75 Such situations have led the NRA to state that:

"Some rationalisation or additions to existing legislation may be necessary to enable NRA to guarantee compliance with statutory quality objectives in such situations. It may prove necessary for the NRA to seek powers of direction in relation to planning approval in order to be able to ensure that statutory quality objectives in controlled waters can be achieved...", (NRA, 1991).

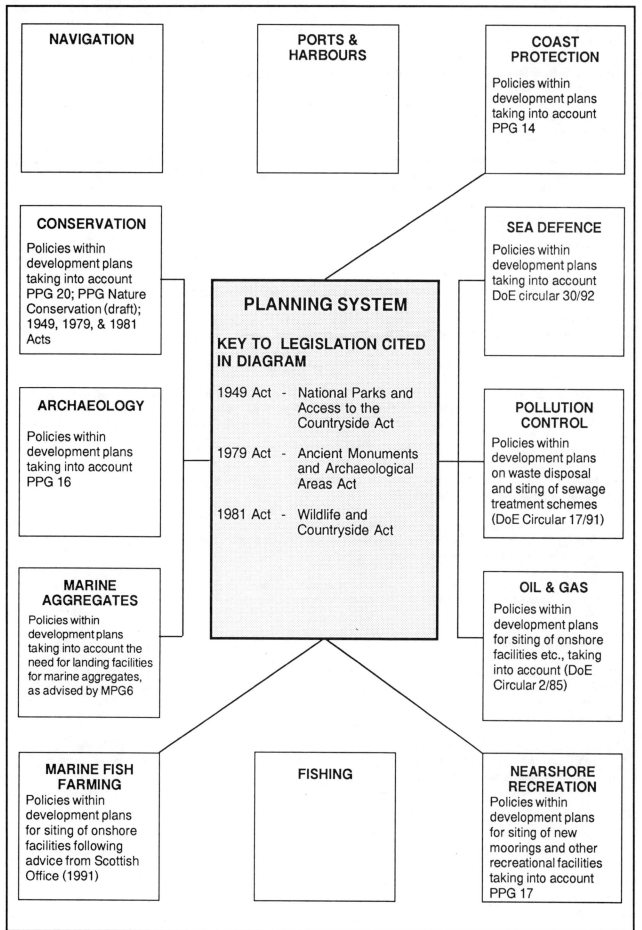

Table 6.9 Selected examples of approaches to hazard management

Set-back

Canterbury City Council; a coastal protection zone has been defined on the unstable London Clay cliffs at Beltinge and Studd Hill. Development is generally not permitted in this zone, as new buildings would exacerbate the present situation and also prejudice future remedial works.

Swale Borough Council; because of the instability problems associated with the London Clay cliffs, a development line has been established in the Leysdown and Warden Bay Local Plan, beyond which no permanent development will be permitted.

Chichester District Council; because of the potential damage to property caused by storm damage, the council has defined a Harsh Marine Environment Setback Line. No residential development, including car parking is permitted within the 15m strip landward of existing or proposed coastal defences unless adequate protection is provided.

Modifications to building design

Shepway District Council; in the Romney Marsh area the authority applies the following criteria in considering proposals for new development:

"Single storey development will not be permitted within areas liable to deep water flooding".

"Within areas liable to shallow water flooding provision should be made for a means of escape from any single storey dwelling to the satisfaction of the District Planning Authority" (Romney Marsh Local Plan).

Swale Borough Council; the following policy has been developed to address flood risk problems:

"Any new dwelling built on land less than 5.3m AOD should contain a means of escape at first floor level, unless the site is protected by secondary defences against flooding. No single storey development will normally be permitted on land less than 4.1m AOD unless there are adequate secondary defences", (The Sheerness, Queensborough and Minster Local Plan).

Retaining wall control

The Hastings Borough Council Act 1988 gives the council considerable control over the construction of retaining walls in areas affected by land instability. S.5 of this Act states:

"...no retaining wall shall be erected otherwise than in accordance with plans sections and specifications approved by the borough council; and if any person erects such a wall in contravention of this subsection he shall be guilty of an offence and liable to a summary conviction ..."

"if any retaining wall is in a state of disrepair as to be dangerous ... the borough council may by notice to the owner or occupier require him to execute such work as may be necessary to obviate the danger.." (Hastings Borough Council Act 1988).

Requirement for stability reports

Shepway District Council; parts of Sandgate are affected by instability and damage has occurred to buildings due to landsliding. In order to prevent such problems arising on new development, a condition is attached to new building permissions requiring developers to obtain specialist advice on the suitability of land for development and to carry out such works as are necessary for ensuring the stability of the site and the adjoining land.

Hastings Borough Council; the council requires a full and adequate site investigation report to be submitted by the developer. Work shall not proceed until and unless measures deemed to be necessary by the local planning authority as a result of the report have been incorporated in the development proposals.

Table 6.10 The Building Regulations in England and Wales (similar provisions apply in Scotland and Northern Island)

> Building Regulations are made by the DoE and Welsh Office to secure "the health, safety, welfare and convenience of persons in and about the building" (The Building Act 1984). They provide a complementary mechanism to the planning system for addressing coastal hazards during development.
>
> The 1991 Building Regulations drew the building industry's attention to the problems that instability may cause to a building and the surrounding area:
>
> "The building shall be constructed so that movement caused by:
>
> (a) swelling, shrinkage or freezing of the subsoil; or
>
> (b) land-slip or subsidence, in so far as the risk can be reasonably foreseen,
>
> will not impair the stability of any part of the building (Requirement A2).
>
> Flood hazards are not specifically addressed by the regulations, although they do consider subsoil drainage requirements.

6.76 In this context, it is important to note that of the 16 development plans examined during the course of this study only 2 contain policies specifically directed towards controlling developments that may impair the quality of coastal waters:

"The County Council will seek to secure the protection and improvement of the quality of the water in the harbours and rivers of south east Dorset and to protect the beaches from pollution", (South East Dorset Structure Plan policy 7.16, approved Sept. 1990).

"There will be a presumption against any form of development that will cause the discharge of effluent in a manner which would be likely to impair the quality of coastal or inland water", (Clwyd County Council Structure Plan policy H12, 1990).

(iii) Conservation

6.77 The overwhelming majority of development plans examined during this study had policies that specifically addressed the conservation of the coast. These policies reflect issues of local and national importance and range from a desire to control the

effects of tourism (eg West Dorset Eastern Area Local Plan) to restricting visually intrusive developments (eg Lorn Local Plan) and the limiting of new marinas (eg Hampshire County Structure Plan):

(In the Heritage Coast) "the provision of car parking and other recreational facilities will be permitted only where an increase in the number of visitors is compatible with the retention of the unspoilt character of the area" West Dorset Eastern Area Local Plan policy EA/L2 (Amendments Oct. 1991).

"There shall be a presumption against proposals for prominent or sporadic development which would have an adverse environmental impact on areas or coasts of regional scenic significance" Lorn Local Plan policy EN 1(A) (Adopted March 1984).

"New marina developments, or proposals for new moorings, will not normally be permitted if their implementation is likely to give rise to additional marine activity which will result in unacceptable levels of congestion in harbours or sailing areas offshore" Hampshire County Structure Plan policy C8 (Submitted May 1991).

6.78 However, the inconsistent or inadequate treatment of other conservation issues in development plans is of concern to many coastal managers. For example, despite clear national guidance on the importance of many conservation designations (eg the draft PPG Nature Conservation and DoE Circular 15/88 (WO 23/88) Environmental Assessment; see Table 6.2 for comparable advice in Scotland) the reliance on the planning system to control potentially damaging development in or around SSSIs has led to criticism from conservation groups.

6.79 In 1990, for example, RSPB published a review of nature conservation policies included within structure plans, for England and Wales (no distinction was made between inland and coastal authorities; Bain et al, 1990). This document also included an analysis of threats posed to Ramsar and SPA sites by proposals within the plans. As a result of their analysis RSPB identified policies aimed at protecting sites of known conservation interest in all plans and, of the coastal authorities, only South Glamorgan did not contain a specific policy for the protection of SSSIs. However, RSPB found that there was a wide variation of wording used in these policies, with 15 out of 31 structure plans for coastal counties having what they described as "inadequate" SSSI policies. This variation was felt to weaken the conservation case when objecting to planning applications:

> "When a structure plan is reviewed, there is a risk that developers will try to exploit weak site safeguard policies in neighbouring structure plans by recommending their adoption by the county council as 'reasonable and pragmatic policies'; councils must guard against this practice for site safeguard will then be governed by the principle of the lowest common denominator. Poorly worded and therefore ineffectual site safeguard policies do not provide a firm enough foundation on which conservation bodies can build a defence for a conservation site", (Bain et al, 1990).

6.80 This analysis highlights wider concerns about the adequacy of conservation policies included within development plans. In this context the DoE Circular 1/92 (succeeded by and incorporated into the draft PPG Nature Conservation) announced that the Secretary of State will normally call in all planning applications (both within SSSI boundaries and outside) which are likely to affect significantly sites of international importance and recognised national importance. The Government has decided not to introduce a presumption against development in SSSIs.

6.81 There has also been widespread reflection on the effectiveness of the heritage coast concept following the publication of the Countryside Commission's statement on heritage coast policies and priorities for England (Countryside Commission, 1992). Shortcomings of the heritage coast concept are seen by many coastal managers to include:

- the definition excludes many attractive, yet unspectacular stretches of coast, including estuaries and flatter coastlines. It also largely ignores areas where restoration work has made notable improvements to the coastline;

- the heritage coast definition offers no specific planning protection over and above normal planning control. Areas falling outside National Parks or AONBs are, therefore, particularly vulnerable to development pressures. However, there remains the opportunity to bring further heritage coasts under the AONB umbrella, as originally outlined in DoE Circular 12/72 (DoE, 1972).

Despite calls for statutory protection of heritage coasts there appears to have been a general reluctance by local authorities and the Countryside Commission to consider designating the coasts as AONBs, a move which the Government has announced it would support (HMSO, 1990);

- the definition does not extend below LWM into offshore waters, yet this is where many development pressures are becoming apparent which could have major impacts on the appearance of the coastline, marine wildlife and archaeological interests;

- the heritage coast programme is perceived by many to be underfunded and relies heavily on volunteer support;

- in many parts of the coast protective ownership, for example, through the National Trust has been found to be the only effective guarantee of conservation success.

6.82 Amongst the proposals presented in the Countryside Commissions new strategy for heritage coasts in England (Countryside Commission, 1992) were measures to increase the effectiveness of the concept:

- reaffirmation of the national importance of the definition through appropriate reference in future planning policy guidance (see PPG 20 Coastal Planning);

- heritage coasts should continue to be defined by local planning authorities, in conjunction with the Commission, in structure and local plans;

- although there are no current plans to extend the present coverage, this position would be reviewed during the mid 1990s;

- rigorous control to preclude all forms of inappropriate development;

- withdrawal of permitted development rights in particular cases;

- EA procedures should be used for all major projects with significant environmental effects on the sensitive landscapes of heritage coasts, including the inter–tidal and inshore waters;

- heritage coast objectives should be adopted by all authorities and organisations with responsibilities for the inter-tidal and inshore waters adjacent to Heritage Coasts.

6.83 The Countryside Council for Wales has welcomed the publication of the Commission's policy statement. It is currently preparing its own statement which will expand and develop the heritage coast concept within the context of broader coastal zone management policies.

(iv) Leisure boating interests

6.84 Local authorities have been advised in PPG 17 that there is a widespread shortage of mooring facilities for boats along the coast of England and Wales (see Table 6.1). Advice is given that development plans can be used to encourage the use of redundant land or disused sites to meet the demand without affecting local or conservation interests. However, the Royal Yachting Association (RYA) has indicated, in discussion, that local planning authorities have not been particularly effective in promoting new moorings by providing consent for land-based facilities such as road access, services or car parking. The RYA reported that, in the past, local authorities have been very sensitive to environmental or local interests when considering applications for planning permission. Often environmental groups see additional moorings as a further threat to intertidal wildlife (eg Rothwell & Housden, 1990) and locals may feel that such facilities disturb their peace and quiet.

6.85 It is becoming apparent that conflict can may also arise between local boat owners and broader sailing interests as a result of potential overcrowding. In the Solent, for example, the Solent Sailing Conference and Hampshire County Council have attempted to halt the development of new moorings, especially in the Hamble and Chichester rivers. The RYA have estimated that a further 85,000 berths will be needed by the year 2001 of which around 60% will be in tidal waters. Such a demand will undoubtedly put considerable pressure on parts of the coastline and, if it is to be met, local planning authorities will need to balance both national recreational needs and local interests.

The extent to which harbour authorities take into account the interests of other groups

6.86 As described in earlier sections, harbour authorities are bound by the Food and Environment Protection Act 1985 with regard to activities which

may involve the deposition of waste or articles in the sea (Figure 6.5). They are also bound by the Protection of Wrecks Act 1973, the Ancient Monuments and Archaeological Areas Act 1979 and the Wildlife and Countryside Act 1981 which prevent the undertaking of operations that may damage nationally recognised conservation sites (see Chapter 5).

6.87 Harbour authorities have recently been given environmental duties (some already had them through provisions in local Acts), through an amendment to the Harbours Act 1964 included within the Transport and Works Act 1992 (Schedule 3). When preparing or considering proposals related to its operations, a harbour authority must now have regard to:

- the conservation of the natural beauty of the countryside and of flora, fauna and geological or physiographical features of special interest;

- the desirability of preserving for the public any freedom of access to places of natural beauty;

- the desirability of maintaining the availability to the public of any facility for visiting or inspecting any building, site or object of archaeological, architectural or historic interest.

They must also take into account any effects which the proposals may have on the natural beauty of the countryside, flora, fauna or any such feature or facility.

6.88 Problems have been reported relating to permitted development work carried out within harbour areas. For example, the Mersey Docks and Harbour Company enjoys exemption under the GDO for port-related activity. In recent years there has been a growth in bulk cargo handling at the expense of containerised trade. This has involved the handling of petroleum coke, scrap iron and grain with serious problems relating to dust and noise. Sefton MBC is reported to be considering applying for an Article 4 direction so that the permitted development rights can be withdrawn and taking action in the High Court and European Commission.

6.89 One of the central issues of concern over permitted development rights in port areas is that many ports have undergone major changes in function since those rights were granted. For example, many ports have declined in significance and had some of their statutory functions transferred to private companies. As a result a

Figure 6.5 Formal mechanisms by which harbour authorities take into account the interests of other coastal activities

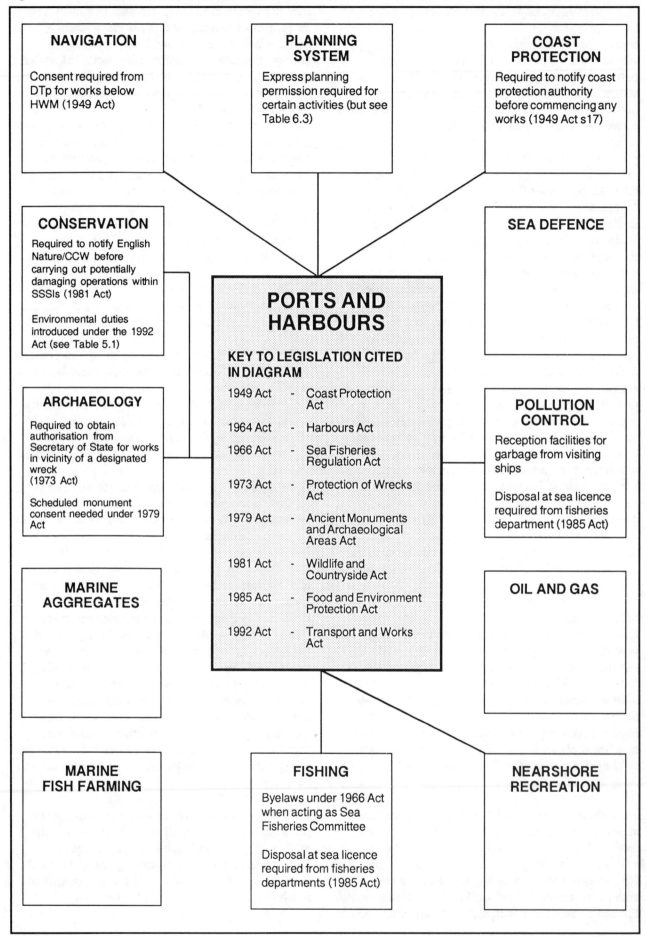

NAVIGATION

Consent required from DTp for works below HWM (1949 Act)

PLANNING SYSTEM

Express planning permission required for certain activities (but see Table 6.3)

COAST PROTECTION

Required to notify coast protection authority before commencing any works (1949 Act s17)

CONSERVATION

Required to notify English Nature/CCW before carrying out potentially damaging operations within SSSIs (1981 Act)

Environmental duties introduced under the 1992 Act (see Table 5.1)

SEA DEFENCE

ARCHAEOLOGY

Required to obtain authorisation from Secretary of State for works in vicinity of a designated wreck (1973 Act)

Scheduled monument consent needed under 1979 Act

PORTS AND HARBOURS

KEY TO LEGISLATION CITED IN DIAGRAM

1949 Act	-	Coast Protection Act
1964 Act	-	Harbours Act
1966 Act	-	Sea Fisheries Regulation Act
1973 Act	-	Protection of Wrecks Act
1979 Act	-	Ancient Monuments and Archaeological Areas Act
1981 Act	-	Wildlife and Countryside Act
1985 Act	-	Food and Environment Protection Act
1992 Act	-	Transport and Works Act

POLLUTION CONTROL

Reception facilities for garbage from visiting ships

Disposal at sea licence required from fisheries department (1985 Act)

MARINE AGGREGATES

OIL AND GAS

MARINE FISH FARMING

FISHING

Byelaws under 1966 Act when acting as Sea Fisheries Committee

Disposal at sea licence required from fisheries departments (1985 Act)

NEARSHORE RECREATION

number of local authorities have expressed the view that they should have a role in determining the nature of new land uses within the old port areas.

6.90 The effects of maintenance dredging have been criticised by many conservation groups because of the potential impact on the marine and estuarine environment, especially as a result of remobilisation of toxic substances and the creation of turbidity problems (eg Clare, 1991). A number of coast protection authorities contacted during this study also expressed concern over the dumping of sediment offshore that would otherwise provide a valuable supply of beach sediment for severely eroded beaches and coastlines. In both instances the relevant fisheries department responsible for granting licences for dumping material at sea can have an important role in resolving these issues.

6.91 The boom in marina development has also brought criticism of port and harbour authorities that they have failed to balance the requirements of their traditional interests with the demand for recreation sailing:

"The role of these authorities is becoming ever more important as water recreational activities continue to grow and new types of craft are developed. Some authorities have not adapted adequately to the changes either in terms of staffing and organisation, or in their changing policies. Some give an overriding priority to commercial shipping and unreasonably restrict recreation uses." (Association of County Councils et al, 1991).

6.92 In other instances, expansion of recreational facilities can threaten both environmental conservation and management (eg Rothwell & Housden, 1990). As harbour authorities receive mooring fees or harbour dues from craft moored within their jurisdiction, the growth in recreational sailing has provided substantial revenue in many harbours. There are feelings that this financial incentive has led some harbour authorities to develop recreational uses in an area at the expense of conservation interests.

6.93 There appear to be growing concerns from other users of the coastal zone over shortcomings in existing harbour arrangements. The expansion of facilities in estuaries invariably conflicts with sensitive environmental issues. At Southampton, for example, over 1,000 ha of land has been reclaimed since 1800, including the loss of extensive marshes and mudflats during the development of the Western Docks. The cumulative effect of even minor developments in an area can be significant, threatening the integrity of the whole estuary ecosystem; **"death by a thousand cuts"** (Hampshire CC, 1991). Dredging and dumping within ports do not require an environmental assessment to be undertaken, although their effect on the marine environment can be significant both in the dredged channel and in the disposal areas. Harbour works and jetties may have a major impact on sediment transport along the coast, as at West Bay, Dorset (Brunsden, 1991).

The extent to which development control systems enable coordinated decision making across the coastal zone

6.94 Harbour authorities may have powers to undertake, control or regulate operations on land, on the sea bed or in harbour waters. These powers can provide a link between decision making throughout that part of the coastal zone which is in their direct interest. Chichester Harbour is an excellent model of integrated management of a coastal area. The **Chichester Harbour Conservancy Act 1971** provided for the control of the harbour and adjoining areas of high landscape value under a single authority (the Chichester Harbour Conservancy) with responsibility for conservancy, maintenance and improvement to take advantage of opportunities for leisure and recreation across the coastal zone (Chichester Harbour Conservancy, 1983). A management plan has been prepared for the Harbour Amenity Area which extends over both the harbour waters and the surrounding land. However, the authority does not control fisheries activity.

6.95 Such a coordinated approach to managing the coastal zone is not available to local planning authorities with the exception of Shetland and Orkney Island Councils which are unique in the UK in that their powers extend to the surrounding Territorial Waters. These powers were developed as a result of residents' fears for the impact of oil and gas related activities on the local economy and environment. The councils have also used their powers to control other activities such as marine fish farming.

6.96 For example, the **Zetland County Council Act 1974** gave Shetland Council the following powers:

- conservancy of and control of development in the coastal area and harbour;

- the promotion of development and improvement of port and harbour services;

- harbour duties, harbour jurisdiction and powers to construct works and acquire land.

6.97 In contrast the boundaries of the planning system throughout the rest of the UK can be strictly defined in terms of its spatial limit (normally MLWM in England and Wales) and the definition of what is considered to be development (see above). **Thus the planning system can only be used to control certain activities in the landward part of the coastal zone**. It does not provide a means of coordinating decision making across the coastal zone.

6.98 Unlike, for example, the powers of a coast protection authority (under the Coast Protection Act 1949 S.18), local planning authorities cannot extend their jurisdiction to control elements of a development that lie below LWM. Although planning advice has been issued to cover certain aspects of offshore activity (see Table 6.1), the seaward limit of the planning system has led a number of local authorities to express a desire to see the limit of jurisdiction of the Town and Country Planning Act 1990 extended to cover coastal waters.

6.99 A direct consequence of the spatial limit of planning control has been the use of Private Bills to obtain consent for development below LWM (see Chapter 2). The approval of works in a Private Act carries automatic planning approval (GDO, 1988 Schedule 2). However, the Transport and Works Act 1992 is likely to have a major effect on the procedures for approval of development below LWM in England and Wales. Under a new order-making system many such projects could be approved outside Parliament (see Chapter 2).

6.100 There are many activities in the coastal zone that lie outside the planning system, although they may be of direct interest to local authorities. This has led a number of authorities to prepare **coastal management plans** to address these broader issues that fall outside the remit of the local planning authority, but are of pressing concern along their coastlines. Examples include:

- Sefton MBC's Coast Management Plan (1989) which provides a framework for resolving issues arising out of multiple land uses in the

dune coastline. The management policies include dune conservation, land management, woodland management, nature conservation, recreation, interpretation and education, and monitoring and research (Table 6.11).

- Northumberland CC's Coastal Management Plan (1991) which addresses a range of issues relevant to that coast: the boundary of the Heritage Coast, the local community, the coastal landscape, nature conservation and geological interest, historical and archaeological interest, recreation and tourism (Northumberland CC, 1991). This plan recognised that near shore waters are of major conservation importance and sensitivity. As a result the offshore boundary of the area covered by the management plan extends to the 10 fathom contour to include island along the coast and the near shore waters.

6.101 Problems have been most acute in the industrial estuaries. These are under considerable development and user pressure which could affect those designated conservation areas which do not receive protection from the planning system because they lie below LWM. These problems are exacerbated by the fact that many estuaries lie at the junction of numerous local authority boundaries. The Thames, for example, extends over 20 local authority areas; the Humber, 14; the Dee falls within 8 councils and two countries. **Estuary management plans** spanning the administrative areas of different authorities and even different countries could provide a framework for resolving such complex issues.

6.102 These coastal and estuary management plans are non-statutory but have been developed within the context of the relevant development plans. Management plans can be supported by the statutory planning system and may point the way forward to the way in which local authorities can begin addressing the complex problems facing coastal managers, rather than dealing with issues in isolation.

Summary

6.103 The main control of development on land is the planning system which is designed to regulate the development and use of land in the public interest, having to recognise both conservation and economic interests. The spatial extent of the planning system is normally limited to MLWM (in

Table 6.11 Coastal planning and management in Sefton Metropolitan Borough (prepared from Sefton, 1989; 1991)

Coast Management Plan

The Sefton Coast Management Scheme has been operating since 1979. It is a partnership between the Council, major landowners, the Countryside Commission and the Forestry Commission for coordinated management of nature conservation and recreation of the tidal flats, open dune systems and grazing marshes. The aims of the scheme can be summarised as:

– management of the open coast as an amenity area, with the emphasis on nature conservation, while making provision, where necessary, for low–intensity recreational uses, compatible with the carrying capacity of the area;

– maintenance of and enhancement of the natural coastline, its habitats and wildlife, in a way compatible with sea defence and coast protection considerations;

– improvement of the landscape quality of the area, where necessary, and management of visitor pressure so that the environment is protected and people's enjoyment and understanding of it enhanced;

– development and enhancement of the role of the coast as an educational resource.

The scheme works through a Management Plan which is reviewed on a 3–4 year cycle and is subject to public consultation. The management objectives and policies are supported by Coastal Planning Zone policies within the Unitary Development Plan.

Coastal Planning Zone

The council has defined a coastal planning zone which includes all beaches and intertidal areas (to MLWM) and the landward area where there is a discernible maritime influence on flora and fauna. A number of specific planning policies have been included within the draft UDP that address the council's coastal policy objectives. These include:

CPZ 1; Development Constraints; consent will not normally be granted for any development proposal within the Coastal Planning Zone which would:

– increase the risk of flooding or coastal erosion through its impact on natural coastal processes, or
– prejudice the capacity of the coast to form a natural sea defence or adjust to changes in conditions, without risk to life or property, or
– increase the need for additional sea walls or other civil engineering works for coast protection purposes except where necessary to protect existing investment, or achieve the Council's strategic planning objectives.

CPZ 2; Requirement for Environmental Assessment; the Council may require an environmental statement to accompany development proposals within the Coastal Planning Zone in which attention should be paid to the following matters and to any ameliorative measures required:

– the coastal process of sediment transport, erosion and accretion,
– the need for coast protection and/or sea defence measures arising from the proposal, and the assessment of the effects of these measures,
– the effect of the development on the nature conservation value of the coast,
– the effect on the landscape and amenity value of the coast,
– any other matters which it is necessary to consider.

CPZ 3; Nature Conservation Sites

CPZ 4; Local Nature Reserves

CPZ 5; Coastal Agriculture

CPZ 6; Coastal Woodlands

CPZ 7; Coast Management Plan; there will be a presumption against any development proposal which conflicts with the aims of the Council with regard to management of the Coastal area.

CPZ 8; Mineral Extraction; there will be a presumption against granting consent for the extraction of sand or other forms of aggregates from within the Coastal Planning Zone.

CPZ 9; Oil and Gas Extraction

113

K

England and Wales). In addition, some activities lie outside the responsibility of the local planning authority. In the coastal zone the most important exception is in harbours where the authorities have a degree of autonomy to operate under statutory powers set out in local Acts or by means of orders made under the Harbours Act 1964.

6.104 Local planning authorities determine planning applications submitted by developers. Their decisions must be made in accordance with their development plans unless material considerations indicate otherwise. The system operates on the basis that development should be allowed, having regard to all the material considerations unless the proposed development would cause demonstrable harm to interests of acknowledged importance (PPG 1, DoE, 1992).

6.105 The DoE and Welsh Office provides national guidance on planning considerations in England and Wales through circulars and PPGs. The most specific to the coastal zone are:

- DoE Circular 2/85 Planning Control over Oil and Gas Operations;

- DoE Circular 17/91 Water Industry Investment: Planning Considerations;

- DoE Circular 30/92 Development and Flood Risk;

- MPG 6 Guidelines for Aggregates Provision in England and Wales;

- PPG 7 The Countryside and the Rural Economy

- PPG 14 Development on Unstable Land;

- PPG 16 Archaeology and Planning;

- PPG 17 Sport and Recreation;

- PPG 20 Coastal Planning;

- PPG 21 Tourism;

- PPG Nature Conservation (draft).

6.106 In Scotland, the Scottish Office issues advice and formal guidance to local planning authorities, many of which have a direct relevance to coastal issues. These cover similar themes to the advice given in England and Wales (see Table 6.2),

with the exception that no formal advice has been issued about coastal hazards.

6.107 The protection of the undeveloped coast is considered to be one of the major successes of the planning system. Since the introduction of planning control in 1947, sporadic development has largely been restricted.

6.108 A number of important weaknesses in the operation of the planning system have been identified. Although these specifically apply to England and Wales a number have a broader relevance for Scotland:

- there has been a lack of coordination between land use planning and decisions over coastal defence strategy. This has led to a need to manage the coast through engineering options rather than development control. This approach has increased the amount of development in vulnerable areas. However, since defences can only reduce risk not eliminate it; the approach could lead to higher losses when extreme events occur;

- the prevailing view in the past has been that hazards such as erosion, landsliding and flooding are a matter for the developer and not a planning issue. As a result some development has proceeded which has subsequently required protection. Guidance has now identified that land instability may be a material planning consideration (PPG 14). However, local planning authorities appear concerned that many hazards are difficult to predict and hazard maps need to be prepared with great care to avoid problems such as adverse effects on property values or litigation;

The planning system could be an important instrument in minimising the risks associated with sea level rise, but this would involve the development of policies to control development in vulnerable locations. Stricter development control, however, is likely to lead to increased pressure for compensation for affected property owners;

- some activities in the coastal zone do not require express planning permission (eg some types of permitted development or development outside planning control) but may increase the risks to adjacent properties from coastal hazards. Indeed, construction of swimming pools and open trench excavations have been shown to contribute to instability problems in

Ventnor, Isle of Wight. This has led to the local authority seeking additional control over many such activities through voluntary agreement or the withdrawal of permitted development rights;

- many local planning authorities have not formulated policies directed towards controlling development which may affect the quality of coastal waters and, in some cases, have been reported to have disregarded NRA advice on water quality implications when determining planning applications;

- although most local planning authorities have developed policies which address conservation of the coast there are concerns that some policies do not provide effective protection to sites of international and national importance. Despite clear national guidance the RSPB found many conservation policies to be "inadequate" and very variable between authorities (Bain et al, 1990);

- the heritage coast concept is seen by many coastal managers as being hindered by the fact that there is no specific planning protection over and above normal planning control;

- although there has been recent national guidance, leisure boating interests are concerned that the planning system views the sailing industry as an unnecessary intrusion which can significantly affect the local environment.

- although major developments require environmental assessment there are a number of smaller projects which could have a major impact on adjacent coastal developments. Some of the more important activities in this context do not require express planning permission and so there is no formal mechanism for reviewing their potential effects.

6.109 A direct consequence of the spatial limits of the statutory planning system has been the use of Private Bills to obtain consent for development below LWM. However, the new order-making procedures introduced by the Transport and Works Act 1992 should ensure a more coordinated approach to controlling projects with elements above and below LWM.

6.110 Unlike, for example, the powers of a coast protection authority (under the Coast Protection Act 1949 S.18), local planning authorities cannot extend their jurisdiction to control elements of a development that lie below LWM. Although planning advice has been issued to cover certain aspects of offshore activity (see Table 6.1), the seaward limit of the planning system has led a number of local authorities to express a desire to see the limit of jurisdiction of the Town and Country Planning Act 1990 extended to cover coastal waters.

6.111 In recent years a number of local authorities have prepared coastal plans to manage various activities which lie outside the statutory planning system. These management plans are non-statutory but could be supported by development plans. Such plans may point the way forward in enabling local authorities to address the complex problems facing coastal and estuary managers rather than dealing with problems in isolation.

6.112 In contrast to planning authorities, harbour authorities are in a unique position in that they may have control over activities above and below LWM and on harbour waters. They rely on statutory powers provided by local Acts for construction and maintenance below HWM to ensure that the works are not challenged in court. In the absence of statutory powers they may seek revision or empowerment orders from the appropriate Secretary of State under the Harbour Act 1964. Harbour authorities also benefit from significant permitted development rights under the GDO, 1988 which include the right to spread dredged material on land.

6.113 Harbour authorities are bound by provisions within existing legislation, but to a large extent may carry out their operations without formal consultation with other interested groups. A number of areas of concern have been identified which mainly relate to the effects of harbour operations on other coastal activities or interests:

- the use of permitted development rights which may have an adverse effect on adjacent developments or other interests;

- routine activities such as maintenance dredging have been reported to cause serious conflict with conservation interests;

- harbour authorities' role in facilitating new marina developments and moorings, with some authorities being criticised for ignoring recreation demands and others for developing recreation uses at the expense of conservation interests.

References: Chapter 6

**Association of County Councils and others,
1991**, Coastal Zone Protection and Planning.
Memorandum of Evidence to the House of
Commons Environment Committee.

Bain, C., Dodd, A. & Pritchard, D., 1990, RSPB
Planscan. A study of development plans in England
and Wales. RSPB Conservation Topic Paper No.
28.

Brook, D., 1989 Physical constraints on the
planning of coastal development. Coastal
Management, Thomas Telford, 43–50.

Brook, D., 1991 Planning aspects of slopes in
Britain. In: R.J. Chandler (ed), Slope Stability
Engineering, Thomas Telford, 69–77.

Brunsden, D., 1991 Coastal and landslide
problems in Dorset. Proceedings of the SCOPAC
conference on Coastal Instability and Development
Planning, Southsea.

Chandler, M.P. & Hutchinson, J.N., 1984,
Assessment of relative slide hazard within a large,
pre–existing coastal landslide at Ventnor, Isle of
Wight. Proc. 4th Int. Symp. on Landslides, Toronto
2, 517–522.

Chichester Harbour Conservancy, 1983,
Chichester Harbour Amenity Area Management
Plan.

Clare, N. (ed), 1991, Marine conservation
handbook. Nature Conservancy Council/English
Nature.

Coard, M.A., Sims, P.C. & Ternan, J.L., 1987.
Coastal erosion and slope instability at Downderry,
south–east Cornwall – an outline of the problem
and its implication for planning. In: M.G. Culshaw,
F.G. Bell, J.C. Cripps and M. O'Hara (eds).
Planning and Engineering Geology. Geological
Society, Engineering Geology Special Publication
No.4, 529–532.

Conway, B.W., 1979, The contribution made to
cliff stability by head deposits in the west Dorset
coastal area. Quarterly Journal of Engineering
Geology. Vol.12, 267–275.

Countryside Commission, 1992, Heritage Coast
Policies and Priorities – Policy Statement.

**Denness, B Conway, B.W., McCann D.M.&
Grainger, P., 1975** Investigation of a coastal
landslip at Charmouth, Dorset. Quarterly Journal of
Engineering Geology. Vol.8, 119–140.

Department of the Environment, 1972, Planning
of the Undeveloped Coast. Circular 12/72. HMSO.

Department of the Environment, 1990
Development on Unstable Land. PPG 14. HMSO.

Department of the Environment, 1990,
Archaeology and Planning. PPG 17. HMSO.

Department of the Environment, 1991 Regional
guidance for East Anglia. RPG 6. HMSO.

Department of the Environment, 1992, General
policy and principles. PPG 1. HMSO.

Department of the Environment, 1992,
Development plans and regional planning guidance.
PPG 12. HMSO.

Department of the Environment, 1992, Sport and
recreation. PPG 17. HMSO.

Department of the Environment, 1992, Coastal
Planning. PPG 20. HMSO.

Department of the Environment, 1992, Tourism.
PPG 21. HMSO.

Earth Science Conservation, 1988, No. 24, March
1988.

Geomorphological Services Ltd., 1987, Review of
research into landsliding in Great Britain. Series D
Vol.3 Legislative and Administrative Provisions
and a review of overseas practice. Report to DoE.

Hampshire County Council, 1991 A Strategy for
Hampshire's Coast. County Planning Department.

Her Majesty's Stationary Office, 1990 This
common inheritance. Britain's Environmental
Strategy. Government White Paper.

Holt, R., 1991 Study of planning policies for
development in flood/erosion risk areas. Hampshire
County Council Planning Department.

Inder, A., 1991 Planning policies for development
in flood/erosion risk areas. Proceedings of the
SCOPAC conference on Coastal Instability and
Development Planning, Southsea, 74–77.

Jones, D.K.C., & Lee, E.M., in press, Landsliding
in Great Britain: a review for the Department of
the Environment. HMSO.

Jordan, M.S., 1991, The implications of the
Ventnor study for the planning authority.
Proceedings of the SCOPAC conference on Coastal
Instability and Development Planning, Southsea.

Kay, R., & Wilkinson, A., 1990, Lessons from the
Towyn Flooding. The Planner, 17 Aug. 1990,
10–12.

Lee, E.M., 1992 Urban landslides: impacts and
management. In R.J.Allison (ed) The coastal
landforms of West Dorset. Geologists Association
Guide No.47, 80–93.

Lee, E.M., & Moore, R., 1989 Landsliding in and
around Luccombe Village, Isle of Wight. HMSO.

Lee, E.M., & Moore, R., 1991, Coastal Landslip
Potential Assessment, Isle of Wight Undercliff,
Ventnor. DoE.

**Lee, E.M., Doornkamp, J.C., Brunsden, D., &
Noton, N.H., 1991a,** Ground Movement in
Ventnor, Isle of Wight. DoE.

**Lee, E.M., Moore, R., Brunsden, D., & Siddle,
H.J., 1991b** The assessment of ground behaviour at
Ventnor, Isle of Wight. In: R.J. Chandler (ed),

Slope stability engineering developments and applications, Thomas Telford, 189–194.

National Rivers Authority, 1991, Evidence to the House of Commons Environment Committee on Coastal Zone Protection and Planning.

Northumberland County Council, 1991 Northumberland Coast Management Plan. Consultation Draft, June 1991.

Owens, S. & Cope, D., 1991 Land use planning policy and climatic change. UK Centre for Economic and Environmental Development. DoE.

Rothwell P & Housden, S, 1990 Turning the Tide: A Future for Estuaries. RSPB.

Scottish Development Department, 1974, North Sea Oil and Gas. Coastal Planning Guidelines.

Sefton MBC, 1989 Coastal management plan.

Sefton MBC, 1991 A plan for Sefton. Draft UDP.

7 Regulation of Development on the Sea Bed

Introduction

7.1 With the exception of some port and harbour areas and other inshore areas ceded for historic reasons, the sea bed between MLWM (or spring LWM in Scotland) and the limit of Territorial Waters, forms part of the **Crown Estate**. The **Continental Shelf Act 1964** extended the Crown's interest in the sea bed beyond the 12 mile territorial limit to the edge of the UK Continental shelf.

7.2 The Crown Estate is managed by a Board of Commissioners whose duties and responsibilities are set out in **The Crown Estate Act 1961**. This Act requires the Commissioners to:

"maintain and enhance the value of the Estate and the return obtained from it, but with due regard to the requirements of good management" (Crown Estate Act, 1961).

7.3 The Crown Estate Commissioners (CEC) manage the sea bed as an asset, like any other holding. Most activities on the sea bed require approval and consent from the CEC. For example, consent has to be sought and paid for when oil pipelines are laid on the sea bed. The CEC operate within private law and not statutory law and, hence, their only powers come through their contracts with leaseholders or licensees.

7.4 However, the Government is responsible for the regulation of most activities below LWM. For example, Government approval is required for:

- orders for harbour works (the Harbours Act 1964);

- depositing materials on the sea bed (the Food and Environment Protection Act 1985 Part II);

- orders for works affecting rights of navigation (the Transport and Works Act 1992);

- consent for construction, depositing or removal of material from below HWM (the Coast Protection Act 1949 S.34);

- works authorised by Private or local Acts;

7.5 The Government is also responsible for the oil and gas industry (see below) and the development of alternative, renewable energy sources such as tidal or wave power generation and wind energy is regulated by the Department of Trade and Industry (DTi). At present, such schemes are generally in the proposal or feasibility stages in the UK, so the regulatory procedures surrounding their development have not yet been fully exercised.

7.6 The Crown Estate, however, has considerable interests in providing licences for two offshore industries; marine aggregate extraction and marine fish farming. Both these activities lie beyond the jurisdiction of the planning system and are currently not controlled by legislation. The industries are, however, regulated by means of non statutory procedures established by the Government.

7.7 Three main types of development on the sea bed are considered in this Chapter: marine aggregate extraction, fish farming and oil and gas development. These activities tend to be concentrated in certain areas such as marine aggregate extraction off the south and east coast of England, marine fish farming in Scotland and oil and gas development off the east coast of Scotland and southern and eastern England.

Marine aggregates

7.8 The marine aggregates industry supplies about 15% of the UK demand for sand and gravel. Much of the 20M tonnes landed each year is extracted off the east and south coasts of England, with smaller amounts off the west coast and Wales (Figure 7.1 Nunny & Chillingworth, 1986). The industry plays an important part in maintaining supplies and reducing pressure to work land of agricultural or environmental value (DoE, 1989). In recent years over 2M tonnes of sand from the sea bed has been pumped onshore to Folkestone as foundation material for the Channel Tunnel terminal area (Parrish, 1990). Sea bed material is increasingly in demand from coast defence engineers, for use in beach replenishment schemes (see Chapter 3). Around 2.5M tonnes is exported to mainland Europe every year.

7.9 **Prospecting licences** are issued by CEC to operators in order to determine whether suitable material exists in commercial quantities. An operator may only apply for a **commercial**

Figure 7.1 Licensed dredging areas in Great Britain (after Murray, 1992)

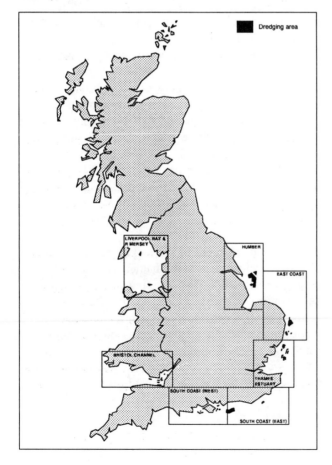

extraction licence on the basis of proven resources within the licence area. Extraction licences are granted in return for royalties on the materials landed.

7.10 There is no specific legislation controlling marine aggregate extraction (which excludes capital and maintenance dredging in harbours and estuaries). The industry is, however, subject to control by the Department of Transport under the Coast Protection Act 1949 (S.34), and in some cases by coast protection authorities under the 1949 Act (S.18; eg South Wight Borough Council; see Figure 3.2). The industry is bound by provisions in the **Merchant Shipping Acts, 1894–1988**, the Protection of Wrecks Act 1973 (see Chapter 5) and the Food and Environment Protection Act 1985 (see Chapter 4).

7.11 Since 1989 the industry has been regulated by means of a consultation procedure known as **The Government View Procedure** (GVP). Applicants for extraction licences submit outline proposals for informal discussion with CEC. The CEC will then undertake informal consultations with groups whose interests may be affected by the proposed dredging, such as coast protection authorities, MAFF, the Welsh Office, SOAFD, the NRA, Internal Drainage Boards, the appropriate Sea Fisheries Committee, local offshore operators, the Department of Transport, Department of Trade and Industry, the Hydrographic Department of The Ministry of Defence, JNCC and other conservation agencies (Table 7.1).

7.12 At the same time, the proposals are referred to consultants (Hydraulics Research Ltd; HRL) for professional advice on whether the proposed operations could have an adverse effect on coast protection interests. The Government decides whether an environmental assessment is required.

7.13 Following the informal consultation stage, a formal dredging licence application is prepared and submitted to the CEC who arrange for it to be advertised in the local press and other appropriate publications. The proposal and supporting information is referred to either **The Minerals and Land Reclamation Division** of the DoE (where appropriate, the Welsh Office, the Scottish Office or DoE (NI)) who are responsible for formulating the Government View.

7.14 In preparing the Government View the coordinating Department consults with other Departments and considers representations from interested parties. If the View is favourable and

Table 7.1 Regulation of sea bed development: licensing and consultation procedures

Activity	Consultation
Marine Aggregate Extraction	coast protection authority; maritime district council; NRA; Internal Drainage Board; Sea fisheries committee; local fisheries interests; local offshore operators; DTp; DNH; MAFF; MoD; the relevant CCC; other environmental interests; minerals planning authorities (DoE, 1989).
Marine Fish Farming	CEC consults with: Leaseholders; Other potential developers; Landowners and tenants interests; SOAFD; Scottish Fisherman's Federation; Local fishermen's association; District Salmon Fishery Board; Salmon Fishery Owners; DTp; HM Coastguard; RYA; Port and harbour authorities; MoD; Scottish Natural Heritage; Scottish Wildlife Trust; RSPB; Association for the Protection of Rural Scotland; National Trust for Scotland; Highlands and Islands Enterprise; Crofter's Commission; Forestry Commission; Regional Planning Authority; General Public (through notices in the press and local post office) (Scottish Office, 1991)
Oil and Gas (Landward)	Prior to award of exploration or appraisal licence DTi will undertake consultations with bodies including: minerals planning authority; interested parties. Prior to award of development licence DTi asks DoE to undertake consultation with; DTp; MAFF; Scottish Office; MoD; CEC; minerals planning authority; NRA; HMIP; coast protection authority; the relevant CCC; Countryside Commission; other environmental interests; (DoE Circular 2/85).
Oil and Gas (Seaward)	Before offering blocks for licence DTi consults: DoE/WO/Scottish Office; the relevant CCC; MAFF; SOAFD; DTp; Health and Safety Executive; CEC; Sea Fisheries Committee.

HRL advises that the proposal will not have adverse effects, CEC can grant a licence. Any conditions required as a result of the View procedure are incorporated into the contractual terms of the licence and are, therefore, enforceable by CEC. If a Department raises an overriding objection to the proposal which cannot be resolved an unfavourable View would be issued and CEC would reject the proposal.

7.15 The marine aggregates industry is represented by the **British Marine Aggregate Producers Association**. The industry has expressed concern over the lengthy consultation periods required to review licence applications. At present it is reported that initial consultations by CEC are taking up to 18 months to reach agreement with other bodies. The association considers the procedure unfair because there is no right of appeal. One objection can result in the rejection of the application, giving rise to claims, for example, that MAFF have an overriding influence on licence applications with respect to fisheries matters. Furthermore, there is no Government guidance on the nature and level of information required by the industry to support licence applications.

Marine fish farming in Scotland

7.16 The marine fish farming industry in Scotland experienced rapid expansion in the 1980s with some 600 leases for fish and shellfish farms being granted by CEC, mainly in the sea lochs of the west coast and islands (Figure 7.2). The industry has grown rapidly over the last 25 years and makes an important contribution to Scotland's rural economy. For example, the value of salmon output in 1990 was around £140M, providing an estimated 6,000 jobs often in areas where employment opportunities are scarce (Scottish Office, 1991).

7.17 Salmon farming involves the use of seawater cages or tanks, with the fish contained in net bags suspended from floating collars. Most installations comprise rafts of cages connected by a series of walkways to help servicing. Each installation is held in position above the sea bed by moorings, hence the need for a lease from CEC or the Shetland Islands Council who have powers to issue licences under the **Zetland County Council Act 1974**.

7.18 A number of authorities have statutory responsibility for the regulation of marine fish

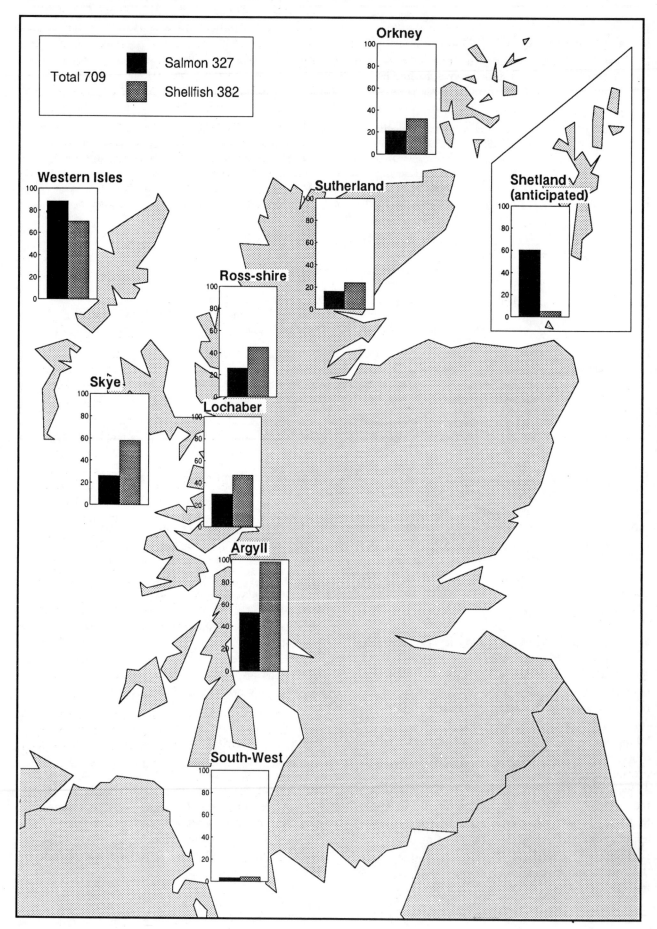

farming, including:

- Scottish Office Agriculture and Fisheries Department (SOAFD), who are responsible for statutory measures under the **Diseases of Fish Acts, 1937 & 1983** and the **Sea Fisheries (Shellfish) Act 1967** to prevent the introduction and spread of serious pests and diseases. All fish farms must, therefore, be registered with SOAFD for disease control purposes;

- Department of Transport, who are responsible for ensuring works do not present a hazard to navigation (under the Coast Protection Act 1949 S.34). Their consent must be obtained for the installation of equipment;

- River purification authorities, who are responsible for safeguarding water quality under the **Control of Pollution Act 1974** (as amended by the Water Act 1989). Their consent is required for the discharge of effluent from fish farms into coastal waters.

7.19 As the farms lie in coastal waters, seaward of LWM, there is no planning legislation which deals with the siting of fish farms in marine waters. Formal planning consent is, however, required for any associated on-shore developments such as servicing, access and storage facilities, although it is reported by COSLA (1988) that sea bed leases have been granted by CEC prior to the submission of planning applications, creating problems for the local planning authorities.

7.20 The Government, in close consultation with CEC, have been progressively developing a framework for reviewing lease applications. The most recent regulatory framework is outlined in the Scottish Office's **"Guidance on the Location of Marine Fish Farms"**, which was published in draft in December 1991 (formal publication is expected in March/April 1993). This document presents strategic guidance on the environmental aspects of the siting of farms. The purpose of the regulatory framework, summarised below, is to enable the development of the industry to take place in a sustainable way, whilst safeguarding the coastal environment.

7.21 Applications to CEC for fish farm leases must be supported by specific information about the proposed farm, including the need for onshore facilities and measures to be taken to safeguard other interests. Following the receipt of the application, CEC will invite comments from the

general public and a wide range of public authorities, agencies and private interest groups (Table 7.1). Applications are also advertised in the local press and in the local post office. Comments must be submitted within 28 days.

7.22 In considering applications CEC attempt to balance fish farming with navigational, fisheries, conservation and other interests. Over 50% of all applications are rejected on this basis and those that are approved are often modified to meet objections before a lease is granted (Murray, 1991). In contentious cases CEC may seek the views of an **Advisory Committee**, with members drawn from the relevant statutory bodies.

Oil and gas

7.23 Rights to explore and exploit oil and gas reserves in Great Britain are vested in the Government. Licenses for developments are awarded by the Department of Trade and Industry (DTi; formerly the Department of Energy) whilst planning decisions on oil and gas matters are the responsibility of the relevant minerals planning authority (see Chapter 6). Two related systems have been established to regulate activities on land (**landward**) and offshore (**seaward**), reflecting the jurisdiction limits of mineral planning authorities who are only responsible for the former. The situation is complicated, however, by the fact that the landward regulations also cover estuaries and the waters around the Scottish islands which lie outside local authority control (Figure 7.3). Thus a third set of procedures is required to deal with activities in the "**landward-marine**" zone.

Landward-marine areas

7.24 Licences are awarded by DTi under the **Petroleum (Production) (Landward Areas) Regulations 1991**. For such areas the DTi serves as licensing authority and de facto mineral planning authority. Where necessary, DTi consults with MAFF and SOAFD about sensitive marine areas. The 1991 Regulations provide licences for **exploration**, **appraisal** and **development**:

- **Exploration** licence applications are invited in formal rounds based on 10km x 10km blocks. Licences are awarded for a 6 year period which permits the licensee to search and drill for oil and gas. It is a condition of the licence that the operator consults with all interested parties and keeps them informed at all stages of operations.

– **Appraisal** licences are required for field assessment of a discovery and are issued for a 5 year period. Before awarding either an exploration or appraisal licence, DTi consults mineral planning authorities and other interests on the need for any restrictions on the proposed operations.

– **Development** licences are awarded provided the operator has prepared a development programme. The licence is valid for 20 years although this may be extended by the Secretary of State.

7.25 Prior to the award of an exploration or appraisal licence, DTi will consult mineral planning authorities and other relevant parties on the need for restrictions to the operations and whether there should be a requirement for the operator to consult or notify interested parties before carrying out any work. Any requirements arising out of this consultation procedure are made a condition of the licence award.

7.26 If an operator wishes to produce from a well sited in an estuary, DTi asks the DoE or Scottish Office to conduct a **Government View Procedure**. During this procedure consultations are held with other Government Departments, minerals planning and coast protection authorities, the NRA and conservation agencies. On the basis of these consultations, the Secretary of State determines the Government View on whether the development licence should be granted by DTi.

Seaward areas

7.27 Oil and gas exploration and development in seaward areas is licensed under the **Petroleum (Production) (Seaward Areas) Regulations 1988** and the **Petroleum (Production) (Seaward Areas) (Amendment) Regulations 1990**. Oil and gas licensing takes place in a cycle which typically takes about two years, each cycle being known as a 'round'. The cycle begins with the DTi consulting the oil and gas industry and other Government departments to establish which blocks (areas of about 200–250 square km) or part blocks the industry is interested in, which blocks may be offered, and whether conditions or restrictions should be attached to the offer. Companies then consider the blocks offered and decide whether to

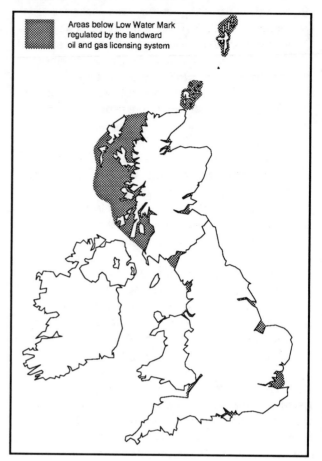

Figure 7.3 The extent of the landward–marine oil and gas licensing system (after NCC, 1986)

Areas below Low Water Mark regulated by the landward oil and gas licensing system

apply. The cycle ends with the Department considering applications and making licence awards.

7.28 The Fisheries and Offshore Oil Consultative Group (FOOCG) was set up in 1974 as a voluntary forum for the exchange of information on general matters concerning the fishing and oil industries in the North Sea. The full Group meets twice a year under the Scottish Office Chairmanship and now has 2 sub-groups which report on technical issues.

The effectiveness of the present approach to regulating sea–bed activities

The extent to which coastal dynamics are considered

7.29 The possible effects of aggregate dredging on coastal sediment transport are recognised and CEC seek professional advice, at the applicants expense, from Hydraulics Research Ltd (HRL) on whether proposed dredging would increase the risk of coastal erosion. As part of their studies, HRL examine:

- whether the area of dredging is far enough offshore so that beach draw–down into the deepened area will not take place;

- whether the dredging will interrupt the supply of material to adjacent beaches;

- whether the dredging will reduce banks which provide protection to the coast by absorbing wave energy;

- whether the dredging will cause, or modify, refraction of waves and thus lead to significant changes in wave pattern.

7.30 If the investigations indicate that there is an unavoidable risk of coast erosion the application is rejected. HRL may suggest restrictions to the proposed operations which would reduce the risk of adverse effects. However, although there is a mechanism for assessing the potential effects of marine aggregate extraction, this has not allayed the fears of a number of coastal protection authorities that coastal erosion may be affected. Concerns have also been expressed about the effects of dredging on sea bed marine communities (see ICES, 1991; Clare 1991).

7.31 The advice given by Hydraulics Research is perceived as not going far enough, being restricted by the general lack of reliable information about offshore sediment movement around the UK coastline. As a result, a number of coastal defence groups have begun to focus their attention on this topic. For example, agreement has recently been reached between the Crown Estate and SCOPAC (see Chapter 3) for the joint funding of research to assess the mobility of sea bed materials for a large area of existing and potential marine dredging activity east and south of the Isle of Wight.

7.32 The principal concern in relation to the fish farming and oil and gas industries is the rapid spread of potential pollutants (see Chapter 4). The regulations made under the **Petroleum (Production) Act 1934**, for example, includes model licence clauses covering avoidance of pollution from offshore oil and gas installations. These require licensees to take all practical steps to prevent the escape of petroleum and report any incident to the Minister and HM Coastguard. Oil spill contingency plans are required by conditions attached to licences before any well is drilled within 25nm of the coast.

The extent to which the environmental implications of schemes are considered

7.33 Environmental assessment forms part of the regulatory procedures for determining licences or leases for sea bed development. In oil and gas developments, for example, the operator is required to prepare an EA in cooperation with the local authority, in addition to environmental, fisheries and other interests. This is designed to ensure that interested parties are fully aware of related offshore activity and where appropriate enable them to help formulate environmental options.

7.34 A preliminary environmental assessment would normally have been carried out by the operator before applying for a seaward licence. Before development consent is granted a formal EA is normally required. Companies are, however, becoming more environmentally conscious and are taking the initiative with such matters. Further informal consultations between the DTi and local agencies with an interest in the site are held to discuss the development plan and the implications of this with all other activities and interests in the area. These would normally include SOAFD, MOD, RSPB, the local Sea Fisheries Committee and fisheries organisations.

7.35 In the marine aggregate industry prior to 1992, CEC and DoE/WO determined the need for EA (in England and Wales). Procedural problems resulted in disagreement between CEC and Government regarding the responsibility, although the situation was resolved in May 1992, with the decision for EA resting with DoE/WO. The decision is made on the basis of a number of criteria which take into account the potential effects on other interests:

- if dredging is proposed within 1km of a Marine Nature reserve or 500m of an historic wreck designated under the Protection of Wrecks Act 1973;

- if the dredging area includes important fisheries spawning areas or nursery ground or lies within an important commercial fishery area;

- if dredging is proposed within water depths of less than 18m.

7.36 The **Environmental Assessment (Salmon Farming in Marine Waters) Regulations 1988** require the competent authority (CEC) to seek an

EA in support of applications for salmon farm leases if the development is likely to have significant effects on the environment. A range of indicative criteria, based on the location, nature and size of proposed operations, have been prepared by the Scottish Office (1991) to guide CEC in determining whether an EA is required.

7.37 The CEC has, however, come under severe criticism from some local authorities and conservation groups for its role in regulating fish farming in the absence of statutory arrangements:

> "As principle landowner in the marine environment, and in the absence of any planning system which covers sea areas, the CEC, under pressure from the Government have assumed a quasi-planning role by default, despite the fact that they are not a publicly accountable body. At the same time the Government views the CEC as independent and has designated them as a "competent authority" for the purposes of the **Environmental Assessment (Salmon Farming in Marine Waters) Regulations, 1988**. Despite the fact that they have a financial interest in the outcome of any assessment the Government has found it necessary to use the CEC as more than merely a landlord " (Wildlife Link, 1991).

> "It is in effect the judge and jury on many developments in the coastal zone... their role should be re-examined, having particular regard to their lack of accountability and the interpretation of their financial objectives" (Association of County Councils et al, 1991).

7.38 Some coastal mangers are concerned that CEC have a vested interest in development which might affect their approach to environmental management. In addition, they are not seen to be publicly accountable in the way that, for example, a local authority is. By being placed in the position similar to an offshore planning authority by the Government, CEC has found itself exposed to mounting criticism from many quarters.

The extent to which the approaches take into account the interests of other groups

(i) Marine aggregate extraction

7.39 The procedures for the determination of extraction licence applications involve widespread consultation amongst relevant government departments, local authorities, coastal defence interests, conservation groups and other local operators (Table 7.1 and Figure 7.4). Only if Government departments agree that the proposed dredging operation is in the public interest will a favourable Government View be given to CEC, perhaps subject to conditions. However, there is still considerable unease of the procedures controlling the marine aggregates industry amongst local authorities, conservation agencies and groups.

7.40 Although there are few complaints levelled at the decisions made, the effectiveness of control over marine aggregate extraction is felt by some local authorities and conservation agencies to be limited by CEC's perceived role as both landlord and licensing authority. Despite local authorities having the opportunity to make their views known in the GVP, it is felt that there is a general lack of involvement at a local level and that public access to the decision making process is not readily apparent. At Filey, for example, marine aggregates prospecting activity led to the formation of the Filey Against Dredging Committee, even though dredging licence applications had not been submitted (Reina, 1991).

7.41 The CEC consider themselves isolated by the industry and Government for holding up aggregate licence applications; the reasons for this include the onerous consultation procedures and the poor level of information supporting each application.

(ii) Marine fish farming

7.42 The Scottish Office regulatory framework for fish farming requires CEC to consult with a very broad range of interests before evaluating the suitability of a particular proposal (Table 7.1 and Figure 7.5). Where conflicts arise with other interests, CEC may seek modifications to the original proposal before deciding whether to approve or refuse the application. An independent Advisory Committee has been established to advise on particularly contentious lease applications. Proposals are referred to the Committee where an objection from one of the statutory bodies is maintained. The Chairman of the Committee may refer applications to the Secretary of State for advice.

7.43 It is recognised that environmental and infrastructural constraints within sea lochs and coastal waters mean that proposals cannot be determined in isolation (Scottish Office, 1991). As a result CEC also takes into account the cumulative effects of the proposed and existing fish farming in an area. In 1989 CEC listed 25 **Very Sensitive**

Figure 7.4 Formal mechanisms by which the marine aggregate industry takes into account the interests of other coastal activities

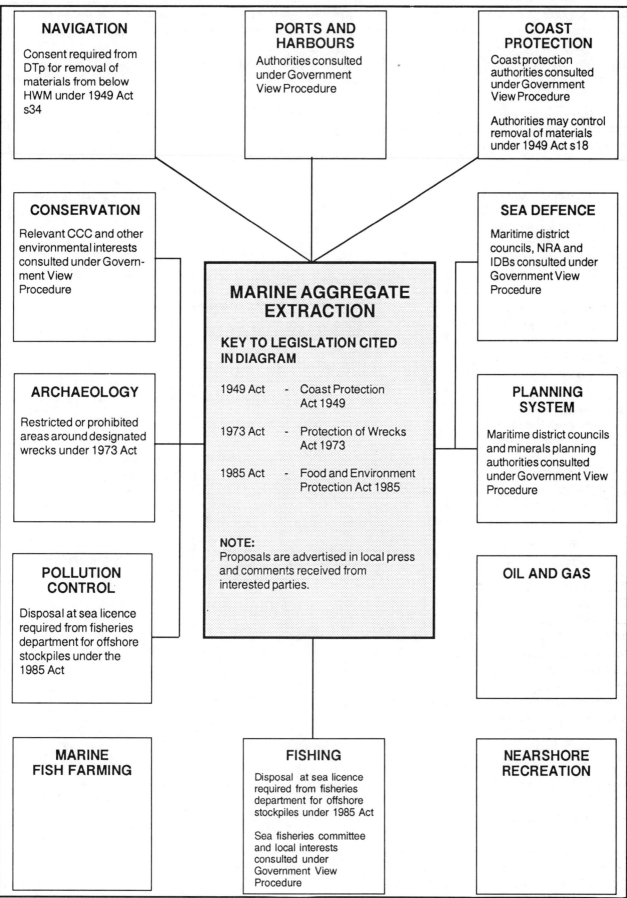

NAVIGATION

Consent required from DTp for removal of materials from below HWM under 1949 Act s34

PORTS AND HARBOURS

Authorities consulted under Government View Procedure

COAST PROTECTION

Coast protection authorities consulted under Government View Procedure

Authorities may control removal of materials under 1949 Act s18

CONSERVATION

Relevant CCC and other environmental interests consulted under Government View Procedure

SEA DEFENCE

Maritime district councils, NRA and IDBs consulted under Government View Procedure

MARINE AGGREGATE EXTRACTION

KEY TO LEGISLATION CITED IN DIAGRAM

1949 Act   -   Coast Protection Act 1949

1973 Act   -   Protection of Wrecks Act 1973

1985 Act   -   Food and Environment Protection Act 1985

NOTE:
Proposals are advertised in local press and comments received from interested parties.

ARCHAEOLOGY

Restricted or prohibited areas around designated wrecks under 1973 Act

PLANNING SYSTEM

Maritime district councils and minerals planning authorities consulted under Government View Procedure

POLLUTION CONTROL

Disposal at sea licence required from fisheries department for offshore stockpiles under the 1985 Act

OIL AND GAS

MARINE FISH FARMING

FISHING

Disposal at sea licence required from fisheries department for offshore stockpiles under 1985 Act

Sea fisheries committee and local interests consulted under Government View Procedure

NEARSHORE RECREATION

Figure 7.5 Formal mechanisms by which marine fish farming takes into account the interests of other coastal activities

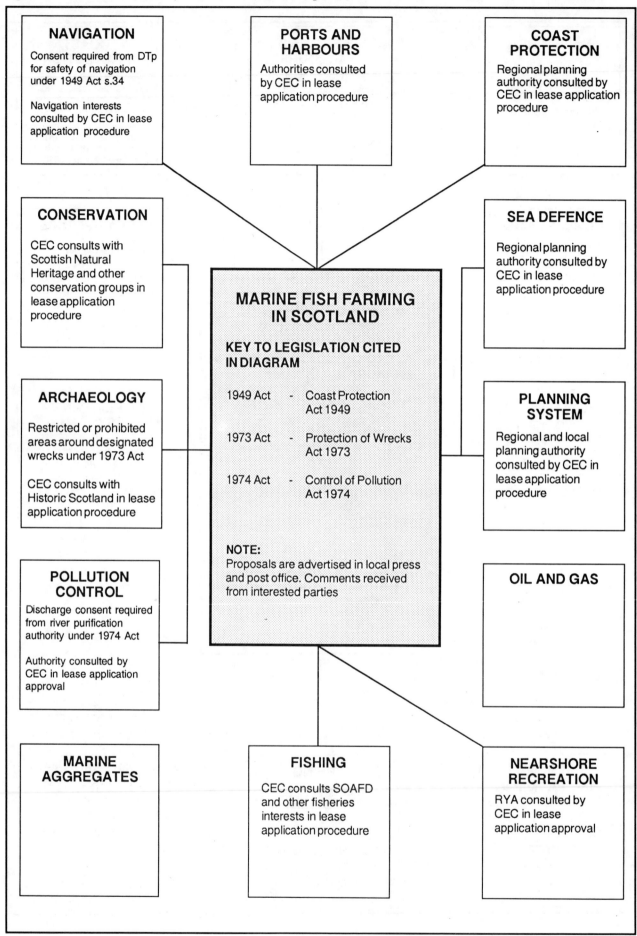

NAVIGATION

Consent required from DTp for safety of navigation under 1949 Act s.34

Navigation interests consulted by CEC in lease application procedure

PORTS AND HARBOURS

Authorities consulted by CEC in lease application procedure

COAST PROTECTION

Regional planning authority consulted by CEC in lease application procedure

CONSERVATION

CEC consults with Scottish Natural Heritage and other conservation groups in lease application procedure

SEA DEFENCE

Regional planning authority consulted by CEC in lease application procedure

ARCHAEOLOGY

Restricted or prohibited areas around designated wrecks under 1973 Act

CEC consults with Historic Scotland in lease application procedure

MARINE FISH FARMING IN SCOTLAND

KEY TO LEGISLATION CITED IN DIAGRAM

1949 Act — Coast Protection Act 1949

1973 Act — Protection of Wrecks Act 1973

1974 Act — Control of Pollution Act 1974

NOTE:
Proposals are advertised in local press and post office. Comments received from interested parties

PLANNING SYSTEM

Regional and local planning authority consulted by CEC in lease application procedure

POLLUTION CONTROL

Discharge consent required from river purification authority under 1974 Act

Authority consulted by CEC in lease application approval

OIL AND GAS

MARINE AGGREGATES

FISHING

CEC consults SOAFD and other fisheries interests in lease application procedure

NEARSHORE RECREATION

RYA consulted by CEC in lease application approval

Areas (VSAs) where environmental considerations and/or the potential for conflict with existing fish farms or other interests posed significant constraints on new farms. These designations were criticised because they were, in part, a measure against over–population of fish farms rather than directed towards marine conservation (Warren, 1991). This view is strengthened by the fact that the Very Sensitive Areas do not include all the sites designated as Marine Consultation Areas (see Chapter 5).

7.44 The current guidance for the location of farms prepared by the Scottish Office (1991) includes an extended list of 44 VSAs, based on advice from the Countryside Commission for Scotland (now SNH), the list of Marine Consultation Areas prepared by NCC in 1990 and other environmental considerations. Within these areas there will be a presumption against new salmon farms, although this will not preclude the establishment of new sites to facilitate improved husbandry where it can be shown that these would make a positive contribution to environmental quality.

7.45 A number of bodies interviewed expressed the view that the expansion of the fish farming industry has led to increased demands on rural infrastructure. For example, it has been claimed that Highland Regional Council has:

"incurred substantial unplanned expenditure in repairing rural roads damaged by the heavy vehicles which service fish farms, yet the siting of these operations is largely outside their control. One such case was the need to upgrade access to Loch a'Choire which initially cost the Council £300,000 and subsequently another £450,000" (Wildlife Link, 1991).

7.46 The Scottish Office regulatory framework, however, requires CEC to liaise closely with planning authorities to ensure the coordination of offshore and onshore impacts of fish farm development. In turn planning authorities are advised to include policies in their development plans which address the effects of marine fish farming on access, the environment and socio-economic issues:

"While planning authorities only exercise control over the onshore aspects of marine fish farm development, the relationship with the offshore aspects is frequently intimate and it is therefore proper for a planning authority to have a policy view encompassing both while

recognising that it has a controlling influence only over the former", (Scottish Office, 1991).

7.47 A number of Scottish local plans reviewed by this study have included policies relating to fish farming in coastal waters; for example:

POL RUR(24) "The District Council will seek the agreement of Crown Estate Commissioners to extend the time period allowed for consultation on applications for licences for fish farming developments below LWM, and to require applicants to submit a draft operational plan with their application indicating the location and extent of development which may be required above LWM as well as that below it".

POL RUR(25) "The District Council will regard coastal water adjoining land recognised as being of scenic importance in POL RUR(1) and being 'sensitive areas' for fish–farm developments. In these waters, the presumption will be against such developments unless it can be justified against the following criteria: landscape impact; economic benefit; effect on conservation or natural and heritage resources; effect on navigation and on other land/water uses and resources", (Islay Jura and Colonsary Local Plan, 1988)

7.48 Similar policies have also been included in the Highland Region Structure Plan. The same council have also prepared a series of non-statutory **framework plans** to guide and control development in areas under particular development pressure, addressing both onshore and offshore issues.

(iii) Oil and gas

7.49 Since 1981, consultations with, among others, the DOE, English Nature/CCW, Scottish Office, Welsh Office, MAFF, MoD, DTp, CEC, and the Health and Safety Executive, have taken place before offering blocks for licence (Table 7.1 and Figures 7.6 and 7.7). This process enables the DTi to evaluate carefully how the licensing of particular blocks might impact upon the various interests concerned and to eliminate blocks with too many restrictions to be worth considering. Any difficulties or conflicts which arise are resolved through discussion and negotiation.

7.50 Throughout an oil and gas development programme the operator is required to take into account navigation, fishing and conservation

L

Figure 7.6 Formal mechanisms by which oil and gas developments in the landward–marine zone take into account the interests of other coastal activities

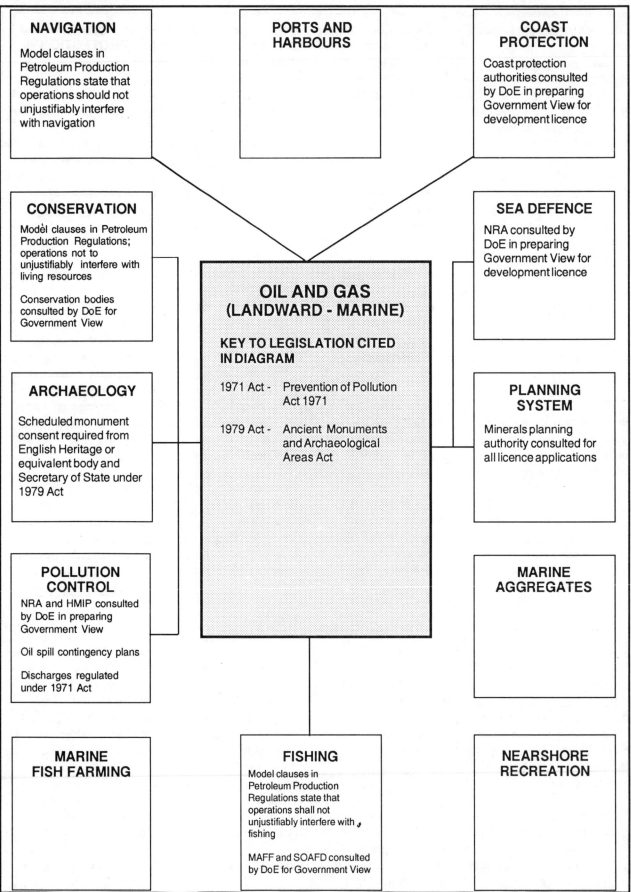

NAVIGATION

Model clauses in Petroleum Production Regulations state that operations should not unjustifiably interfere with navigation

PORTS AND HARBOURS

COAST PROTECTION

Coast protection authorities consulted by DoE in preparing Government View for development licence

CONSERVATION

Model clauses in Petroleum Production Regulations; operations not to unjustifiably interfere with living resources

Conservation bodies consulted by DoE for Government View

SEA DEFENCE

NRA consulted by DoE in preparing Government View for development licence

OIL AND GAS (LANDWARD - MARINE)

KEY TO LEGISLATION CITED IN DIAGRAM

1971 Act - Prevention of Pollution Act 1971

1979 Act - Ancient Monuments and Archaeological Areas Act

ARCHAEOLOGY

Scheduled monument consent required from English Heritage or equivalent body and Secretary of State under 1979 Act

PLANNING SYSTEM

Minerals planning authority consulted for all licence applications

POLLUTION CONTROL

NRA and HMIP consulted by DoE in preparing Government View

Oil spill contingency plans

Discharges regulated under 1971 Act

MARINE AGGREGATES

MARINE FISH FARMING

FISHING

Model clauses in Petroleum Production Regulations state that operations shall not unjustifiably interfere with fishing

MAFF and SOAFD consulted by DoE for Government View

NEARSHORE RECREATION

Figure 7.7 Formal mechanisms by which oil and gas developments in the seaward zone take into account the interests of other coastal activities

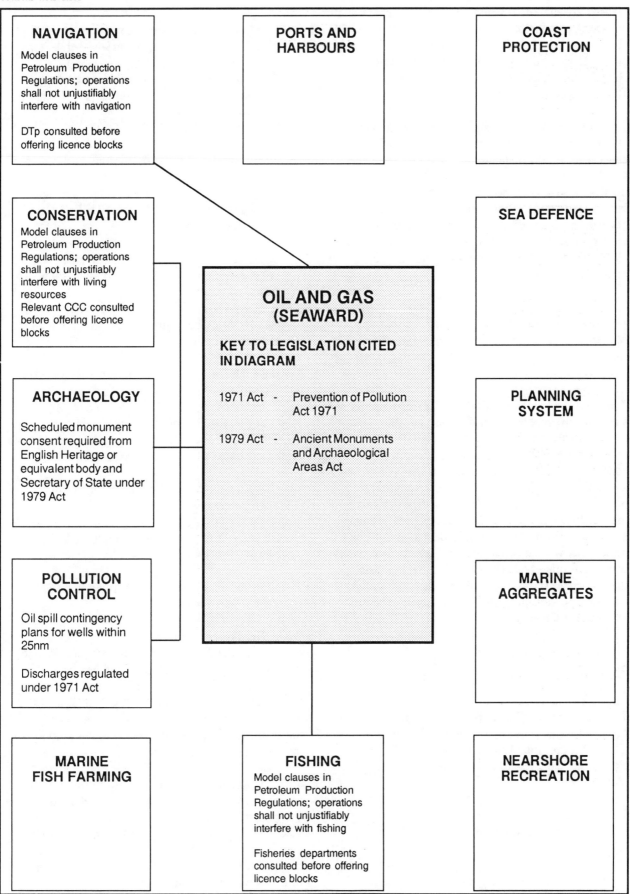

NAVIGATION

Model clauses in Petroleum Production Regulations; operations shall not unjustifiably interfere with navigation

DTp consulted before offering licence blocks

PORTS AND HARBOURS

COAST PROTECTION

CONSERVATION

Model clauses in Petroleum Production Regulations; operations shall not unjustifiably interfere with living resources
Relevant CCC consulted before offering licence blocks

SEA DEFENCE

OIL AND GAS (SEAWARD)

KEY TO LEGISLATION CITED IN DIAGRAM

1971 Act – Prevention of Pollution Act 1971

1979 Act – Ancient Monuments and Archaeological Areas Act

ARCHAEOLOGY

Scheduled monument consent required from English Heritage or equivalent body and Secretary of State under 1979 Act

PLANNING SYSTEM

POLLUTION CONTROL

Oil spill contingency plans for wells within 25nm

Discharges regulated under 1971 Act

MARINE AGGREGATES

MARINE FISH FARMING

FISHING

Model clauses in Petroleum Production Regulations; operations shall not unjustifiably interfere with fishing

Fisheries departments consulted before offering licence blocks

NEARSHORE RECREATION

interests. Indeed, within both the landward and seaward regulations (see above) model licence clauses are included which state that licensees shall not carry out operations in or about the licence area to unjustifiably interfere with navigation or fishing or the conservation of living resources (**The Petroleum (Production) (Landward Areas) Regulations 1991**; Schedule 3, clause 15).

7.51 In general the oil and gas industry is very aware of the obvious potential conflicts with conservation and recreational interests, and has developed nature conservation guidelines with the then NCC (NCC, 1986). For example, at Furzey Island, in Poole Harbour, environmental issues have been given priority consideration throughout the exploration and development phases (Abraham, 1990) which has been widely commended by conservation bodies.

The extent to which the approaches enable coordinated decision making across the coastal zone

7.52 All the sea bed activities described in this Chapter have onshore implications and the regulatory procedures include consultation requirements that can enable a degree of coordination in decision making across the coastal zone. For example, by virtue of consultation between CEC and planning authorities the siting of marine fish farm installations can be conditional upon policies directed towards development control on land as well as environmental issues in coastal waters. In this context it should be reemphasised that, as coast protection authorities, local authorities can seek powers to control dredging in offshore waters (see Chapter 3).

Summary

7.53 The sea bed forms part of the Crown Estate. Most activities require approval and consent from CEC who are bound to maintain and enhance the estate, but with regard to the need for good management.

7.54 Development on the sea bed must comply with a number of key provisions in existing legislation:

- Coast Protection Act 1949 S.34 for safety of navigation;

- Protection of Wrecks Act 1973 for preservation of valuable wrecks;

- Food and Environment Protection Act 1985 Part II for dumping of materials in the sea;

- Control of Pollution Act 1974 and Water Resources Act 1991 for controlling discharges into coastal waters.

7.55 In addition operators may have to take account of byelaws made by various authorities and bodies, including:

- harbour authorities, for the control of movement of vessels;

- NRA or RPA's, for discharge of effluents into coastal waters and for protection of salmon and trout fisheries;

- Sea fisheries committees, for protection of fisheries;

- the relevant CCC to restrict entry into Marine Nature Reserves.

7.56 In the absence of statutory frameworks, regulatory procedures have been established which are based on wide ranging consultation:

- Government View Procedure for marine aggregates;

- Scottish Office regulatory framework for marine fish farming;

- DTi licensing rounds and Government View Procedures for oil and gas.

7.57 The present arrangements are designed to ensure that the activities do not have significant adverse impacts on other parts of the coastal zone and have, in some cases, been criticised for being too strict. This may not be a disadvantage in the coastal zone where there is often considerable uncertainty about the effects of human activity on habitats and sediment transport.

7.58 A number of the criticisms outlined earlier are concerned not so much with whether the system works but whether it an appropriate mechanism for addressing conflicting resource demands below LWM. It is understandable that many of the local authorities and bodies contacted in this study have compared the approaches for regulation offshore with the more familiar planning system on land.

7.59 The most apparent contrasts between the approaches is the absence of strategic plans covering a variety of sea bed uses and less local access to the decision making process in the non-statutory frameworks. Indeed, this has led many authorities to suggest that the planning system should be extended over offshore waters with local planning authorities assuming responsibility for many sea-bed activities, as is the case in the Shetland Isles (see Chapter 6).

7.60 The scale of decision making, however, is an important factor in assessing the effectiveness of control mechanisms in the coastal zone. Unlike the planning system which tends to consider coastal processes at the site specific level (see Chapter 6) the national or regional perspective of the sea bed regulatory systems allows proposals to be judged in terms of their broader implications to coastal dynamics or the economy. Such decision making also benefits from the concentration of marine experience held within a department. This is often in direct contrast with the planning system where it is rare to find specialist earth scientists or ecologists working for local authorities. For the regulation of aggregate dredging operations, the national perspective also enables a close link to develop between research into sea bed sediment mobility and decision making, with the DoE commissioning research which is directly relevant to assisting the formulation of the Government View (eg the recent HRL study of marine sand extraction in Liverpool Bay; HRL, 1992).

References: Chapter 7

Abraham, K.S., 1990, Wytch Farm development stresses environmental responsibility. World Oil, April 1990, 85–94.

Association of County Councils and others, 1991, Coastal Zone Protection and Planning. Memorandum of Evidence to the House of Commons Environment Committee.

Clare, N. (ed), 1991, Marine conservation handbook. Nature Conservancy Council/English Nature.

Convention of Scottish Local Authorities, 1988, Marine fish farming in Scotland. April 1988.

Department of the Environment, 1989, Procedure Note for Offshore dredging for sand, gravel and other minerals.

Hydraulics Research Ltd, 1992 Marine sand extraction in Liverpool Bay. Report to DoE.

International Council for the Exploration of the Sea, 1991, Cooperative research report on effects of marine aggregate extraction on fisheries. Report of the ICES Working Group.

Murray, A., 1991 The Crown Estate: Management of Marine Assets. Ecos 12(2), 7–11.

Nature Conservancy Council, 1986, Nature conservation guidelines for onshore oil and gas development.

Nunny, R.S., & Chillingworth, P.C.H., 1986, Marine dredging for sand and gravel. HMSO.

Parrish, F., 1990 Coastal management: the practitioners viewpoint. In Houston J & Jones C (eds) Planning and Management of the Coastal Heritage, Symposium Proceedings, Southport, 1989, 28–31.

Reina, P., 1991, Fear for the coast. Surveyor, 3/10 Jan. 1991, 12–14.

Scottish Office Environment Department, 1991, Guidance on the location of marine fish farming. Consultative draft December 1991.

Warren, L., 1991 The role of the Crown Estate in Coastal and Sea-use Management. Ecos 12(2), 11–15.

Wildlife Link, 1991, A selection of case studies illustrating the need for coastal zone management in the UK.

8 Regulation of Activities on and in the Sea

Introduction

8.1 An important distinction must be made between the regulation of activities on the sea bed and those on or in the sea. The sea-bed is the property of private owners, often the Crown Estate, and activities may be regulated by means of licences, leases or orders, issued by CEC or the relevant Government Department. In contrast, there are strong public rights covering many traditional uses of the sea such as fishing, navigation and bathing. These rights can be removed or restricted by specific legislation (eg fisheries legislation, Table 8.1) or regulated by international agreements (eg control of pollution from vessels) and local byelaws (eg establishment of marine nature reserves; Table 8.2).

Control of shipping and navigation

8.2 The freedom of navigation is a long standing right, confirmed by the **United Nations Convention on the Law of the Sea 1982** (UNCLOS III). Working through the International Maritime Organisation (IMO), the Department of Transport uses a variety of measures to minimise the risk of accidents to shipping in UK waters.

8.3 Account has to be taken of the **innocent passage** through the seas around the UK, including territorial waters. However, sea lanes can be established for improving the safety of navigation **(General Provisions on Ships' Routing; IMO Resolution 572 (14))**, although no ship is obliged to follow a specific route. Measures taken include **Areas to be Avoided**, where navigation is hazardous or it is exceptionally important to avoid accidents. These are designed to protect particularly ecologically sensitive areas by keeping certain categories of vessels out, although they are only practicable where there are safe all-weather alternative routes (DoE, 1991). Two such areas have been established in UK waters; off the Pembrokeshire coast and the west coast of Shetland. Other measures include the provision of pilotage in the English Channel and southern North Sea and a requirement to report all dangerous cargoes.

8.4 Under the **Protection of Wrecks Act 1973** S.2 **prohibited** areas may be designated around a site if a vessel is in a condition which makes it a potential danger to life or property or if it needs protection from unauthorised interference. It is an offence to enter a prohibited area. This provision is administered separately to the archaeological provisions described in Chapter 5, by the Department of Transport. These powers have only been used with respect to one wreck, the "Richard Montgomery" in the Thames.

8.5 The implementation of the **Channel Navigation Information System** in 1972 has seen a decline in accidents by 85% despite increases in shipping. The system does require radar scanners and other equipment which occasionally have been sited in areas of great conservation vale.

8.6 The DTp's controls on commercial shipping are being progressively extended to all craft for trade and hire. Small recreational craft are not, however, regulated in the same way.

Control of fishing

8.7 Under the EC Commission Common Fisheries Policy, agreed in 1983, only UK vessels are allowed to fish in a 0-6nm zone around the UK. In a 6-12nm zone around the UK specific countries are allowed to carry out fishing, according to

Table 8.1 Summary of fisheries legislation

Legislation	Comment
Sea Fisheries Act 1868	Registration of sea fishing boats.
Salmon Fisheries (Scotland) Act 1868	Regulation of salmon fishing in Scotland.
Sea Fisheries Act 1883	Enforces international agreements on policing fisheries in the North Sea.
Sea Fisheries (Scotland) Amendment Act 1885	Secretary of State may make byelaws for prohibiting or regulating trawling in defined areas.
Fisheries Act 1891	Enforcement of an agreement between Great Britain and Belgium.
North Sea Fisheries Act 1893	Enforces a convention on liquor traffic amongst fishermen.
Illegal Trawling (Scotland) Act 1934	Amends enforcement of law prohibiting beam and otter trawling in Scotland.
Salmon and Freshwater Fisheries (Protection) Act 1951	Prohibits poaching of salmon within 1 mile of LWM.
Sea Fish Industry Act 1962	Regulation of sea fish and shellfish by appointment of sea fishery officers.
Fishery Limits Act 1964	Extends limit of British fisheries to include Northern Ireland
Sea Fisheries (Regulation) Act 1966	Establishes sea fisheries committees (S1&2) with powers to make byelaws. Appointment by SFC of sea fisheries officers to enforce byelaws. Harbour authorities or NRA can be appointed as SFC where the area is under their jurisdiction. Applies to England and Wales only.
Sea Fisheries (Shellfish) Act 1967	Minister may make, by order, byelaws for establishment or regulation of shellfish fisheries. Holders of orders have exclusive rights of deposition, propagating, dredging, fishing for and taking shellfish.
Sea Fisheries (Conservation) Act 1967	Consolidates provisions for regulation of sea fisheries and authorises measures for increase or improvement of marine resources. Includes: – restrictions on commercial use of undersized fish (S1) – regulations of nets and gear (S3) – licensing of fishing boats (S4) – powers to restrict fishing by order of the Minister (S5) – powers to take measures to increase or improve resources (S10)
Sea Fisheries Act 1968	Regulation of sea fisheries operations. Details powers of sea fisheries officers.
Sea Fish Industry Act 1970	Consolidates provisions for the regulation and administration of the sea fisheries industry.
Salmon and Freshwater Fisheries Act 1975	Regulates obstructions to the passage of fish up rivers, including waters below HWM. Defines offences in blocking passage of fish.
Fishery Limits Act 1976	Extends limits to 200nm from baselines.
Fisheries Act 1981	Establishes the Sea Fish Industry Authority with duty to promote the efficiency of the industry in the UK. Minister may, by order, enforce EEC restrictions or other obligations.
British Fishing Boats Act 1983	Regulation of fishing boats
Inshore Fishing (Scotland) Act 1984	Provisions for regulation of inshore fishing. Secretary of State may make orders to regulate sea fishing in Scottish waters.

136

Table 8.1 (cont) ...

Legislation	Comment
Salmon Act 1986	Establishes Salmon Fishery Districts within coastal limits of a district and extending seaward for 3nm from MLWS and landward to include the whole catchment. Secretary of State has power to make regulations for various aspects including obstructions in rivers and estuaries to the passage of salmon. Establishes district salmon fishery boards for protection or improvement of fisheries, stocking or increase in salmon.
Water Act 1989	NRA has duty to maintain, improve and develop salmon, trout, freshwater and eel fisheries within 6nm from baselines.
Sea Fisheries (Wildlife Conservation) Act 1992	Requires Ministers and relevant bodies to have regard to the conservation of flora and fauna in discharging their functions under Sea Fisheries Acts.

species and area. In the remaining areas of the UK's 200nm fisheries limit EC countries have equal access, whereas non–EC countries are only allowed to fish by agreement.

8.8 Conservation of fish stocks in UK waters is achieved through the EC **Common Fisheries Policy** which controls operations in all waters under the jurisdiction of member states. Annual regulations agreed by the Council of Ministers, specify total allowable catches and national quotas which can be caught for fish species of major economic interest. EC Regulation No 3094/86, as most recently amended in June 1992, provides technical measures for conservation of fishery resources, including mesh sizes, minimum size limits and restrictions on certain types of fishing. Member states may also take unilateral steps to conserve fish stocks, such as the UK's measure to require the use of square mesh panels in some nets, helping young fish to escape and reproduce.

8.9 The sea fisheries industry is controlled through a wide variety of legislation, covering aspects such as conservation of fish stocks to the regulation of fishing boats (Table 8.1).

8.10 In England and Wales **Sea Fisheries Committees** (SFCs), have powers to make byelaws controlling fisheries, under **The Sea Fisheries Regulation Act 1966** (S.5). The 12 committees are established by MAFF and include members from local authorities and the NRA. Constituent local authorities are responsible for their funding and proceedings under local government legislation. The committees have jurisdiction to 3nm offshore, although Ministers have now agreed to extend this,

on application, to 6nm principally to assist shellfish conservation. Byelaws, which have to be confirmed by the Minister, may be made for:

– restricting or prohibiting the fishing or taking of all or any specified sea fish in specified areas or at specified times;

– restricting or prohibiting any specified method of fishing;

– regulation, protection and development of fisheries for shellfish.

8.11 Sea fisheries byelaws must not affect any byelaws made by the NRA, rights under Private Acts or Royal Charter or affect the powers of local authorities to discharge sewage. Where a sea fisheries district adjoins or overlaps an estuary the Minister may confer sea fisheries committee powers on the NRA or the harbour authority (S.18).

8.12 The shellfish industry is controlled through provisions in the **Sea Fisheries (Shellfish) Act 1967** (as amended by the **Sea Fisheries (Shellfish) Act 1973**), which empowers Ministers to make orders to establish, maintain or regulate shellfish fisheries.

8.13 Under the **Salmon Act 1986** salmon fishery districts can be established, extending seaward for 3nm from spring LWM. Salmon fishery boards have powers to protect or improve salmon fisheries. As part of its responsibilities to maintain, improve and develop fisheries the NRA has substantial duties and byelaw–making powers in

Table 8.2 Byelaws for control of near shore leisure boating

Activity	Control mechanism
Control of use of NRA's waterways (eg Rye Harbour) for: – regulating sailing, boating, bathing, fishing – registration of boats – sanitary appliances to prevent pollution	Byelaws made by NRA under Water Resources Act 1991 S.20, confirmed by relevant Minister[*].
Control of pollution in controlled waters prohibiting or regulating: – washing or cleaning – vessels with water closets	Byelaws made by NRA under Water Resources Act 1991 S.210, confirmed by Minister[*].
Sea defence schemes: – regulating the use of watercourses or banks to prevent damage to flood defences.	Byelaws made by NRA under Water Resources Act 1991 S.210, confirmed by Minister[*]. **Byelaws must not conflict with the operation of byelaws made by harbour, navigation or conservancy authority.**
Control of movement of ships in harbours	Byelaws made by harbour authorities under Harbours Act 1964 S.22, confirmed by appropriate Minister.
Control of recreational craft up to 1000m beyond LWM for the prevention of danger, obstruction or annoyance to bathers: – regulating speed – preventing dangerous navigation – requiring use of silencers	Byelaws made by local authorities under Public Health Act 1961 S.76, confirmed by the appropriate Secretary of State. **Must be consistent with byelaws made by harbour authorities.**
Control of public bathing by regulating: – permitted bathing areas – siting of bathing huts – the navigation of recreational craft to prevent dangers to bathers.	Byelaws made by local authorities under Public Health Act 1936 S.231, confirmed by appropriate Secretary of State. **Must be consistent with byelaws made by harbour authorities.**

[*] A notice of the byelaws must be made in the national press, and to affected persons and relevant authority officers.

respect of salmon and migratory trout to a distance of 6nm around the coast of England and Wales.

8.14 In those Regions where the NRA manages sea fisheries, the duties and powers are contained in the 1966 Act, the **Sea Fisheries (Conservation) Act 1967** (S.18), the **Salmon and Freshwater Fisheries Act 1975**, the **Salmon Act 1986** and the **Water Act 1989**.

8.15 In Scotland, there are no local committees, with control provided through **The Inshore Fishing (Scotland) Act, 1984**. The Act enables the Secretary of State for Scotland, after consultation with the fishing industry, to make orders regulating fishing in waters up to 6nm offshore. The current orders include all–year and seasonal restriction on the use of mobile fishing gear in areas which are very sensitive from a fisheries conservation perspective, restrictions on suction dredging for shellfish, seasonal restrictions on lobster and creel fishing in certain areas and limitations on the length of vessels fishing in the Firths of Clyde and Forth.

8.16 In Northern Ireland the fishing industry is regulated by the Departments of Agriculture, Environment and Economic Development, although there is no specific legislation governing the industry.

8.17 Since 1992 the **Sea Fisheries (Wildlife Conservation) Act 1992** requires Ministers and SFCs to endeavour to achieve a reasonable balance between environmental considerations (the conservation of marine flora and fauna) and the other factors which are to be taken into account for the purposes of sea fisheries measures, when exercising their powers under sea fisheries legislation (S.1). However, this new Act does not provide powers to control fisheries solely for environmental reasons.

The control of leisure sailing and near shore recreation

8.18 In recent years there has been a dramatic increase in the popularity of water sports in many areas around the coast. Problems arise not because the craft are unsafe but that sports such as boating, water skiing, boardsailing and jet–skiing may not be compatible with other leisure activities in bathing waters and can lead to disturbance of wildlife habitats (eg Davidson et al, 1991).

8.19 All leisure sailors, whether they are in ocean–going yachts or on jet–skis are bound by the same international agreements as commercial craft. Freedom of navigation and unimpeded peaceful passage are closely guarded rights which are central to the enjoyment of leisure boating. However, these rights can be regulated or restricted through the use of byelaws either to regulate movement in harbours (see Chapter 6), for the safety of bathers or to control pollution in coastal waters (Table 8.2).

8.20 Under the **Public Health Act 1961** (S.76) and the **Local Government (Miscellaneous Provisions) Act 1976** (S.17), local authorities may make byelaws covering the use of the sea up to 1km offshore to:

- regulate the speed of leisure craft (ie all recreational craft from sailing boats to windsurfers and jet–skis);

- regulate the use of leisure craft to prevent danger to other sea users;

- require the use of effective silencers.

8.21 Under the **Public Health Act 1936** (S.231) local authorities may make byelaws to regulate the areas in which bathing is permitted and control the passage of leisure craft within these areas. However, byelaws made under both Acts must be consistent with byelaws made by harbour authorities. Similar powers are provided under the **Civic Government (Scotland) Act 1982**.

8.22 The powers provided in the 1936 and 1961 Acts are widely considered to be inadequate with particular problems arising from the difficulty and cost of enforcement, and problems in defining separate zones for sail or power craft. However, use of the powers has led to the development of zoning policies to prevent accidents on some

stretches of beach at, for example, Hayling Island, Studland Bay and Colwyn Bay.

8.23 The importance of the powers for water safety is clear, providing a valuable tool for beach management. In this context, the **Royal Life Saving Society** and the **Royal Society for the Prevention of Accidents** are currently preparing policy guidelines which could lead to accepted standards of practice for beach management. This document, "Safety on British Beaches – Guidance for Operators" is being produced with the support of the Home Office.

The effectiveness of the approaches to the regulation of sea use

8.24 To a degree it is inappropriate to judge the effectiveness of the mechanisms for regulating sea use by the same criteria as used for the control of development on land or the sea bed. The consideration of the dynamic nature of the coastal zone is largely focused on the devastating nature of storm events (see, for example, Lamb, 1991), rather than the impact of the activities on coastal processes. However, it has been recognised that trawling can cause resuspension of sediment and lead to deposition of fine material in areas of low tidal currents (ICES, 1991).

8.25 There are no requirements for environmental assessment of sea use. The activities can, however, affect marine and coastal ecosystems, through:

- disturbance by shipping, leisure craft, water sports and bathing (see Clare, 1991);

- accidental or unlawful discharge of harmful pollutants (see Chapter 4);

- direct destruction of sea bed organisms by trawling (ICES, 1991). Indeed, has been estimated that virtually every part of the North Sea is trawled 3 times a year, affecting not only the sea bed communities but also the fish stocks (Gubbay, 1992).

8.26 It would be wrong to imply that sea users did not take other interests into account. The observation of international agreements on the disposal of garbage and byelaws to control pollution of coastal waters (see Chapter 4), the extensive legislative provisions for conservation of fish stocks, byelaws to control movement in harbours and to protect the safety of bathers all provide important mechanisms for ensuring other interests are appreciated (Tables 8.1 and 8.2).

8.27 Marine conservation interests can also be taken into account in a variety of ways including:

- the discouragement of access into sensitive areas (Areas to be Avoided), the prohibition of garbage disposal in Special Areas (see Chapter 4), limitations on access around designated historic wrecks and, in some circumstances, the restriction of access by pleasure boats in Marine Nature Reserves (see Chapter 5);

- protection of fish stocks through legislation (Table 8.1), sea fisheries committee and NRA byelaws and EC fisheries regulations;

- the various voluntary codes prepared by the RYA to ensure leisure boaters appreciate their environmental responsibilities. These include the "Clean Code" prepared in 1990 to provide information on how to deal with litter and other effluents and the "Yachtsman's Guide for Environmental Care" prepared in 1987. In addition around 80,000 individuals undertake the RYA Seamanship courses each year which emphasise the need for environmental awareness.

8.28 It must be emphasised that the byelaw-making provisions in the Public Health Acts provide an important mechanism for extending local authority control over sea use close to the shore. If used in conjunction with other local authority powers, could enable coordinated decision making on various aspects of leisure sailing from provision of landward access to moorings (under planning legislation) to avoidance of bathing areas. However, enforcement of byelaws remains the most pressing problem restricting local authority use of their powers.

References: Chapter 8

Clare, N. (ed), 1991, Marine conservation handbook. Nature Conservancy Council/English Nature.
Davidson, N.C., d'A Laffoley, D., Doody, J.P., Way, L.S., Gordon, J., Drake, C.M., Pienkowski, M.W., Mitchell, R. and Duff, K.L., 1991 Nature conservation and estuaries in Great Britain. Nature Conservancy Council.
Department of the Environment, 1991, Coastal policy. Memorandum by DoE and other Government Departments. Evidence to the House of Commons Select Committee on the Environment.
Gubbay, S., 1992, Marine nature conservation in the coastal zone. In M.G.Barrett (ed) Coastal zone planning and management, Thomas Telford, 83–90.
International Council for the Exploration of the Sea, 1991, Cooperative research report on effects of marine aggregate extraction on fisheries. Report of the ICES Working Group.
Lamb, H.H., 1991, Historic storms of the North Sea, British Isles and Northwest Europe. Cambridge University Press.

9 Issues in Coastal Planning and Management

Coastal management: Geographical perspectives

9.1 A key theme throughout the Report has been the special nature of the coast:

- as a **physical heritage** where the land and sea meet in unique coastal landscapes and where the built environment reflects our maritime history;

- where **human activity** is influenced by the juxtaposition of land and water; and

- where the **physical processes** of erosion, deposition and flooding have an important influence on the morphology and use of the land and the sea bed.

9.2 In attempting to define the coastal zone it is readily apparent that there can be no single definition for many stretches of coast. One of the key problems is the need to reconcile the contrasting perspectives of those involved with the **management of coastal resources** (eg sea fisheries, waste disposal, marine aggregates) and **management of coastal hazards** (eg erosion and flooding). The approach adopted by this study (Figure 1.1) has recognised the importance of both the human and physical geographical systems (the interactive and dynamic zones, respectively) and the narrow hazard zone where they interact.

9.3 Particular coastal environments present a unique combination of **resources and constraints** to and **opportunities** for development or use, which need to be taken into account in the management of a coastline. The nature and significance of these factors will depend on a combination of (Figure 9.1):

- **the physical character**; landforms, materials and processes;

- **the natural heritage**; landscapes, habitats and living resources;

- **the coastal use**; past and present development, historic interest and technological hazards.

9.4 The development and use of the coastal zone is influenced by these three characteristics which are interlinked to produce the unique nature of a stretch of coast. It is clear, therefore, that planning and management considerations will not be uniform around the coast, but reflect a combination of **local** (eg site conditions), **regional** (eg demand for employment opportunities; sediment transport), **national** (eg demand for aggregates for the construction industry) and **international** (eg pollution of the seas around the UK) factors.

9.5 The coastal zone presents unique management challenges for coastal managers. These include special problems related to the contrasting nature of marine and landward activity in the interactive zone and issues related to the operation of coastal processes in the dynamic zone:

(i) **interactive zone;**

- the traditional rights of freedom of navigation and fishing in the sea are in marked contrast to ownership of land resources;

- at sea many different uses may occur in the same area (multiple use), often leading to conflict between users;

- the environmental effects of many sea uses are not immediately apparent. For example, the detection of harmful pollutants from waste materials requires sophisticated analytical

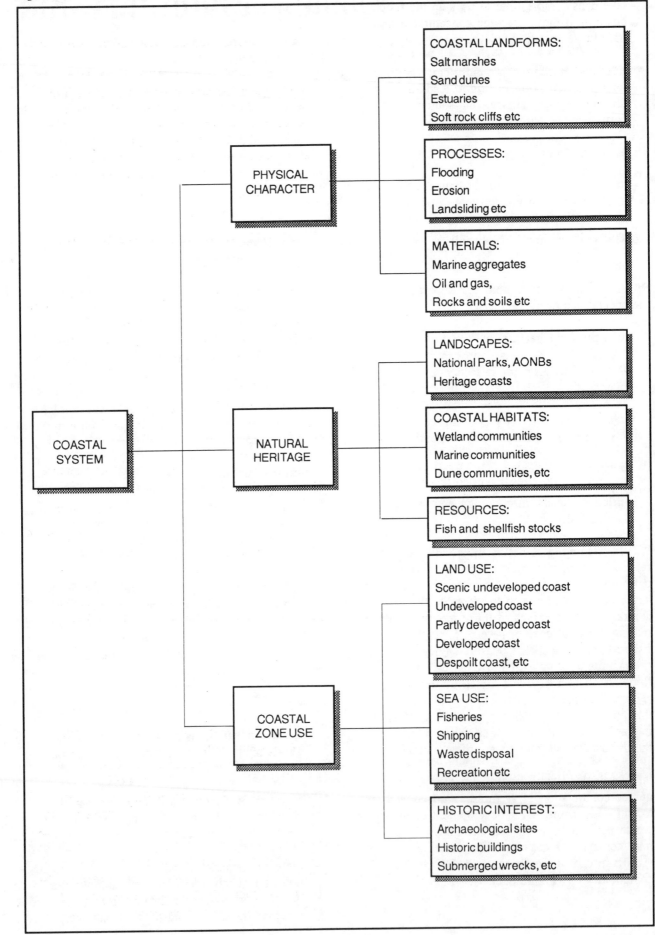

techniques. In addition, the contaminants may take considerable time to pass up the food chain until they become concentrated and harmful to marine life;

- tides and currents can rapidly carry pollutants far from their point of origin, leading to difficulties in identifying the source of particular contamination problems.

(ii) **dynamic zone:**

- there is an inherent conflict between the need to protect against erosion and flooding and the need to allow coastal landforms to adjust to natural processes. Coastal defences, for example, may be necessary to protect vulnerable developments or heritage sites, but may also lead to a disruption of the supply of sediment to nearby tourist beaches;

- development on the coast may lead to significant changes elsewhere within a coastal system. These changes can affect both landforms which provide natural coastal defences and the habitats which they support;

- the cumulative effects of development on a coastal system may take many years to become apparent. Indeed, past responses to the threat of erosion and flooding have led to many long term problems facing coastal managers.

9.6 In the past the coastal zone has tended to be seen as the boundary between the land and the sea, rather than an integrated unit. This is reflected by different legislative and administrative provisions for controlling activity on land, sea bed and at sea. Separate mechanisms have also evolved to manage the impact of man on the physical environment and to minimise the risks associated with coastal development (conservation, pollution control and coastal defence).

9.7 The foregoing Chapters 3 to 8 have provided a brief outline of the current legislative and administrative frameworks for controlling activity in the coastal zone. These Chapters have also addressed the effectiveness of the provisions in terms of the extent to which the administrative systems:

- consider coastal dynamics;

- take the environmental effects of a project into account;

- take into account the interests of other groups; and

- enable coordinated decision making across the coastal zone.

9.8 The main issues of concern within each of the areas of interest have been described in the relevant Chapters and are summarised in Table 9.1. The purpose of this Chapter is to highlight the key issues relevant to the wider context of coastal management within which the planning system operates.

The planning system as an instrument for coastal management

9.9 It must be stressed that there are limits to what can be achieved, in the coastal zone, under the planning system. It is designed to regulate the development and use of land in the public interest, with the limit of local planning authority jurisdiction normally around low water mark (see Chapter 6). In addition, planning legislation should not normally be used to secure objectives achievable under other legislation. However, the planning system, through development plans and control of development, is an important instrument in determining the way the coast is developed and conserved.

9.10 Many of the land use issues which need to be addressed on the coast are not unique to the coast. However, the dynamic nature of the coastal environment and the special character of coastal resources and land use heightens the significance of some issues and requires specific policies to be formulated.

Planning policies for the coast

9.11 The coastal environment contains important **landscapes and habitats** which should be protected and preserved. These assets, however, cannot be separated from the **physical characteristics** of the coast which, to a large extent, have shaped them. The **development and use** of the coast is also constrained by the physical environment (eg hazards, steep slopes etc.,) and the need to protect conservation interests. Thus these factors (the physical character, natural heritage and coastal use; Figure 9.1) should be the focus of specific land use policies prepared to protect the

Table 9.1 Key issues of concern in the coastal zone

Coastal Defence (Chapter 3)

Lack of appreciation of powers available to coast protection authorities for controlling removal of material from the sea bed (para 3.14).

Legacy of defence works which have disrupted sediment transport or promoted accelerated erosion (paras 3.32–3.36).

Establishment of coastal defence groups which reflect pattern of sediment movement rather than administrative boundaries (para 3.44).

Lack of reliable and useful data on coastal processes on which policy decisions can be made (para 3.51).

Lack of coordination between coastal defence strategy and land use planning (para 3.54).

No requirement for EA with coast protection schemes (para 3.57)

Limited consideration of leisure sailing interests in sea defence schemes (para 3.65).

Problems of reconciling coast protection and conservation interests (paras 3.71–3.75).

Absence of coordinated decision making for schemes that involve works immediately above and below LWM (para 3.78).

Separation of coast protection and sea defence responsibility in England and Wales (para 3.80).

Pollution Control (Chapter 4)

Concerns over garbage disposal regulations at sea outside special areas (para 4.10).

Limited resources allocated to deal with accidental spillages at sea (para 4.37).

Concerns that bathing water improvements apply to only a limited part of the coastline (para 4.44).

Lack of agreement over the effects of contaminants on marine life, reflecting inadequate scientific information (para 4.49).

Concern from port authorities over the cost of providing garbage reception facilities (para 4.50).

Potential confusion between authorities and bodies with a responsibility for pollution control and conservation, as highlighted by the Kimya incident in Caernarfon Bay (para 4.56).

Concerns over the achievement of bathing water quality standards (para 4.62).

Conservation (Chapter 5)

The need for additional protection for areas of landscape conservation value in Scotland (para 5.9).

The omission of important nature conservation sites from the SSSI network (para 5.8).

The lack of protection for wetland sites which meet Ramsar criteria, but lie outside the SSSI network (para 5.33).

The limited number of important wrecks protected by the 1973 Act (para 5.47).

The lack of resources for identifying new archaeological sites in coastal waters (para 5.49).

Lack of reliable information about recent habitat loss (para 5.62).

The potential effects of sea level rise on intertidal habits and the need to consider options for restoring habitats (paras 5.63–5.65).

The need to recognise the value of submerged archaeological sites as indicators of long term coastal changes (para 5.66).

The effect of the heritage coast definition on concentrating "unsuitable" development in estuaries (para 5.67).

The lack of formal consultation arrangements for SSSI designation and concerns that national conservation interests can take precedence over the local economy (para 5.72).

The potential effects of common law rights and traditional activities, permitted development and development authorised by private Acts on SSSIs (para 5.73).

The lack of progress in designating Marine Nature Reserves (para 5.79).

Concerns over the preservation of archaeological sites below LWM (paras 5.84–5.85).

The problems involved in achieving conservation objectives for habitats covering the intertidal range because of the limit of local authority jurisdiction (para 5.88).

The Planning System (Chapter 6)

The reluctance of some local planning authorities to take landslide and flood risk into account when preparing development plans and determining planning applications (paras 6.40–6.56).

The absence of specific planning policy advice concerning coastal risks in Scotland (para 6.57).

Concerns that a number of activities that do not require express planning permission may increase the risk to adjacent properties from natural hazards (para 6.58 and 6.61).

Table 9.1 (cont) ....

The Planning System (cont ...)

The lack of coordination between land use planning and coastal defence strategy (paras 6.67–6.70).

The absence of a mechanism to provide compensation to property owners affected by stricter development control in areas prone to landsliding, erosion or flooding (para 6.73).

Lack of consideration of NRA water quality objectives in development plan policies (para 6.74).

Inconsistent or inadequate treatment of conservation issues in development plans (paras 6.78–6.80).

Calls to improve the effectiveness of the heritage coast definition (para 6.81).

Lack of consideration of leisure sailing interests in development plans (paras 6.84–6.85).

Concerns over lack of local planning authority powers to control activities below LWM, especially within estuaries (paras 6.98–6.102).

Ports and Harbours (Chapter 6)

Concerns over the exercise of certain permitted development rights within operational land (paras 6.88–6.89).

Concerns over the effects of maintenance dredging on marine conservation interests (para 6.90).

Concerns over harbour authority's role in facilitating new marina developments (paras 6.91–6.93).

Marine Aggregate Extraction (Chapter 7)

The lengthy periods required for the Government View Procedure and the absence of a right to appeal over rejected applications (para 7.15).

Concerns about the potential impact of dredging on coast erosion and marine conservation interests, and the lack of reliable information on the mobility of sea bed materials (paras 7.30–7.31).

Concerns over the limited local involvement in decision making procedures and the absence of local planning authority jurisdiction below LWM (paras 7.40 and 7.59).

Marine Fish Farming (Chapter 7)

The perceived conflict of interest arising out of CEC's role as the "competent authority" for environmental assessment and their financial responsibilities in managing the Crown Estate (paras 7.36–7.38).

The limited consideration of marine conservation interests in the Very Sensitive Area definition (para 7.43).

Concerns over the onshore impacts of the rapid expansion of the marine fish farming industry and the absence of local planning authority jurisdiction below LWM (para 7.45).

Sea Use (Chapter 8)

Problems of enforcement of byelaws to control recreational craft and water sports (para 8.22).

Concerns about the effects of sea uses on marine conservation interests, resulting from disturbance, discharge of pollutants and trawling (para 8.25).

coastal environment addressing, as appropriate, the following topics:

(i) **physical character**
  – the risks to development posed by flooding, erosion and unstable land;
  – conservation of important geological sites and landforms;
  – the importance of erosion, deposition and flooding to the maintenance of coastal habitats and landforms.

(ii) **natural heritage**
  – conservation of habitats;
  – landscape conservation;
  – the cumulative effects of development;

(iii) **land use**
  – tourism and recreation;
  – leisure sailing;
  – major developments;
  – archaeological or historic sites;
  – historic buildings;
  – minerals;
  – energy;
  – pollution control;
  – housing;
  – traffic.

9.12 The recently published PPG 20 Coastal Planning (DoE, 1992) provides guidance to local authorities on planning policy for coastal areas of England and Wales, covering all of the topics identified above. It sets out the general context for policy and identifies a range of key policy issues:

– conservation of the natural environment;

– development, particularly that which requires a coastal location;

– risks, including flooding, erosion and land instability; and

– improving the environment, particularly of urbanised or despoiled coastlines.

9.13 In Scotland, specific coastal planning policy guidance is restricted to addressing the pressures of North Sea oil and gas developments. Advice is contained within the **Coastal Planning Guidelines** (SDD, 1974) and the **National Planning Guidelines** (SDD, 1981) which identify:

– **preferred development zones**; areas within which sites for appropriate oil and gas related developments should be encouraged;

– **preferred conservation zones**; areas of particular national importance, where oil and gas related developments would generally be inappropriate.

The Effectiveness of Current Land Use Policies

9.14 The planning system is entirely capable of taking into account the human, natural heritage and physical elements of the coastal environment. However, there is a difference between what **can be achieved** within the present framework and what **is achieved** by many local planning authorities.

9.15 Since 1947, the planning system has been effective in arresting the spread of piecemeal development along the **scenic undeveloped coast**. For example, in England and Wales, land use policies within development plans have played an important role in the success of designated National Parks and AONBs and those stretches of coastline defined as heritage coasts, following advice given in:

– DoE Circular 12/72 (WO 36/72) Planning of the Undeveloped Coast (now cancelled by PPG 20);

9.16 In Scotland, protection of National Scenic Areas has been achieved by means of development control restrictions outlined in:

– SDD Circular 51/77 Development Control in National Scenic Areas (as amended by Circular 9/87);

9.17 Local planning authorities have to balance conservation interests with the need to make adequate provision for development and economic growth. Nature conservation designations such as National Nature Reserves, Local Nature Reserves and SSSIs provide protection for areas of the **undeveloped** coastline as well as some developed stretches. Many estuaries lie within the **developed** coast, but have been recognised to be of international conservation importance, reflected by their designation as Ramsar and SPA sites.

9.18 The planning system is an important instrument in achieving nature conservation objectives above LWM, through the inclusion of land use policies within development plans that take into account the following guidance (see also Table 6.2 for advice in Scotland):

- DoE Circular 32/81 (WO 50/81) Wildlife and Countryside Act 1981 (to be cancelled by the forthcoming PPG Nature Conservation);

- DoE Circular 27/87 (WO 52/87) Nature Conservation (to be cancelled by the forthcoming PPG Nature Conservation);

- DoE Circular 1/92 (WO 1/92) Planning Controls over SSSIs (to be cancelled by the forthcoming PPG Nature Conservation);

- PPG 7 The Countryside and Rural Economy.

9.19 Concern has been expressed, however, over the inconsistent or inadequate treatment of many nature conservation objectives within development plans (Bain et al, 1990; see Chapter 6).

9.20 The planning system has also had a significant role in protecting sites of archaeological interest (above LWM). The importance of protecting sites of national value, in England and Wales, has recently been stressed in:

- PPG 16 Archaeology and Planning.

9.21 Advice on policies for historic buildings and conservation areas is contained in:

- DoE Circular 8/87 (WO 61/87) Historic Buildings and Conservation Areas – Policy and Procedures.

9.22 The planning system has been less effective in addressing issues related to the **physical character** of the coast (see Chapter 6). Indeed, the prevailing view, in the past, has been that hazards such as erosion, landsliding and flooding are a matter for the developer and not a planning issue. As a result development has proceeded which has subsequently required protection, such as at Durlston Bay, Dorset. In recent years, however, the Government has emphasised the need for these problems to be taken into account in development plans in England and Wales, through:

- PPG 14 Development on Unstable Land;

- PPG 20 Coastal Planning;

- DoE Circular 30/92 (MAFF FD 1/92; WO 68/92) Development and Flood Risk;

9.23 Within the context of this advice, the planning system has an important role in minimising risks, especially in light of the possible

effects of sea-level rise, through refusing permission to develop in vulnerable locations or making permission conditional on special building measures. To date, however, no advice specifically addressed at the management of natural hazards has been issued in Scotland.

Coastal management

Introduction

9.24 The Government White Paper "This Common Inheritance" (HMSO 1990) identifies three critical issues for the environment:

- the need to resolve the conflicts between pressures for development and mobility, and the conservation of what is best in the environment;

- the need to maintain economic growth without making excessive demands on natural resources;

- the need to combat the dangers of pollution without jeopardising economic growth.

9.25 The dynamic physical nature of the coastal zone, together with the ever increasing problems of balancing conflicting, and occasionally incompatible, demands on the limited resources dictate that the regulation of separate activities in isolation is unlikely to meet these objectives. The linkages between activities (Figure 9.2) and their close relationship with the physical environment highlight the need for a **coordinated approach to decision making**, involving all appropriate interests and activities.

9.26 It is important to emphasise that the present coastal management frameworks have evolved over different time scales and for a variety of different reasons. As a result they do not all address the problems of linkages between activities or consider environmental implications in the same ways or to the same degree.

9.27 Powers generally relate to a requirement to perform specific duties, such as maintaining water quality (eg the NRA, under the Water Resources Act 1991 or the River Purification Authorities under the Control of Pollution Act 1974), protecting sites of conservation value (eg English Nature and its counterparts in Scotland and Wales, under the Wildlife and Countryside Act 1981),

147

Figure 9.2 Examples of the common areas of interest between different coastal zone activities

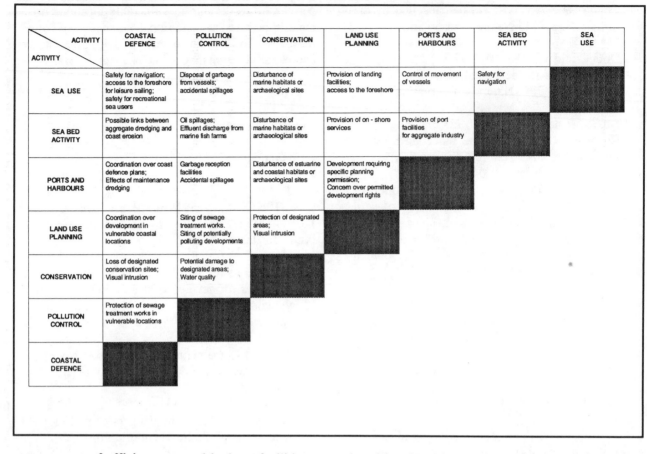

management of efficient port and harbour facilities (harbour authorities, under the Harbours Act 1964) and protection against the effects of erosion (coast protection authorities, under the Coast Protection Act 1949).

9.28 Most of the current coastal zone responsibilities reflect past economic climates (eg harbour authorities, with the importance of many traditional ports having declined in recent years), historic ownership patterns (eg CEC), the result of urgent needs for action to prevent loss of life and investment (eg the powers for flood defence), have been acquired in response to specific EC directives (eg monitoring bathing water quality by the NRA or RPAs) or simply developed because of a pressing need for regulation of a rapidly expanding industry (eg CEC's role in the control of marine fish farming in Scotland).

9.29 The complexity of arrangements in the UK is further heightened by the different legislative provisions, policy context and responsible authorities that form the framework for coastal management in each of the four constituent countries; England, Scotland, Wales and Northern Ireland. Just as there can be unique issues along particular coastlines, there can be contrasting responses in the four separate countries. For the sake of brevity this Report has been biased towards the management framework in England and Wales, although significant differences have been highlighted where appropriate. It is clear, however, that there can be no single statement on the effectiveness of coastal management in the UK; each country has adopted its own responses to the issues that are currently relevant along their coastlines.

The Framework

9.30 The framework for coastal management can be viewed as a complex system; change in one area (eg increased demand, intensification of use or change in management practice) will often lead to change and tension elsewhere. The effect of the heritage coast definition is an example, diverting development towards less valued landscapes and estuaries where it may cause conflict with other conservation interests.

9.31 The key elements of the various regulatory systems in England and Wales are summarised in Table 9.2, which highlights that there is no consistent approach. Management takes place at a variety of scales from local to national, often not in

148

Table 9.2 Summary of the main features of the various regulatory systems relevant to coastal management in England & Wales

REGULATORY SYSTEM	LEGISLATION	AUTHORITY	SCALE OF DECISION-MAKING	PREPARATION OF STRATEGIC PLANS	CONSULTATION	ENVIRONMENTAL DUTIES	PUBLIC PARTICIPATION
Coast Protection	Coast Protection Act 1949 (Also see Table 3.2)	Maritime district councils as promoters or regulators of schemes.	Local, but increasingly within context of National (MAFF/WO) and Regional (Coastal Defence Group) considerations, (Table 3.1).	Trend towards regional scale plans, through Coast Defence Groups, (Table 3.6).	Wide ranging consultation required under 1949 Act, (Table 3.8)..	None.	Proposals advertised, anybody may object. If objections are not withdrawn a local inquiry or hearing can be held.
Sea Defence	Water Resources Act 1991 Land Drainage Act 1991 (Also see Table 3.2)	NRA as promoters or regulators of schemes	Regional, but increasingly in context of Regional and National Coastal Defence Strategies, (Table 3.1).	Trend towards regional scale shoreline management plans.	Limited requirements to consult. Guidelines published by MAFF/DOE/WO which recommend consultation with a wide range of conservancy agencies and groups.	- to further conservation of natural heritage. - to have regard for sites of archaeological interest. - to take into account effect of proposals on conservation interests.	None.
Waste Disposal at Sea	Food and Environment Protection Act 1985 Part II	MAFF	National.	No.	No specific consultation requirements, (Table 4.1).	- to protect the marine environment and its living resources.	None.
Discharge of Prescribed Processes	Environmental Protection Act 1990	HMIP	National.	No.	Limited consultation, including NRA and MAFF, (Table 4.1).	None.	Local inquiry or hearing may be held in relation to discharge application.
Discharge to Water	Water Resources Act 1991	NRA	Regional.	No.	Must consult EN/CCW before carrying out or authorising works that may affect an SSSI, (Table 4.1).	- to further conservation of natural heritage. - to have regard for sites of archaeological interest. - to take into account effect of proposals on conservation interests.	NRA required to give notice of discharge consents in press. Objections can be made and may lead to a local inquiry.
Development on Land	Town and Country Planning Act 1990 Planning and Compensation Act 1991	Local planning authority	Local, but within context of national and regional policy guidance, (Tables 6.1 and 6.2).	Preparation of development plans. All planning decisions made in accordance with policies in development plans, unless material considerations indicate otherwise.	Wide ranging consultation required when preparing development plans and determining planning applications, (Tables 6.6 and 6.7).	No formal duties.	Public consulted in development plan preparation Objections may lead to an Examination in Public or local inquiry.

Table 9.2 (cont...)

REGULATORY SYSTEM	LEGISLATION	AUTHORITY	SCALE OF DECISION-MAKING	PREPARATION OF STRATEGIC PLANS	CONSULTATION	ENVIRONMENTAL DUTIES	PUBLIC PARTICIPATION
Landscape Conservation - National Parks - AONBs	National Parks and Access to the Countryside Act 1949.	Secretary of State, proposed by Countryside Commission and CCW.	National	Management plans prepared by countryside body and local authority.	Local authority, (Table 5.4).	Defined by conservation legislation.	Public informed by notice in national and local press. Local inquiry or hearing may be held to resolve objections.
Landscape Conservation - heritage coast	None	Defined by Countryside Commission and CCW, together with local authorities.	Local and National.	Management plans prepared by countryside body and local authority, (Table 5.5).	Landowners and other bodies concerned, (Table 5.4).	Defined by conservation legislation.	Public invited to comment.
Wildlife Conservation - National Nature Reserves	National Parks and Access to the Countryside Act 1949.	Secretary of State, proposed by conservancy council.	National.	Management plans.	No formal requirements. Agreement with owner, leasee or occupier, (Table 5.4).	Defined by conservation legislation.	Notice published in press. Local inquiry or hearing may be held to resolve objections.
Wildlife Conservation - SSSIs	Wildlife and Countryside Act 1981.	Secretary of State, proposed by conservancy council.	National.	Nature Conservation and Geological Conservation Reviews.	Owners and occupiers (Table 5.4).	Defined by conservation legislation.	None.
Wildlife Conservation - Marine Nature Reserves	Wildlife and Countryside Act 1981.	Secretary of State, proposed by conservancy council.	National.	Management plans.	Secretary of State shall consult with any appropriate group. Extensive informal consultation by conservancy council.	Defined by conservation legislation.	Notice given to all interested parties. Local inquiry or hearing may be held to resolve objections to designation or byelaws.
Archaeology - scheduled monuments and archaeological areas	Ancient Monuments and Archaeological Areas Act 1979.	Secretary of State, local authority.	National and Local.	None.	Consultation with local authorities, (Table 5.4).	Defined by conservation legislation.	Notice in national and local press. Local inquiry or hearing may be held.
Archaeology - wrecks	Protection of Wrecks Act 1973.	Secretary of State, DNH.	National.	None.	Any appropriate bodies, (Table 5.4).	None.	None.

Table 9.2 (cont ...)

REGULATORY SYSTEM	LEGISLATION	AUTHORITY	SCALE OF DECISION-MAKING	PREPARATION OF STRATEGIC PLANS	CONSULTATION	ENVIRONMENTAL DUTIES	PUBLIC PARTICIPATION
Development in Harbours: Harbour orders (Also see Table 6.3).	Harbours Act 1964.	DTp.	National.	No.	No specific consultation requirements.	Harbour authorities must have regard to: - conservation of the natural heritage. - preserving freedom of access to archaeological or historic sites. - the effect of proposals on	Local inquiry or hearing may be held to resolve objections to applications for harbour orders.
Land drainage consents.	Water Resources Act 1991.	NRA control through byelaws.	Regional.	No; although may operate within context of shoreline management plans.	No specific requirements.	NRA has statutory environmental duties (see Sea Defence, above).	Byelaws advertised with notices served to affected parties. Local inquiries may be held to resolve objections.
Marine Aggregate Extraction	None.	Government: DoE coordinates Government View Procedure.	National.	No.	Wide ranging consultation carried out. (See Table 7.1)	None.	Applications advertised in press.
Marine Fish Farming	None.	CEC.	National.	No; but Scottish Office (199 guidance does identify locational and operational constraints.	CEC invite comments from a wide range of bodies. (See Table 7.1)	Crown Estate Commissioners must maintain and enhance the value of the estate, with due regard to requirements of good management.	Applications advertised in press.
Oil and Gas	None.	DTi.	National.	No.	Wide ranging consultation carried out. (See Table 7.1)	None.	None.
Shipping	Various Merchant Shipping Act.	DTp.	National.	No.	No specific requirements.	None.	None.

151

Table 9.2 (cont...)

REGULATORY SYSTEM	LEGISLATION	AUTHORITY	SCALE OF DECISION-MAKING	PREPARATION OF STRATEGIC PLANS	CONSULTATION	ENVIRONMENTAL DUTIES	PUBLIC PARTICIPATION
Sea Fishing	Various Fisheries Acts. (See Table 8.1).	MAFF Sea Fisheries Committees may make byelaws.	National and Regional.	No.	No specific requirements.	None.	Local inquiries or hearing can be held to resolve objections to sea fisheries byelaws. Byelaws must not affect rights under Private Acts or Royal Charter.
Near Shore Recreation	Public Health Act 1936, 1961 Local Government (Miscellaneous Provisions) Act 1976.	Local Authority may make byelaws.	Local.	No.	No specific requirements.	None.	Byelaws must be consistent with byelaws made by harbour authorities. Secretary of State may hold a local inquiry to resolve objections to byelaws.

the context of strategic plans or clearly defined national strategies and with varying degrees of public participation or access to the decision making process.

9.32 In general, the framework comprises three key components:

- **legislation and regulations** which define responsibilities and provide powers;

- **policy advice** which sets the management context;

- **linkages** between authorities, managers and users through which decision makers can take into account the views of other interests.

9.33 In the UK, with separate legislation and policy for many of the different types of coastal activity, the linkages provide the means for:

- anticipating problems before they arise;

- coordinating management decisions to ensure that uses do not interfere with other interests;

- ensuring that coastal management reflects local needs as well as national policy;

- resolving conflicts when they arise.

9.34 The formal mechanisms by which decision makers take into account the interests of other coastal users have been described in the preceding Chapters 3–8. These links are summarised in Figures 9.3 and 9.4. However, it is important to stress that both Figures show only **points of contact** between different interest groups. They are not necessarily the optimum links and, in many cases, their effectiveness has been questioned, as between marine conservation and navigation and sea fishing interests (see Chapter 5).

Dominant Issues

9.35 The main concerns within each of the areas of interest have been described in the relevant Chapters and summarised in Table 9.1. Individual issues can, of course, be addressed in a variety of ways, including new legislation or regulations and policy guidance. Indeed, this is a common characteristic of coastal management in the UK where the frequent amendments make it difficult to determine exactly what the current position is. However, it is important to view these concerns in

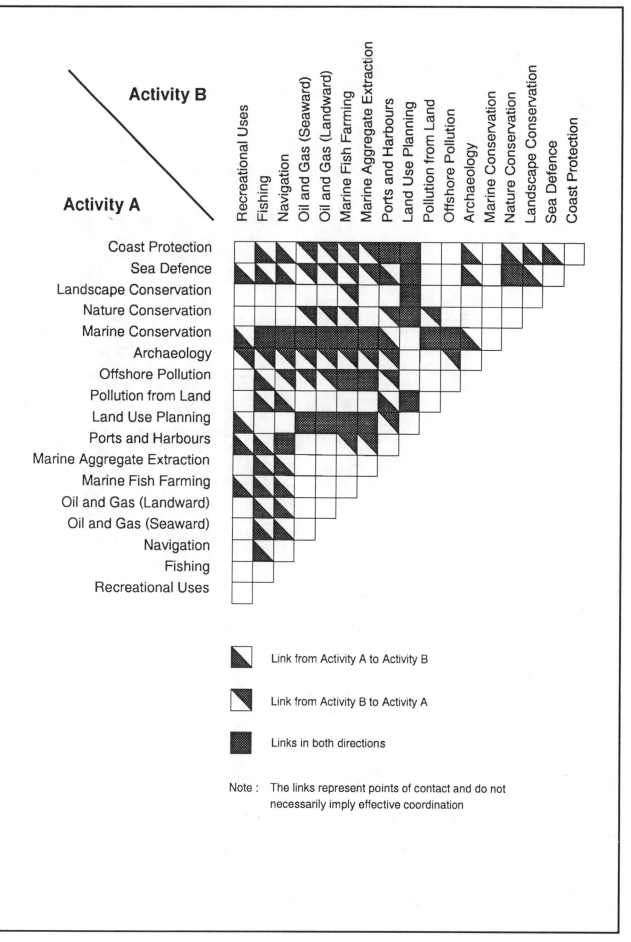

Figure 9.4 Summary of the links between different interest groups in the coastal zone, in England

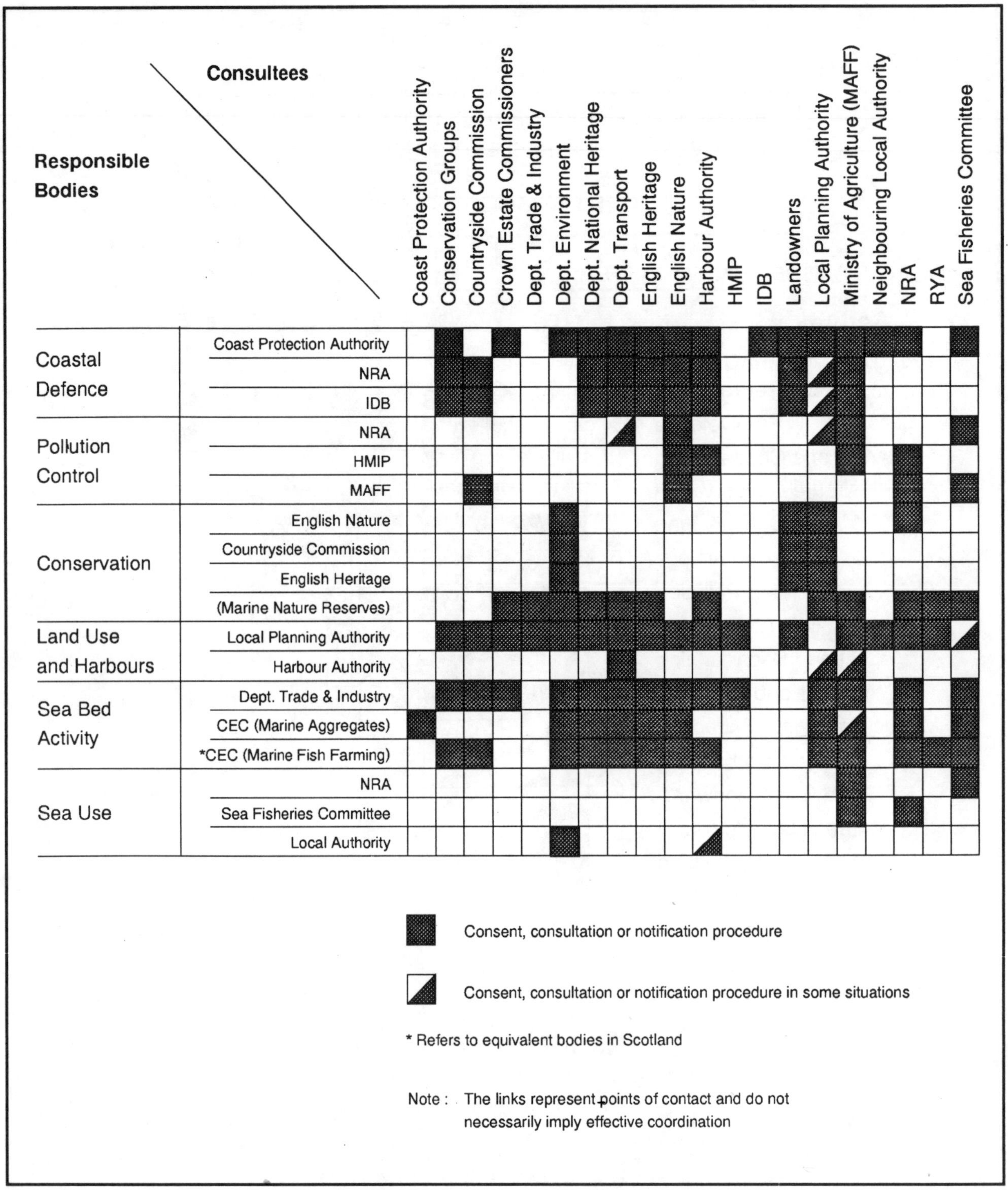

Consultees (columns):

1. Coast Protection Authority
2. Conservation Groups
3. Countryside Commission
4. Crown Estate Commissioners
5. Dept. Trade & Industry
6. Dept. Environment
7. Dept. National Heritage
8. Dept. Transport
9. English Heritage
10. English Nature
11. Harbour Authority
12. HMIP
13. IDB
14. Landowners
15. Local Planning Authority
16. Ministry of Agriculture (MAFF)
17. Neighbouring Local Authority
18. NRA
19. RYA
20. Sea Fisheries Committee

Responsible Bodies (rows), grouped:

Responsible Body	Row
Coastal Defence	Coast Protection Authority
Coastal Defence	NRA
Coastal Defence	IDB
Pollution Control	NRA
Pollution Control	HMIP
Pollution Control	MAFF
Conservation	English Nature
Conservation	Countryside Commission
Conservation	English Heritage
Conservation	(Marine Nature Reserves)
Land Use and Harbours	Local Planning Authority
Land Use and Harbours	Harbour Authority
Sea Bed Activity	Dept. Trade & Industry
Sea Bed Activity	CEC (Marine Aggregates)
Sea Bed Activity	*CEC (Marine Fish Farming)
Sea Use	NRA
Sea Use	Sea Fisheries Committee
Sea Use	Local Authority

Legend:

■ Consent, consultation or notification procedure

◣ Consent, consultation or notification procedure in some situations

* Refers to equivalent bodies in Scotland

Note : The links represent points of contact and do not necessarily imply effective coordination

---

a broader context which examines how decision making in one administrative system can lead to conflict with other interests. These interlinkages can be analysed in terms of the dominant issues in coastal management:

– the effects of protecting vulnerable communities from coastal hazards (Figure 9.5);

– the effects of reconciling competing coastal activities or land uses (Figure 9.6).

Hazard management: Protection of vulnerable communities

9.36 Coastal defence works have been very successful in protecting communities, industrial

Figure 9.5 Coastal hazard management: a summary of issues and responses

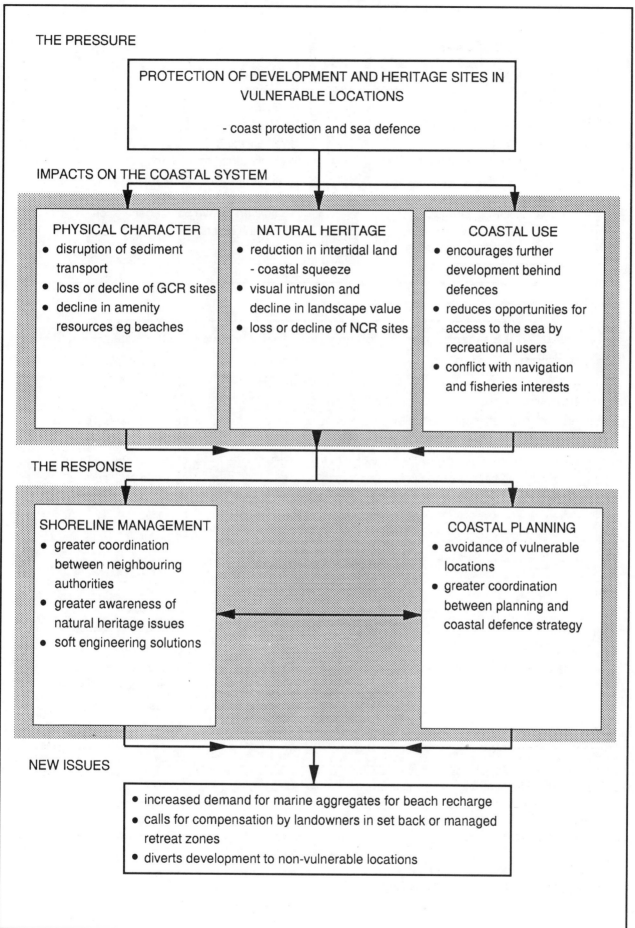

THE PRESSURE

PROTECTION OF DEVELOPMENT AND HERITAGE SITES IN VULNERABLE LOCATIONS

- coast protection and sea defence

IMPACTS ON THE COASTAL SYSTEM

PHYSICAL CHARACTER
- disruption of sediment transport
- loss or decline of GCR sites
- decline in amenity resources eg beaches

NATURAL HERITAGE
- reduction in intertidal land - coastal squeeze
- visual intrusion and decline in landscape value
- loss or decline of NCR sites

COASTAL USE
- encourages further development behind defences
- reduces opportunities for access to the sea by recreational users
- conflict with navigation and fisheries interests

THE RESPONSE

SHORELINE MANAGEMENT
- greater coordination between neighbouring authorities
- greater awareness of natural heritage issues
- soft engineering solutions

COASTAL PLANNING
- avoidance of vulnerable locations
- greater coordination between planning and coastal defence strategy

NEW ISSUES

- increased demand for marine aggregates for beach recharge
- calls for compensation by landowners in set back or managed retreat zones
- diverts development to non-vulnerable locations

Figure 9.6 Coastal resource management: a summary of issues and responses

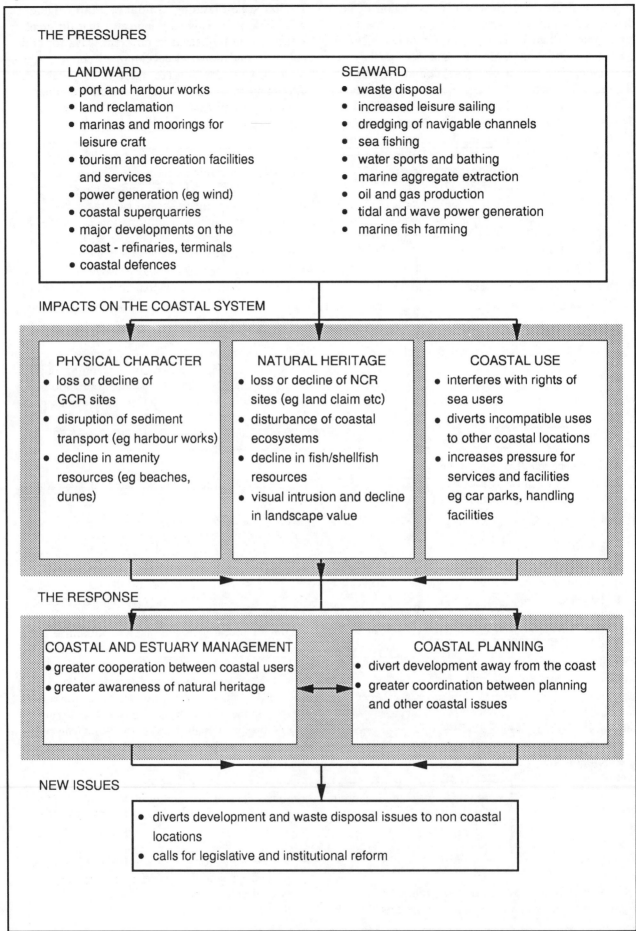

THE PRESSURES

LANDWARD
- port and harbour works
- land reclamation
- marinas and moorings for leisure craft
- tourism and recreation facilities and services
- power generation (eg wind)
- coastal superquarries
- major developments on the coast - refinaries, terminals
- coastal defences

SEAWARD
- waste disposal
- increased leisure sailing
- dredging of navigable channels
- sea fishing
- water sports and bathing
- marine aggregate extraction
- oil and gas production
- tidal and wave power generation
- marine fish farming

IMPACTS ON THE COASTAL SYSTEM

PHYSICAL CHARACTER
- loss or decline of GCR sites
- disruption of sediment transport (eg harbour works)
- decline in amenity resources (eg beaches, dunes)

NATURAL HERITAGE
- loss or decline of NCR sites (eg land claim etc)
- disturbance of coastal ecosystems
- decline in fish/shellfish resources
- visual intrusion and decline in landscape value

COASTAL USE
- interferes with rights of sea users
- diverts incompatible uses to other coastal locations
- increases pressure for services and facilities eg car parks, handling facilities

THE RESPONSE

COASTAL AND ESTUARY MANAGEMENT
- greater cooperation between coastal users
- greater awareness of natural heritage

COASTAL PLANNING
- divert development away from the coast
- greater coordination between planning and other coastal issues

NEW ISSUES
- diverts development and waste disposal issues to non coastal locations
- calls for legislative and institutional reform

156

developments or heritage sites from the threat of erosion and flooding. However, construction of the defences has had a range of effects on the coastal zone; from "coastal squeeze", the encouragement of further development behind the defences to the disruption of sediment transport around the coast (Figure 9.5). Many of these concerns are now the focus of attention of the recently established coastal defence groups, often in **shoreline management plans** with their emphasis on the consideration of "soft engineering" options (Chapter 3) or have been addressed in recent planning policy advice (PPG 14; PPG 20; DoE Circular 30/92).

9.37 From a planning perspective, however, there are two key aspects that are worthy of further comment:

- the need for earth science information to support coastal planning;

- the need for greater coordination between coastal planning and coastal defence.

The Need for Earth Science Information in Support of Coastal Planning

9.38 The past reluctance of some local planning authorities to consider natural hazards a planning issue reflects the concern that many damaging events are difficult to predict and that hazards maps need to be prepared with great care to avoid problems such as adverse effects on property values or litigation. However, any moves towards greater precaution and tighter development control to ensure hazards are fully considered in the planning process needs to be based on a sound knowledge of the coastal environment.

9.39 The recently completed study of the landslide problems at Ventnor, Isle of Wight, was one of a number of research projects funded by the DoE that have been aimed at developing techniques to help local planning authorities respond to physical constraints to development (Lee & Moore, 1991). The Ventnor study involved the assessment of the **ground behaviour** of different parts of the landslide complex, the Undercliff, within which the town was built. This formed the basis for **landslide management strategies** that reflect variations in stability rather than a blanket approach to the problem (Lee et al, 1991a, 1991b).

9.40 Knowledge of the ground behaviour at Ventnor was incorporated within the existing planning framework through the preparation of a 1:2,500 scale **Planning Guidance Map** (Figure 9.7; Table 9.3). This map indicates that different areas need to be treated in different ways for both policy formulation and development control. Areas were recognised which are likely to be suitable for development, along with areas which are either subject to significant constraints or mostly unsuitable.

9.41 The procedures developed for handling planning applications within the town reflect the importance of the developer undertaking appropriate investigations and supplying the authority with sufficient information to enable them to consider the application (Figure 9.8). The planning authority then determines whether a proposed development should proceed, in accordance with the development plan and taking into account all material considerations of which instability is only one.

9.42 The Ventnor study provides a useful framework for the formulation of planning policies in coastal areas prone to landsliding, erosion and flooding through its approach to understanding:

- the dynamics of the appropriate physical system;

- the nature, frequency and cause of the hazards;

- the ways in which problems can be best investigated and managed to reduce the likelihood of a damaging event or minimise the impacts resulting from such events;

- the most appropriate ways of addressing the issues within the planning system, to ensure proper precautions are taken to minimise risks.

9.43 Indeed, the lesson for other authorities is clear; the first priority when addressing the problems of hazard prone areas is to improve the understanding of the physical processes (Figure 9.9). Subsequent management strategies can only be prepared on the basis of adequate earth science information.

9.44 The second theme within the present research contract is of direct relevance to this issue, as it involves:

- the identification of earth science information needed for sound decision making in the coastal zone;

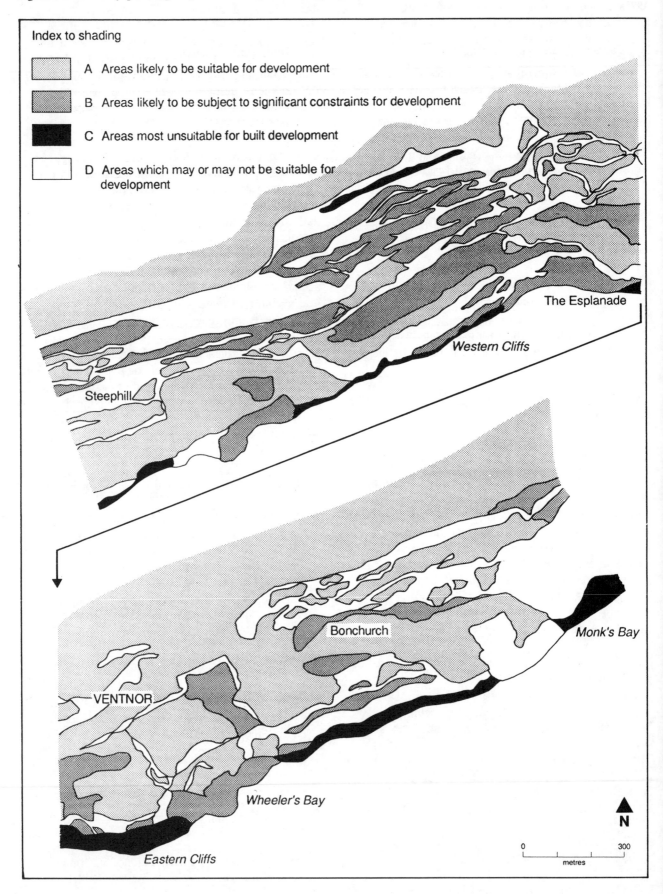

Table 9.3 Planning guidance categories for management of landslide problems in Ventnor, Isle of Wight (after Lee & Moore, 1991).

Category	Development Plan	Development Control
A	Areas likely to be suitable for development. Contemporary ground behaviour does not impose significant constraints on Local Plan development proposals.	Results of a desk study and walkover survey should be presented with all planning applications. Detailed site investigations may be needed prior to planning decision if recommended by the preliminary survey.
B	Areas likely to be subject to significant constraints on development. Local Plan development proposals should identify and take account of the ground behaviour constraints.	A desk study and walkover survey will normally need to be followed by a site investigation or geotechnical appraisal prior to lodging a planning application.
C	Areas most unsuitable for built development. Local Plan development proposals subject to major constraints.	Should development be considered it will need to be preceded by a detailed site investigation geotechnical appraisal and/or monitoring prior to any planning applications. It is likely that many planning applications in these areas may have to be refused on the basis of ground instability.
D	Areas which may or may not be suitable for development but investigations and monitoring may be required before any Local Plan proposals are made.	Areas need to be investigated and monitored to determine ground behaviour. Development should be avoided unless adequate evidence of stability is presented.

– establishing the best means for obtaining, managing, maintaining and presenting information for these purposes.

9.45 The results of this task will be presented during 1994.

The Need for Coordination between Coastal Planning and Coastal Defence

9.46 The past lack of coordination between land use planning and coastal defence strategy has been one of the most serious problems in coastal management (see Chapter 6). The consent for development in vulnerable locations has, in some cases, led to the need for publicly funded protection from erosion or flooding.

9.47 Conflicts have often arisen between the interests of local property owners and national conservation priorities. In some instances important habitats or geological sites are affected in order to protect property. In other instances threatened development remains unprotected because of the need to preserve the character of the unspoilt coast.

9.48 In recent years there has been a growing concern about the traditional response to the threats posed by natural hazards in the coastal zone. The erosion of the cliffs at Fairlight Village, East Sussex, and the 1990 floods at Towyn, North Wales are amongst the best known examples of the difficulties facing many coastal communities. Often the response to damaging events has been to call for expensive coast protection or sea defences. However, coastal engineering is only one of a range of policy options available for a coast defence strategy. The choice of option should depend on the nature of the coastline (whether it is eroding or accreting; developed or undeveloped), land use policies, conservation needs, benefits, costs and resources.

9.49 Decisions to proceed with engineering works need to be made within the framework of a range of planning policies. Indeed, it is beginning to be recognised that, in many situations, there needs to be a shift away from engineering based solutions towards anticipatory measures designed to provide better warnings of difficult ground conditions and vulnerable locations, thus reducing the impact on the economy of such hazards.

9.50 Sound policy formulation and decision making over coastal defence issues requires an appreciation of the relevant scale of operation of coastal processes. From the coastal defence perspective, the creation of **coast defence groups**

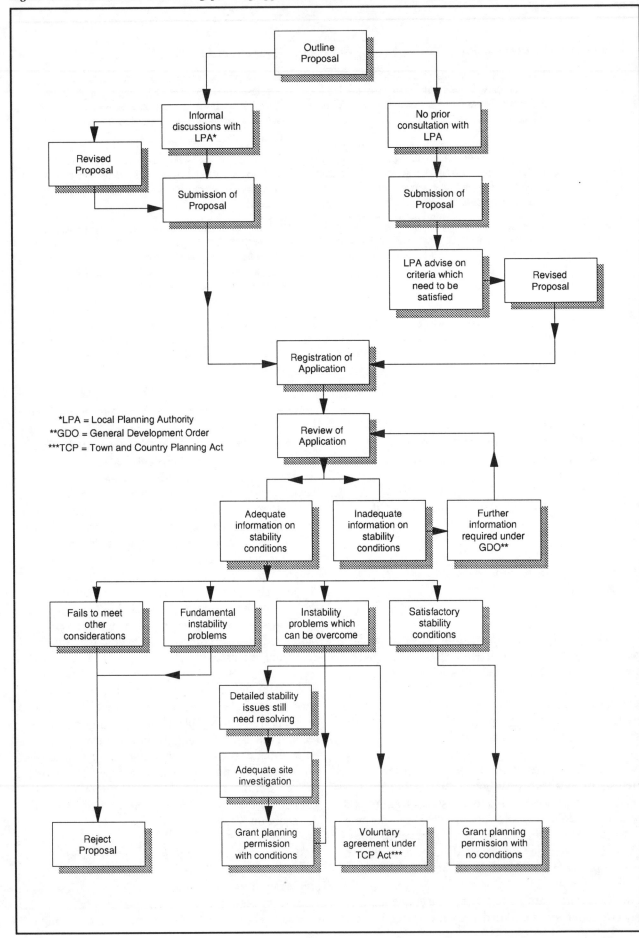

*LPA = Local Planning Authority
**GDO = General Development Order
***TCP = Town and Country Planning Act

Figure 9.9 The importance of monitoring, forecasting and prediction of events in hazard management (after Jones and Lee, in press)

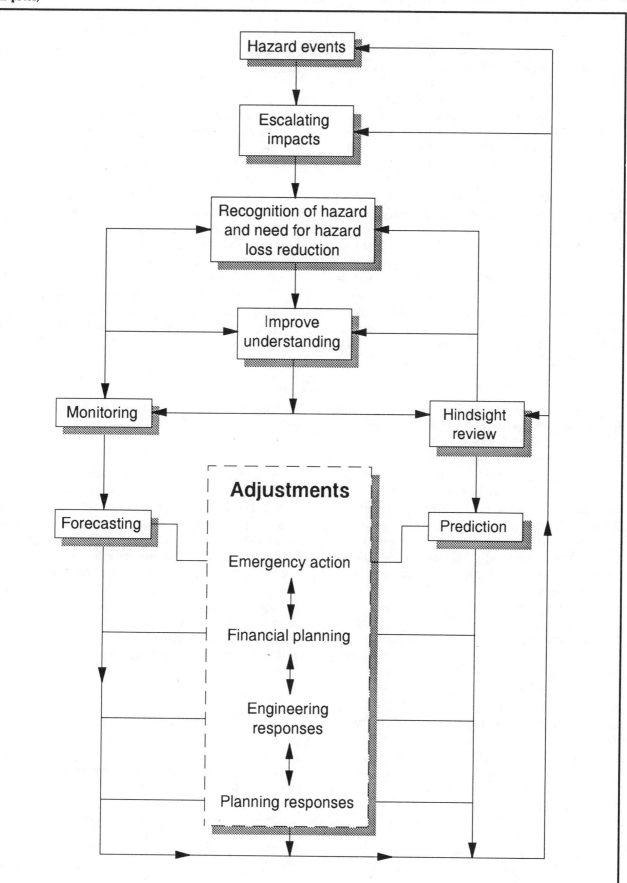

(Figure 3.4) provide a forum for this broader awareness of coastal systems. A similar regional perspective for related land use planning issues could be provided through the **regional planning groups** (Figure 6.3) and the incorporation of consistent policies within development plans.

9.51 It is clear that the two types of regional groups have evolved to address different needs; this is reflected by their different geographical context (Figure 9.10). Coastal defence groups have been established to improve coordination over the management of coastal defence issues, whereas regional planning groups provide a broad development framework for a region, addressing issues that need to be considered on a wider scale than a single county or district (see Chapter 6). However, liaison between the two groups could provide an effective means of coordinating forward planning and coastal defence objectives over large stretches of coastline. In addition, such a forum could help ensure that related land use policies are consistent between neighbouring authorities and do not simply transfer problems from one part of the coast to another.

9.52 Development plan policies prepared by local planning authorities should address the need to prevent further development in vulnerable locations and, thereby, avoid the need for new coastal defence works. In some low lying areas, options for coastal defence may include a policy for managed retreat rather than improving existing defences. Coastal defence groups and regional shoreline management plans clearly have an important role in providing planners with reliable information about the nature and extent of the physical constraints to development and providing a broad understanding of coastal processes.

9.53 There is, however, no clear mechanism for coordination between coastal defence groups and regional planning units. It remains unlikely, therefore, that the present arrangements will provide an effective means of coordinating broad planning and coastal defence objectives or enable related land use policies to be formulated that are consistent between neighbouring authorities.

Future Concerns

9.54 The trend towards a less confrontational approach to hazard management is likely to have a number of significant effects:

– an increase in demand for marine aggregates for beach recharge schemes, requiring a strategic awareness of the availability of potential sources and a sound national policy for the management of the marine resource (Arthurton, 1993);

– tighter development control in vulnerable areas or managed retreat policies are likely to lead to calls for compensation of affected property owners. As Owens & Cope (1992) note, the law would have to be changed to permit property owners in a hazard zone to be compensated, although such costs may compare favourably with those of improving defences. It should also be recognised that managed retreat or set–back policies are likely to conflict with archaeological interests in these areas;

– there will be land requirements for relocating development away from the coastal zone. This may lead to increased pressure for development in areas currently protected by countryside or Green Belt policies.

Resource Management: Reconciling competing demands

9.55 Figure 9.6 summarises the key issues involved in coastal resource management, identifying the main pressures in both the landward and seaward elements. The impacts of these coastal activities range from interference with the rights of other users or diverting incompatible uses to other locations, to the decline or damage in conservation interests through land claim or disturbance. Perhaps the most pressing issue for resource management is the problem of coordinating activity and decision making across the coastal zone, with particular difficulties experienced in the area immediately above and below LWM.

Coordination of Activity Across the Coastal Zone

9.56 The existing planning system provides an effective mechanism for dealing with many of the landward issues. Indeed, the recent PPG 20 emphasised that the opportunities for further coastal development may be limited:

"Where the coastal zone is only a small part of the territory of a local planning authority it is reasonable to expect provision of land, for

Figure 9.10 The composition of coastal defence groups and planning regions in England and Wales (as of 1992)

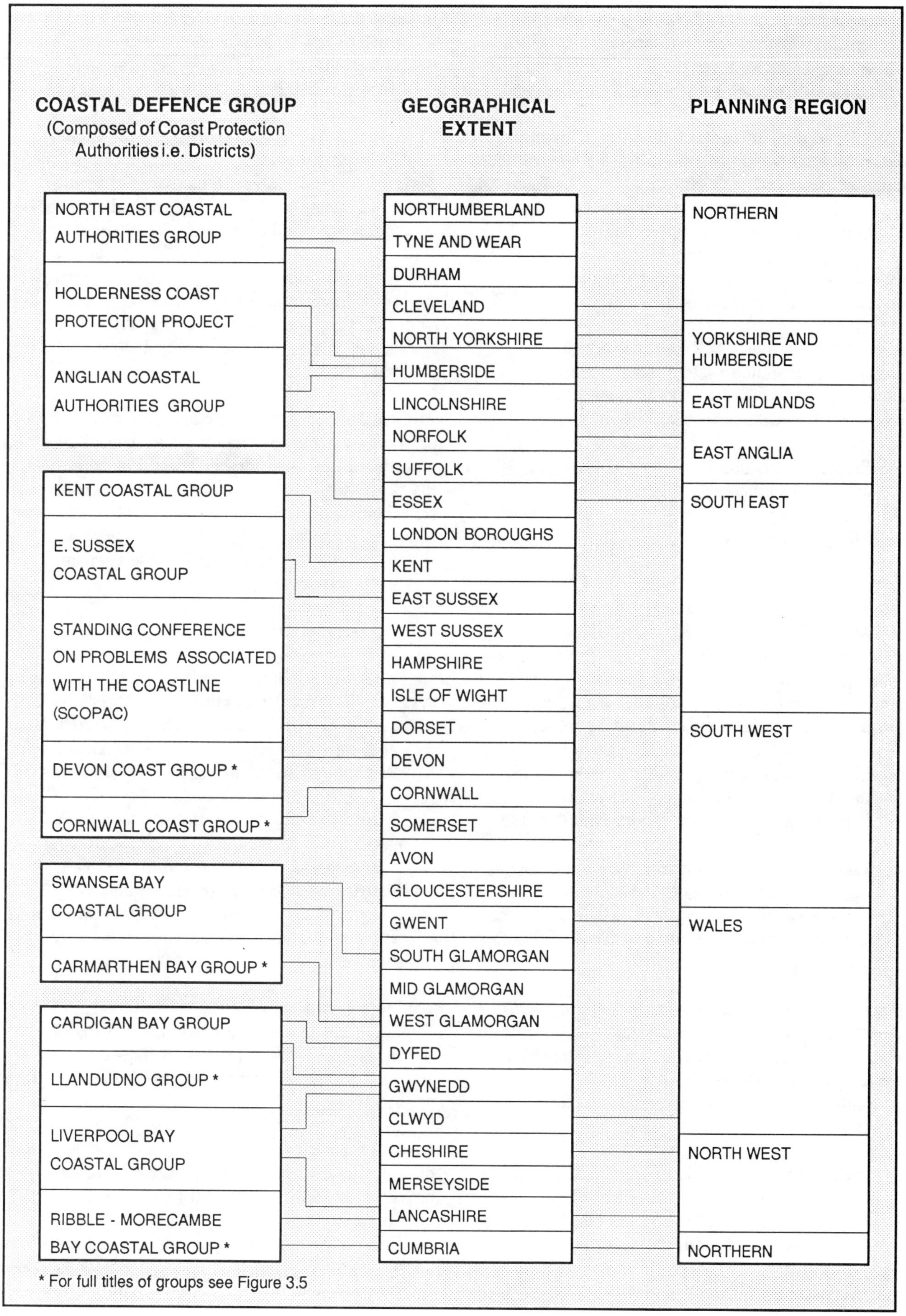

COASTAL DEFENCE GROUP (Composed of Coast Protection Authorities i.e. Districts)	GEOGRAPHICAL EXTENT	PLANNING REGION
NORTH EAST COASTAL AUTHORITIES GROUP	NORTHUMBERLAND	NORTHERN
	TYNE AND WEAR	
	DURHAM	
HOLDERNESS COAST PROTECTION PROJECT	CLEVELAND	
	NORTH YORKSHIRE	YORKSHIRE AND HUMBERSIDE
	HUMBERSIDE	
ANGLIAN COASTAL AUTHORITIES GROUP	LINCOLNSHIRE	EAST MIDLANDS
	NORFOLK	EAST ANGLIA
	SUFFOLK	
KENT COASTAL GROUP	ESSEX	SOUTH EAST
	LONDON BOROUGHS	
E. SUSSEX COASTAL GROUP	KENT	
	EAST SUSSEX	
STANDING CONFERENCE ON PROBLEMS ASSOCIATED WITH THE COASTLINE (SCOPAC)	WEST SUSSEX	
	HAMPSHIRE	
	ISLE OF WIGHT	
	DORSET	SOUTH WEST
DEVON COAST GROUP *	DEVON	
	CORNWALL	
CORNWALL COAST GROUP *	SOMERSET	
	AVON	
SWANSEA BAY COASTAL GROUP	GLOUCESTERSHIRE	
	GWENT	WALES
CARMARTHEN BAY GROUP *	SOUTH GLAMORGAN	
	MID GLAMORGAN	
CARDIGAN BAY GROUP	WEST GLAMORGAN	
	DYFED	
LLANDUDNO GROUP *	GWYNEDD	
	CLWYD	
LIVERPOOL BAY COASTAL GROUP	CHESHIRE	NORTH WEST
	MERSEYSIDE	
RIBBLE - MORECAMBE BAY COASTAL GROUP *	LANCASHIRE	
	CUMBRIA	NORTHERN

* For full titles of groups see Figure 3.5

163

example, for housing and employment to be made elsewhere in the district. Thus, in the coastal zone, development plan policies should normally not provide for development which does not require a coastal location." (PPG 20; DoE, 1992).

9.57 Resolution of conflicts between competing demands requires close cooperation between a wide range of interested authorities and bodies. The consultation arrangements within the statutory planning system (see Tables 6.6 and 6.7) and planning policy advice notes and circulars provide the mechanism for ensuring that this objective can be achieved for land use issues.

9.58 Although many activities are beyond the remit of the planning system, local planning authorities are advised to take account of the landward implications of such activities through:

- DoE Circular 2/85 Planning Control over Oil and Gas Operations;

- MPG6 Guidelines for Aggregates Provision in England and Wales;

- Scottish Office Guidance on the Location of Marine Fish Farms.

9.59 Local planning authorities have also been advised about the need to consider the effects that development can have on the coastal zone:

"Local planning authorities should recognise that on–shore development can often have an impact off–shore. They should take this into account when making planning decisions. Likewise, when considering the environmental impacts of developments outside the coastal zone, local planning authorities will still need to consider the effects on that zone". (PPG 20; DoE 1992).

9.60 Local authorities have an important role in coordinating activity in the coastal zone because of their many varied responsibilities; from land use planning to their involvement in sea fisheries committees. Their influence across the coastal zone can also involve:

- regulation of near shore recreation through the control of on–shore facilities for leisure sailing (under the planning legislation) and the control of recreation craft within 1km of the shore;

- control of the removal of material from the sea bed, by order under the Coast Protection Act 1949 S.18. South Wight Borough Council have made use of these powers to ensure adequate protection of marine archaeological sites (Tomalin, 1992).

9.61 The coastline, however, marks a fundamental change in jurisdiction from administration of the land by local authorities to the national level regulation of the sea. There are well developed procedures for regulating sea bed and sea use, although these do not directly allow a balance to be made between economic and other interests with the environment and safety factors on a sustainable basis. This has led to concerns that there is no equivalent of the planning system below LWM (eg Gubbay 1990).

9.62 In the absence of an equivalent to the planning system, with its extensive consultation procedures, the Government View Procedure and EA processes provide the alternative mechanisms for taking into account the interests of other coastal activities. However, these procedures are not always required to be invoked in the decision making processes offshore.

9.63 Consultation requirements for other regulatory systems are not always as comprehensive as those required by the planning system. The formal mechanisms (ie legislative and administrative provisions) by which activities take into account the interests of other coastal users have been summarised in Figure 9.3 which reveals:

- the most extensive consultation procedures are associated with marine aggregate extraction, marine fish farming, and the oil and gas industry i.e. the more recent regulatory frameworks. In contrast, older frameworks such as for regulating port and harbour activity involve less extensive consultation;

- the contrast between the consultation requirements prior to designating areas of landscape and nature conservation on land, with those required for Marine Nature Reserves.

9.64 A clearer indication of the links between the different interest groups in the coastal zone is provided in Figure 9.4 which highlights the requirements for consent, consultation or notification by those groups responsible for various coastal activities with other interested groups. The limited consultation over port and harbour, pollution control, land–based conservation and sea use issues is in marked contrast to the requirements for coastal defence, land use planning and sea bed activities.

9.65 Despite these opportunities for coordination through consultation or statutory provisions, there is a tendency for coastal zone issues to be compartmentalised as either landward or seaward concerns. This, of course, is a reflection of past attitudes to the use of the coast. Increasing pressure from competing uses and the concerns raised by the possible effects of sea level rise will heighten the need to improve the arrangements for coordinating decision making. In this context, the framework for resource management probably lags behind that for hazard management which has undergone considerable changes within the last decade.

Coordination of activity immediately above and below LWM

9.66 It must be stressed that unique problems arise around LWM because of the change in administrative arrangements. For example:

- the need to obtain consent from different authorities, and by different procedures, for elements of the same scheme that lie immediately above and below LWM;

- the problems of achieving conservation objectives on land immediately below LWM, because of the absence of a comparable approach to the protection afforded by the planning system above LWM.

9.67 In this context, the seaward limit of the planning system is arbitrary and does not reflect the nature of some coastal issues which may involve development immediately below LWM (eg the construction of a marina or barrage). In such circumstances there is no provision under existing legislation for local planning authorities to extend their jurisdiction seawards, in contrast to the powers of coast protection authorities under the Coast Protection Act 1949 S.18. Local authorities can, of course, seek to extend their jurisdiction through special legislation, as was the case with the Zetland County Act 1974 which gave Shetland Council powers to control development within territorial waters.

9.68 It is likely that the new order making procedures introduced by the Transport and Works Act 1992 will address some of the issues in controlling developments above and below LWM. These procedures should reduce the need for private Acts for projects affecting rights of navigation and may encourage greater local participation in decision making through objections and, if called for by the local authority, affected landowners or the Secretary of State, local public inquiries.

Management Plans

9.69 In recent years some local authorities have become more aware of the complex issues that can arise in the coastal zone. This has led a number of individual authorities to address these issues in coastal management plans, including (see Chapter 6):

- Sefton MBC's coast management plan (1989; see Cox, 1990);

- Northumberland County Council's management plan (1991).

9.70 In addition, Hampshire County Council has prepared a coastal strategy (Hampshire County Council 1991).

9.71 Although these management plans have been largely prepared by local authority planners, they address many non–land use issues and do not have the same status as the statutory development plans prepared under the planning legislation. In addition, these plans cover those issues relevant to the particular stretch of coast and, hence, they are not consistent in style and content.

9.72 Within estuaries the problem of balancing demands for coastal resources has been most acute, with incompatible land and sea uses competing for the same space. For example:

- harbour authorities need to maintain the efficiency and competitiveness of ports and harbours by deepening channels for larger vessels and improving facilities;

- heavy industry has been attracted to estuaries because of the easy access to imported raw materials and, in the past, the ability to dilute and disperse toxic waste products in the river;

165

N

- developers see tidal mudflats as potential marina and housing development sites (eg Crompton, 1992; Horsley, 1992);

- the shellfish industry views estuaries, tidal mudflats and sand banks as potential shellfisheries or shellfish farms;

- conservation groups see estuaries as internationally important breeding grounds and wintering areas for millions of birds, with the tidal mudflats supporting distinctive and unique habitats (eg Rothwell & Housden, 1990).

9.73 In the past, effective management within estuaries has been hindered by the large numbers of local authorities and organisations with a responsibility for control or regulation of activities and the reported poor communication between them (see Chapter 6). Recent attempts to address these problems include the establishment of the **National Coasts and Estuaries Advisory Group** (to coordinate local authority interests; King, 1992), the increasing numbers of estuary liaison groups such as the Mersey, the Dee and the Neath and the preparation of non–statutory **estuary management plans** in a number of areas. For example:

- the Mersey Estuary Management Plan (see Cox 1992);

- the Exe Estuary study (see Brooke 1991).

9.74 Hampshire County Council's strategy for the coast is of particular relevance in this context because of the attention paid to management problems within the Solent.

9.75 Chichester Harbour is an excellent model of integrated management of a coastal area. The **Chichester Harbour Conservancy Act 1971** provided for the control of the harbour and adjoining areas of high landscape value under a single authority (the Chichester Harbour Conservancy) with responsibility for conservancy, maintenance and improvement to take advantage of opportunities for leisure and recreation across the coastal zone (Chichester Harbour Conservancy, 1983). A management plan has been prepared for the Harbour Amenity Area which extends over both the harbour waters and the surrounding land. However, the authority does not control fisheries activity.

9.76 In Scotland, Highland Regional Council has prepared a series of sea loch **Framework Plans** to guide and control marine fish farming developments. These framework plans are designed to supplement the statutory local plan and are suggested as a guide to CEC in the issue of seabed leases (eg the Loch Hourn Framework Plan, Highland Regional Council, 1989).

Towards coastal zone management

9.77 The House of Commons Environment Committee (Table 9.4) described coastal zone management as balancing:

"demands for coastal zone resources, to promote their sustainable use and, as far as possible, to resolve conflicts of use by integrating planning and management within coastal "cells" that are defined by natural coastal processes rather than by administrative boundaries." (House of Commons Environment Committee, 1992).

9.78 It is clear that non–statutory management plans are becoming an important element in the coordination of decision making over hazard and resource management issues. Three separate types of plan are emerging: shoreline, estuary and coastal. Although they address different aspects of management in different parts of the coastal zone (Figure 9.11) there is potential for considerable overlap both in terms of the issues covered and the participating authorities and bodies (Figure 9.12).

9.79 Although these management plans can be complemented by appropriate land use policies within development plans, their present ad–hoc nature and overlapping areas of interest may hinder their role in improving the effectiveness of coastal planning. Indeed, there is currently no mechanism for coordinating different plans covering the same stretch of coast, nor linking with plans produced in neighbouring authorities.

The Relationship between Management Plans and the Planning System

9.80 Figure 9.13 presents a framework for the integration of coastal planning and management plans, based on:

- appreciation of the nature of the **coastal environment**;

Table 9.4 The House of Commons Environment Committee

The Environment Committee is appointed to examine the expenditure, administration and policy of the Department of the Environment and associated public bodies.

The Committee has power to:

- send for persons, papers and records, to sit notwithstanding any adjournment of the House, to adjourn from place to place, and report from time to time;

- appoint specialist advisers either to supply information which is not readily available or to elucidate matters of complexity within the Committee's order of reference;

- communicate to any other such committee its evidence and any other documents relating to matters of common interest; and

- meet concurrently with any other such committee for the purposes of deliberating, taking evidence, or considering draft reports.

During the 1991–92 Session the Committee met to consider aspects of coastal management. The aim of the inquiry was to investigate existing policies and responsibilities for planning and protecting the coastal zone with a view to making recommendations to the Government. The Committee received over 80 submissions of written evidence and heard evidence from 15 groups of witnesses.

The Committee's report, **Coastal Zone Protection and Planning**, was published in April 1992 and addressed 5 main themes:

- the National Framework;
- Planning in the Coastal Zone;
- Coastal Protection and Sea Defence;
- Nature Conservation in the Coastal Zone;
- Coastal Zone Management.

In July 1992 the Government published their response to the Committee's report, which was presented to Parliament by the Secretary of State for the Environment. This document sets out the Government's programme of action to address the coastal issues identified in the Committee's report.

- the **information needs** for planning and management;

- the development of appropriate **strategies** at national, regional and local scale;

- the appropriate **responses** to planning and management issues.

9.81 Amongst the key points highlighted by this framework are:

- both planning and management strategies should be appropriate to the relevant coastal **system** (eg sediment transport cell, coastal landslide system, estuary, etc.);

- planning and management strategies need to be prepared in the context of an appreciation of the **constraints** resulting from the dynamic nature of the relevant coastal system;

- the need for decision making to be supported by surveys of coastal **resources** and monitoring to determine how they are responding to current levels of exploitation and usage;

- the important role of **Environmental Assessment** in ensuring that activities do not have an adverse effect on the coastal system;

- the central role of strategic plans highlights an increased emphasis on **preventive** measures rather than reacting to individual problems at specific sites.

9.82 The planning system can address land use issues of relevance to the overall coastal management objectives, with **Regional Planning Guidance** providing an opportunity for addressing issues that need to be considered on a wider scale than a single county or district. Management plans could provide the necessary strategic framework for addressing local hazard and resource management issues. However, in contrast with the planning

Figure 9.11 The hierarchy of management plans that address issues in the coastal zone

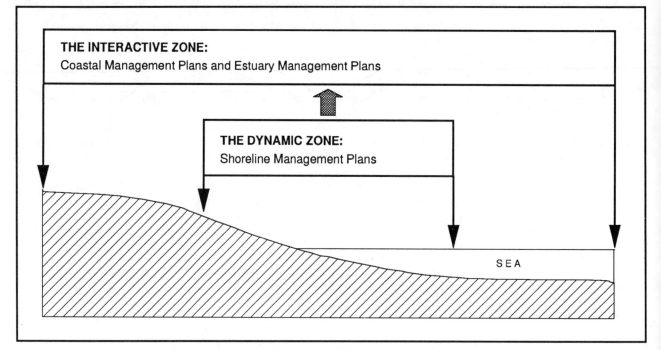

system, there is no national or regional guidance on the aims and objectives of coastal management. There is also no statutory equivalent to the development control process for ensuring that coastal activities are in accordance with management plan policies.

Coastal Planning and Management: The Geographical Context

9.83 In the past, there has been a tendency for individual local authorities to concentrate on local issues such as protection of the undeveloped coast, provision of tourist and recreation facilities and preservation of valuable habitats. However, coastal processes often operate over a much broader scale than individual local authority boundaries (Gubbay, 1991a,b; 1992a). As a result land use policies in one area may have an effect on the coastal zone in neighbouring areas. For example:

- developments in one area may lead to damage of sensitive habitats along the coast because of the rapid spread of pollution;

- reclamation of intertidal land in one area may lead to increased pressure on wetland habitats in another.

9.84 The contrast between the scale of planning and management activity and the scale of problems associated with the dynamic nature of the coast are

illustrated, with reference to East Anglia, in Figure 9.14. This demonstrates that issues such as the disruption of coastal sediment transport, loss of intertidal wetlands and offshore pollution are best viewed over the whole region (and sometimes beyond). The apparent mismatch between the administrative units and the relevant physical units is further emphasised by the way sediment moves around the East Anglian coast, with the scale of the "sediment cells" significantly broader than that of the local authority units.

9.85 It is clear, therefore, that decision making by coastal authorities needs to reflect an awareness of the appropriate scale of physical or ecological systems. This notion has gathered considerable support in recent years. For example, the recent House of Commons Environment Committee stated:

"We recommend that the Government consider how best to establish, resource and empower regional Coastal Zone Management Groups based on natural coastal "cells" as the linchpin of integrated protection and planning of the coastal zone". (House of Commons Environment Committee, 1992).

9.86 Whilst the importance of sediment transport cells for coastal defence along many parts of the UK coast cannot be disputed, it is by no means clear that such cells will be relevant for other aspects of coastal management, most notably land use planning and regulation of sea uses (Lee,

168

Figure 9.12 Common areas of overlap between the variety of management plans currently being prepared in the coastal zone

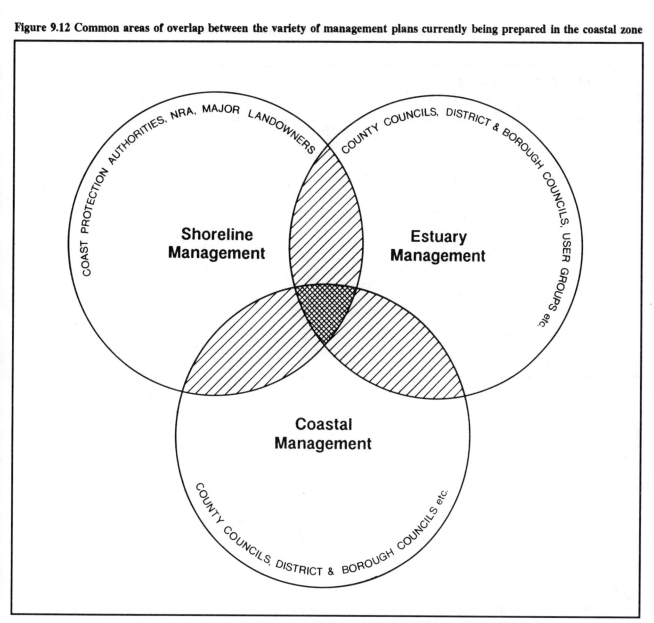

1993). Indeed, as the Ventnor example described earlier has shown, many coastal problems need to be considered in the context of the behaviour of the appropriate **coastal landform**. In Ventnor, the local planning authority is concerned with ensuring that development or redevelopment does not affect the stability of adjacent parts of the landslide system.

9.87 Similar concerns may take precedence on low lying coastal plains or estuary floodplains, where development may affect flood risk. On dune coasts activities such as grazing or harvesting of marram grass may lead to an increased potential for wind erosion, as occurred during the Culbin Sands disaster of 1694 when 20–30km² of the Culbin estate was buried beneath up to 30m of wind blown sand from the coastal dunes (Bain, 1922; Steers, 1937). Coastal communities also need to be aware of the potential problems that can be

transmitted from inland. Indeed, the 1952 Lynmouth floods tragically demonstrated the need to be aware of hazard events transmitted rapidly through a catchment (Kidson, 1953).

9.88 Broad sediment transport cells are not necessarily the most appropriate framework for ensuring that a strategic view is taken over coastal zone issues. However, the principle that decision making should be based on an awareness of both the **site** and the **situation** is of major importance to coastal managers. This awareness should extend to an understanding of how the effects of activities at a particular location can be transmitted over a wider area and vice versa ie. the **area of influence**. In the case of migratory bird feeding grounds or the spread of marine pollutants this may require an appreciation of the international context. In the case of housing development away from the

169

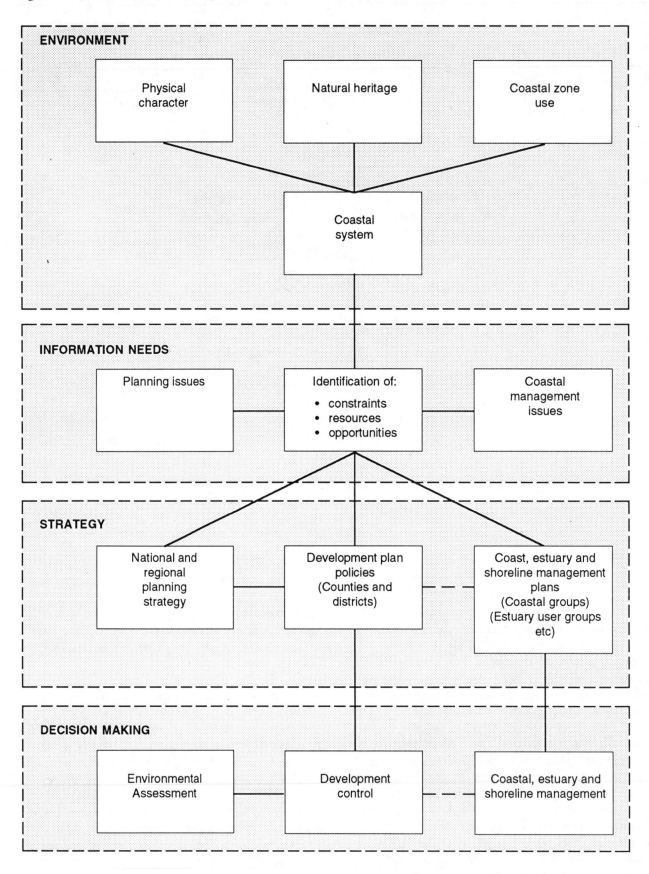

Figure 9.14 The contrast between the scale of planning and management activity and the problems related to coastal dynamics in East Anglia

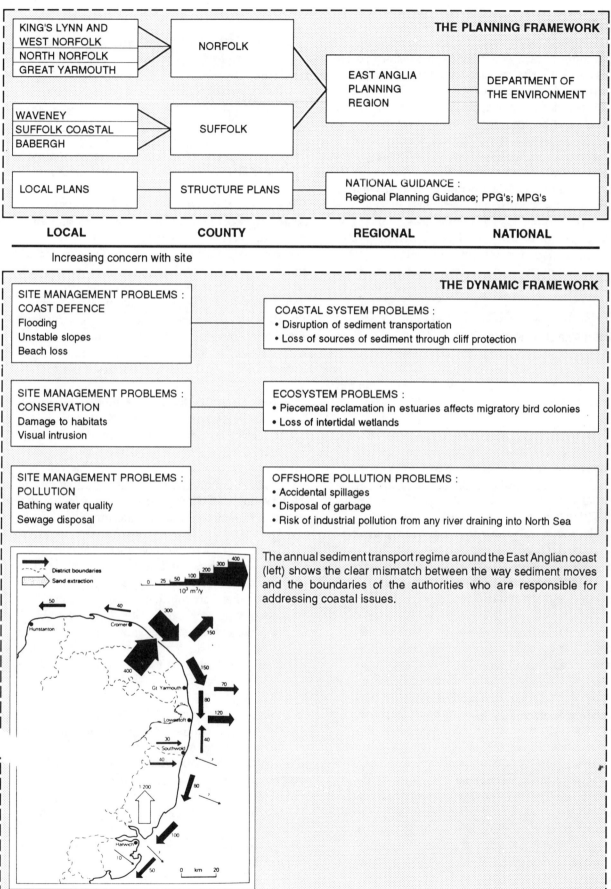

THE PLANNING FRAMEWORK

KING'S LYNN AND WEST NORFOLK
NORTH NORFOLK
GREAT YARMOUTH
→ NORFOLK

WAVENEY
SUFFOLK COASTAL
BABERGH
→ SUFFOLK

NORFOLK and SUFFOLK → EAST ANGLIA PLANNING REGION — DEPARTMENT OF THE ENVIRONMENT

LOCAL PLANS — STRUCTURE PLANS — NATIONAL GUIDANCE : Regional Planning Guidance; PPG's; MPG's

LOCAL   COUNTY   REGIONAL   NATIONAL

Increasing concern with site

THE DYNAMIC FRAMEWORK

SITE MANAGEMENT PROBLEMS :
COAST DEFENCE
Flooding
Unstable slopes
Beach loss

COASTAL SYSTEM PROBLEMS :
• Disruption of sediment transportation
• Loss of sources of sediment through cliff protection

SITE MANAGEMENT PROBLEMS :
CONSERVATION
Damage to habitats
Visual intrusion

ECOSYSTEM PROBLEMS :
• Piecemeal reclamation in estuaries affects migratory bird colonies
• Loss of intertidal wetlands

SITE MANAGEMENT PROBLEMS :
POLLUTION
Bathing water quality
Sewage disposal

OFFSHORE POLLUTION PROBLEMS :
• Accidental spillages
• Disposal of garbage
• Risk of industrial pollution from any river draining into North Sea

District boundaries
Sand extraction
0   25   50   100   200   300   400
10³ m³/y

The annual sediment transport regime around the East Anglian coast (left) shows the clear mismatch between the way sediment moves and the boundaries of the authorities who are responsible for addressing coastal issues.

171

dynamic zone, the area of influence will be much smaller.

9.89 The scale at which decisions are made is of central importance to coastal management. Unlike the planning system which tends to consider coastal processes at the site specific level (see Chapter 6) the national or regional perspective of the sea bed regulatory systems allows proposals to be judged in terms of their broader implications to coastal dynamics or the economy. Such decision making also benefits from the concentration of marine experience held within a department. This is often in direct contrast with the planning system where it is rare to find specialist earth scientists or ecologists working for local authorities. This benefit needs to be set against the importance of public participation in the development and implementation of coastal management plans and policies (Gubbay, 1992b). Indeed, one of the main reasons for the success of the heritage coast definition has been the widespread public support for the management objectives.

Coastal Planning and Management: Understanding Coastal Behaviour

9.90 Most coastal landforms are not static. Understanding how landforms have developed in the past can give a valuable insight into the potential for future change and provide a scientific basis for planning and management policies. For example, the assessment of ground behaviour at Ventnor, Isle of Wight, has enabled landslide management strategies to be developed that take into account the historical patterns of ground movement and structural damage.

9.91 Coastal managers should be aware of the potential for coastal change and the interactions between coastal processes, landforms and the habitats which they support. These changes can be **periodic** (cyclic) with the landforms or habitats responding to events by altering their shape or nature and then recovering and returning to the previous state. Examples include changes in beach profiles in response to storms or the periodic reductions in plant and animal communities in response to changes in environmental conditions. In other instances, change is **progressive** as in the retreat of an eroding cliff. Distinguishing between long term progressive change and cyclic change with periodicities of many decades is a particular problem for coastal managers faced by only a limited period of records. In addition, many of the

environmental effects of coastal zone development or activity may take many decades to become apparent:

- the gradual build up of contaminants that may be harmful to marine life;

- the cumulative effects of small developments on, for example, important habitats or flood risk;

- the disruption of sediment transport and the subsequent adjustment of coastal landforms.

9.92 In the past coastal change has tended to be regarded as detrimental to human interests, with the emphasis placed on resisting rather than accommodating or avoiding the effects of coastal processes. This is readily apparent in past attitudes to coastal defence, but has also influenced approaches to coastal conservation. For example, the 1979 Berne Convention on the Conservation of European Wildlife and Habitat requires parties to take appropriate measures to ensure the conservation of habitats and obliges them to:

"have regard to the conservation requirements of the areas protected ... so as to avoid or minimise as far as possible any deterioration of such areas" (Berne Convention, 1979).

9.93 These requirements are directed towards the preservation of important habitats and ignore the ephemeral nature of coastal landforms:

"Any attempt to preserve these habitats will, in the long term, produce the opposite effect of forcing disequilibrium on the coastline by preventing its evolution towards stability. Attempting to prevent natural periodic changes in these ephemeral wetlands could be likened to an attempt to prevent bird migration – the change is necessary for survival", (Pethick, 1992).

9.94 It is now recognised that understanding coastal changes can be a fundamental component of effective shoreline management and soft engineering; from allowing unprotected cliffs to erode and supply sediment to beaches to the regeneration of salt marshes through managed retreat. On the Anglian coast, for example, the NRA has recognised the importance of the need to understand the operation of coastal processes and their effect on coastal landforms (Halcrow, 1991; Child, 1992). In addition to the Sea Defence Management Study described in Chapter 3 (Table

172

3.7), an annual programme of monitoring has been instigated at a cost of £0.26M per year. The aim of the monitoring programme is to collect reliable information on:

- **forcing components** (ie energy inputs); wind, tides and water levels;

- **response components** (ie changes); aerial surveys, hydrographic surveys, beach surveys and inspections.

9.95 Long term monitoring of coastal behaviour is also necessary for establishing the impact of exploitation of coastal resources and assessing maximum sustainable yields from coastal waters. In this context Cook et al (1992) have advocated a mass balance approach to considering the physical exploitation of shallow seas, identifying the balance between the destruction of the resources of the sea, the impact of the loss of nonrecoverable resources, the natural ability of recoverable resources to reconstitute their conditions and the stress of resource extraction.

Improving the Framework for Coastal Management

9.96 It is not the aim of this Report to recommend particular changes to the framework for coastal management in the UK. However, the developing interest in management plans for both hazard and resource management is a clear indication that the framework for coastal management is changing in response to pressing issues on particular coasts. However, this development is likely to be constrained by the ad hoc nature of these plans and their uncertain relationship with the statutory regulatory frameworks such as the planning system. In this context, a variety of solutions to the current coastal management problems have been advocated:

- new coastal zone legislation (eg Gubbay, 1990);

- institutional change (eg the establishment of a coastal zone management unit; Gubbay 1991a, 1992a);

- consolidation of existing legislation (eg Hampshire County Council 1991);

- extension of local planning authority jurisdiction beyond LWM (eg Association of County Councils et al 1991);

- reorganisation of responsibilities in the coastal zone (Houston & Jones, 1990; Local Authorities Association 1991).

9.97 Whilst these solutions may involve major institutional or legislative change they should not be viewed as a panacea for coastal management. Effective coastal management will depend on close coordination and cooperation between different interest groups to ensure that acceptable solutions are found to the conflicting resources demands. Indeed, it is clear that the links between bodies representing different interests provide the opportunity to ensure that the enormous variety of points of view are heard. In many areas and activities, however, there is a need to strengthen existing mechanisms for coordination (see Table 9.1).

9.98 It is important that the future framework for coastal management is suitable for both hazard and resource management, whilst ensuring that these two key elements are not considered in isolation. The regulatory frameworks should take into account the interests of other coastal zone users and provide effective mechanisms for resolving conflicts. Effective coastal management should also involve a broad strategic perspective at national and regional level and an appreciation of the nature of coastal change, including an awareness of the implications of sea level rise. Decision making needs to be based on adequate scientific understanding of coastal constraints and resources and able to take into account the potential effects of activities or uses on other coastal zone interests. This will require an improved understanding of coastal systems and the interrelationships between coastal landforms and the habitats which they support.

9.99 It should be recognised that coastlines of different character will need different management approaches. Indeed, a nation having more than one type of coast will need to have flexibility in its coastal management framework to allow for appropriate local adjustments.

9.100 However, it is almost inevitable that differences in perception and responsibilities between the numerous authorities, groups and landowners with an interest in the coastal zone will stimulate conflict:

"Almost every proposed solution carries the seeds of conflict, and with good reason, because not only is one man's solution often to the detriment of another, but there are

173

commonly differences in opinion about the effectiveness of proposed solutions amongst professional environmental managers" (Cooke, 1984).

References: Chapter 9

Arthurton, R., 1993 Marine sand and gravel: resources and exploitation. Towards a better coast – a strategic approach to coastal zone management. NERC seminar, London, March 1993.

Bain, C., Dodd, A. & Pritchard, D., 1990, RSPB Planscan. A study of development plans in England and Wales. RSPB Conservation Topic Paper No. 28.

Bain, G., 1922, The Culbin Sands or the story of a buried estate. Nairn (Nairnshire Telegraph).

Brooke, J., 1991, Coastal zone management. Unpublished paper to NW RTPI conference on Coastal Planning and Management, Chorley, Nov. 1991.

Chichester Harbour Conservancy, 1983, Chichester Harbour Amenity Area Management Plan.

Child, M.W., 1992, The Anglian Management Study. In M.G. Barrett (ed) Coastal zone planning and management. Thomas Telford, 253–267.

Cook, P.J., Fannin, N.G.T. & Hull, J.H., 1992, The physical exploitation of shallow seas. In K.J. Hsu & J. Thiede (eds) Use and Misuse of the Seafloor, John Wiley & Sons, 157–180.

Cooke, R.U., 1984, Geomorphological hazards in Los Angeles. George Allen and Unwin.

Cox, T.M., 1990, Coastal planning and management in a metropolitan area. In J. Houston & C.R. Jones (eds) Planning and management of the coastal heritage. Sefton MBC, 32–36.

Cox, T.M., 1992, Coastal zone planning. In M.G. Barrett (ed) Coastal zone planning and management, Thomas Telford, 181–193.

Crompton, D.A., 1992, Cardiff Bay – microcosm of conflicts. In M.G. Barrett (ed) Coastal zone planning and management. Thomas Telford, 139–142.

Department of the Environment, 1992, Coastal Planning. PPG 20, HMSO.

Gubbay, S., 1990 A Future for the Coast : Proposals for a UK Coastal Zone Management Plan. Marine Conservation Society and The World Wide Fund for Nature.

Gubbay, S., 1991a, A definition of the "coastal zone" for UK coastal zone management programmes. Marine Conservation Society discussion paper CZM/1.

Gubbay, S., 1991b, A coastal zone management "unit" for the UK. Marine Conservation Society discussion paper CZM/2.

Gubbay, S., 1992a, Regions for coastal zone management. Marine Conservation Society discussion paper CZM/3.

Gubbay, S., 1992b, Marine nature conservation in the coastal zone. In M.G. Barrett (ed) Coastal zone planning and management. Thomas Telford, 83–90.

Sir William Halcrow and Partners, 1991 Sea Defence Management Study for Anglian Region.

Hampshire County Council, 1991 A Strategy for Hampshire's Coast. County Planning Department.

Her Majesty's Stationary Office, 1990 This common inheritance. Britain's Environmental Strategy. Government White Paper.

Highland Regional Council, 1989, Loch Hourn Framework Plan. Marine Fish Farming Policy Paper No.9.

Horsley, M.J., 1992, Development pressures in an area of declining human resources. In M.G. Barrett (ed) Coastal zone planning and management. Thomas Telford, 125–138.

House of Commons Environment Committee, 1992, Coastal zone protection and planning. HMSO.

Houston, J. & Jones, C., 1990, Planning and management of the coastal heritage. Symposium proceedings, Southport.

Jones, D.K.C., & Lee, E.M., in press, Landsliding in Great Britain: a review for the Department of the Environment.

Kidson, C., 1953, The Exmoor storm and the Lynmouth floods. Geography, 38, 1–9.

King, G.A.D., 1992, Setting the scene: the planning dimension. In M.G. Barrett (ed) Coastal zone planning and management. Thomas Telford, 37–45.

Lee, E.M., 1993, The political ecology of coastal planning and management in England and Wales: policy responses to the implications of sea level rise. Geographical Journal Vol.159, 169–178.

Lee, E.M., & Moore, R., 1991, Coastal Landslip Potential Assessment, Isle of Wight Undercliff, Ventnor. DoE.

Lee, E.M., Doornkamp, J.C., Brunsden, D., & Noton, N.H., 1991a, Ground Movement in Ventnor, Isle of Wight. DoE.

Lee, E.M., Moore, R., Brunsden, D., & Siddle, H.J., 1991b The assessment of ground behaviour at Ventnor, Isle of Wight. In R.J. Chandler (ed), Slope stability engineering developments and applications, Thomas Telford, 189–194.

Local Authorities Association, 1991, Coastal zone protection planning. Memorandum of Evidence to the House of Commons Environment Committee, Oct. 1991.

Northumberland County Council, 1991
Northumberland Coast Management Plan.
Consultation Draft, June 1991.

Owens, S. & Cope, D., 1991 Land use planning
policy and climatic change. UK Centre for
Economic and Environmental Development. DoE.

Pethick, J., 1992, Natural change. In M.G. Barrett
(ed) Coastal zone planning and management.
Thomas Telford, 49–63.

Rothwell P & Housden, S, 1990 Turning the
Tide: A Future for Estuaries. RSPB.

Scottish Development Department, 1974, North
Sea Oil and Gas. Coastal Planning Guidelines.

Scottish Development Department, 1981,
National Planning Guidelines: Priorities for
development planning.

Sefton MBC, 1989 Coast management plan.

Steers, J.A., 1937, The Culbin Sands and
Burghead Bay. Geographical Journal, 90, 498–529.

Tomalin, D., 1992 Maritime archaeology as a
coastal management issue: a Solent case study from
the SCOPAC coast. In Proceedings of the
SCOPAC seminar The Regional Coastal Groups:
After the House of Commons Report, 93–112.

Appendix A   Defining the Coastal Zone

There is no clear definition of the extent of the coastal zone relevant to the UK. To an extent this is a reflection of the dispersed nature of responsibility and jurisdiction in the coastal zone with each separate element (land, sea bed and sea) providing the focus of attention for different authorities and bodies. Because different bodies with remits in the coastal zone are interested in different objectives there is no consistent perception of what area coastal zone management should be addressing.

In most cases the boundaries are defined in terms of limits of jurisdiction eg Controlled Waters (3nm; the NRA's responsibility for water quality), mean low water mark (the normal seaward limit of planning control in England and Wales) and the landward boundaries of maritime district councils. Occasionally the limits have been defined by the limit of influence of coastal processes (eg the landward extent of Canterbury City Council's coastal process units) or the landward limit of sea views (eg some Heritage Coast designations).

The absence of a clear statement of what constitutes the coastal zone can be seen to have focused attention away from integrated coastal management towards management within the traditional administrative systems. By attempting to define the coastal zone as a coherent unit it must be recognised that the definition itself challenges the traditional sub–divisions.

One of the main problems in defining the coastal zone is the complex interlinkages between both human and physical systems. A three–tier approach to defining the coast has, therefore, been proposed which recognises the importance of both the human and physical systems and the narrow zone in which the two systems interact to create coastal risks (Figure 1.1):

(i)   a broad coastal activity zone, or **interactive zone** where human activities are influenced by or can influence the quality of the whole coastal zone. This zone may extend as far inland or seaward as necessary to control activities which may have an impact on the coast. Such activities and, hence, boundaries may include:

- polluting activities within a river catchment;

- the extent of visual intrusion resulting from development both offshore and on land;

- the limit of potential disturbance to important terrestrial and marine habitats

In practice the boundaries to this zone are likely to be either **administrative** (eg the limits of offshore jurisdiction) or **arbitrary** (eg the use of the coast road as the inland limit of a Heritage Coast).

(ii)   narrow coastal process zone, **the dynamic zone** (within the interactive zone), which is directly affected by offshore and nearshore natural processes (eg storm surges, erosion, deposition, flooding, landslides). The limits of this zone may be more rigorously defined using geomorphological or ecological criteria, such as:

- potential extent of a specified return period flood;

- the potential coastal cliff retreat over a specified period;

- the seaward limit of offshore–onshore sediment transport.

(iii)   a narrow **hazard zone** defined as the
landward area potentially susceptible to
damage from coastal processes. Such
damage may include potential loss of life
as well as property damage.

The boundaries of this zone may be the
same as the landward limits of the dynamic
zone, but the areas defined need to be
classified according to the magnitude and
frequency of damaging events. If
development has already taken place in
such hazard zones, special management
considerations may be needed.

It is important to stress that these zones also have
definable limits along the coastline, corresponding
to physical systems, such as estuaries or sediment
transport cells, for the dynamic zone and
administrative areas for the interactive zone. A
combination of these physical and human system
boundaries are relevant in the hazard zone.

This framework for defining the coastal zone
recognises the importance of the coastline for
economic activity and development, and the natural
hazards inherent in such a dynamic environment.
However, not all the coastal zone is threatened by
coastal hazards; this has an important bearing on
the management requirements of the coastal zone.

The definition also recognises that conditions vary
considerably around the UK and, hence, the precise
criteria needed to define the coastal zone will vary.
However, the basic principles will remain the
same:

-   the limit of the human system is defined by
    appropriate administrative units within which
    activities are influenced by or can influence the
    coast. Activities or development within this
    zone may have an effect on the ability of the
    coast to support other activities. Polluting
    activities within the river catchment or out at
    sea, for instance, may have an adverse effect
    on the local tourist trade by causing fears for
    personal health or, simply, by making a resort
    unattractive.

-   the dynamic zone is defined by the area within
    which coastal, river or offshore processes can
    directly affect the coast. Clearly any
    development within this zone may have an
    important effect on the operation of coastal
    processes and, hence, may lead to changes in
    coastal landforms.

-   the hazard zone is defined by the area within
    which human development faces a degree of
    risk from coastal processes. These risks, of
    course, may be minimised by the adoption of
    hazard management strategies which can
    include engineering measures and planning
    responses.

This flexible definition also provides a framework
for reviewing how effective coastal management
has been within the different zones and the
improvements to practice needed to cope with the
anticipated future trends in sea–level rise and
development pressure.

Printed by HMSO, Edinburgh Press
Dd 297657 C10 11/93 (216928)CRC